THE PARENT'S POCKET CHECKLIST

The Parent's Pocket
CHECKLIST

An

Essential Guide

to Pregnancy

KIM ARRINGTON JOHNSON

Published by Comm Brevity Publishing, Boston, MA
Cover design by Anne Marie Denton

Interior design by Ryan Scheife / Mayfly Design and typeset in the Whitman and Helvetica Neue typefaces

Editing by Sarah Menkedick
All other photo and illustration credits are listed at the end of the book.

Kim Arrington Johnson
Visit the book website at www.parentspocketchecklist.com.
Printed in the United States of America

First edition

This book is not intended as a substitute for the advice of health care professionals.

Although the author and publisher have made every effort to ensure that the information in this book was correct at press time, the author and publisher do not assume and hereby disclaim any liability to any party for any loss, damage, or disruption caused by errors or omissions.

Library of Congress Cataloging-in-Publication Data
Johnson, Kim Arrington.
    The Parent's pocket checklist : an essential guide to pregnancy / by Kim Arrington Johnson.
    p. cm.
    ISBN 978-0-9891136-0-1 (pbk.)
    ISBN 978-0-9891136-1-8 (EPUB)
    ISBN 978-0-9891136-2-5 (Kindle)
    Series : The Parent's pocket checklist.
    Includes index and bibliographical references.
1. Pregnancy. 2. Prenatal care. 3. Childbirth. 4. Postnatal care. 5. Pregnancy. 6. Childbirth. 7. Breastfeeding. I. Title. II. Series.
RG525 .J639 2015
618.2/4—dc23   2014919822

For Brad, Katie, and Lauren

Contents

· · · · · · · · · ·

A Word of Gratitude

. . . .

First and foremost, this book would not have been possible without the love and support of my husband, Brad.

I am also sincerely grateful for my mom, brother, grandmothers, in-laws, and other family members who believed in me from the beginning. With special mention, I would like to thank my dad, who is no longer with us, but who shared his special insight on life and passion for the written word.

I am also thankful for many others who have inspired this work: for my early science teachers, especially Mike Shaw, who creatively and passionately brought my favorite subject to life in the small town of King, NC, encouraging scientific curiosity for life; for my obstetrician, Dr. Jane Piness, who delivered my children with loving care and introduced her brilliant and balanced approach to this field.

I am also sincerely grateful for the people who helped bring this book to life: for my all-around go-to helper and collaborator, Audrey Mangan, for her support with all of The Parent's Pocket Checklist projects and their distribution; for my book reviewers, Kristin Busse, Leslie Riesenhuber, and Susanna Visuri, who shared their honest feedback and encouraged me toward the finish line; for my editor, Sarah Menkedick, who challenged me to reveal more of my own story and spurred me on to re-write the book; for my friend and former squadron mate, Natalie "JJ" Caruso, who helped format this project into viable form; for my early proofreading and editing team, Cathy Johnson and Sharon Weller, who taught me grammar rules that I never knew; for my friend and fellow Dukie, Susan Hazard, who helped craft the book's survey; for the hundreds of parents who filled out the survey, provided feedback, or agreed to an interview, generously sharing their practical tips while shaping the book's content;

for my mommy friends, especially my Mothers of Preschoolers (MOPS) group, who helped me keep it together through some long days as a new parent and reminded me that moms are world influencers; and finally, for my children, Katie and Lauren, who bring immense joy to my life and inspire me to be a better person.

Introduction

. . . .

When I was pregnant for the first time, I wanted to know everything about having a baby. So I read one pregnancy book after another and hunched over my computer for hours at a time searching for golden nuggets of parenting wisdom. My mom, who is a former schoolteacher, asked if I had enrolled in a college course for baby. A college course would have only scratched the surface.

For better or worse, I am part of an information generation, and we like to over-research everything. What are the best restaurants, best schools, best apps, and the best deals on the best products available? From the moment that pregnancy was confirmed, I wanted preeminent advice for all things baby. Yet there is a problem with 24-7 access to infinite information—filtering out all the junk wastes precious time and having too many choices paralyzes us. Today, a Google search for "best baby products" returns 536 million hits in .3 seconds, while popular websites bombard expecting couples with pop-up ads, click-through links, and endless advertisements. I haven't even mentioned the 600 to 800 page books about what to expect. There is no shortage of helpful information out there, but it's too much. Here lies the inspiration for this book—to create a crisp, concise guide covering only the most relevant pregnancy and baby information. I wanted to write a book so efficient that Dad might actually read it.

I must admit that I had lots of extra time on my hands for reading and research while pregnant and caring for my firstborn. I had recently quit my job and needed an intellectual outlet—that's a euphemism for "I was a total mess." I had spent my adult life racing from one action-packed environment to another—from the U.S. Naval Academy to flight school to flying in fighter jets (as an F-14 Tomcat RIO and F/A-18F Super Hornet

WSO) to business school at Duke to Goldman Sachs—to finally, being at home all day with a baby. While I was thrilled and blessed to be a mom, I was also lonely and disheartened. The unpaid work that I was doing was barely valued, and my new boss mostly complained. Nobody told me that motherhood would be so complex.

Determined to share my knowledge and not spend naptime discouraged, I created a simple web site and a mommy blog. The web site was designed to steer expecting parents to "best of" pregnancy and baby information, while the blog covered a breadth of parenting topics. The blog's intent was not to rant and rave or blast other parents for their choices. I wanted it to be informative, yet reflective of me—a warm, yet slightly satirical "Moderate mom"—who advocates all things eco-friendly, but isn't about to eat her own placenta; who supports breastfeeding, but refuses to call it mommy nirvana; who subscribes to attachment parenting, but encourages independence when the time is right; who believes in vaccines for the good of all, yet questions the effects on some; and who respects the highest levels of research, yet understands that parenting is both art and science. I wanted to prove that you don't have to live on the fringe to be interesting. Tiger moms and earth moms may sell books and blog ads, but good parenting requires balance. Once I started writing, checklists naturally emerged.

I spent my twenties and early thirties relying on checklists in aviation. Checklists helped me sort through complex problems (like an engine fire), and they also helped my fallible memory recall the mundane (such as startup and shutdown procedures). In Naval Aviation, the aircraft's pocket checklist, called the PCL, was so indispensable that it sat in a special pocket in the leg of my anti-gravity suit for fear it would become detached in an emergency or upside-down flight. You never wanted to be in a situation and not know what the PCL had to say.

While pregnancy and parenting may not be as fast-paced as flying in a fighter jet, it is loaded with pitfalls and important yet forgettable minutiae. For example, a good hospital packing list could be the key to having your camera or phone charger for taking birth photos cherished for a lifetime, while avoiding a list of medications or toxins while pregnant could be lifesaving or life changing. In his book *Checklist Manifesto*, Harvard professor, surgeon, and public health journalist, Atul Gawande, maintains that a well-designed checklist can improve outcomes for

Last flight in the F/A-18F Super Hornet (the only flight that ends with your life vest deployed.) Notice the pocket checklist, or PCL, secured in the bottom left pocket of my G-suit.

Inspiration for this book. A closer look at a pocket checklist used in Naval Aviation.

teams around the world, including business groups, construction crews, emergency responders, airline crews, and surgical units. I contend that families are perhaps the most fundamental "teams" on the planet.

Checklists make a complex world simpler; yet a book that encourages streamlining and efficiencies for families does not imply that we are all the same. Not every expecting parent comes from a privileged starting point—with access to healthcare, emotional readiness for parenthood, extra income for baby gear (much less eco-friendly baby gear), and support from a spouse, family, and friends. However, it is my genuine belief that parenting can be immensely joyous in almost any circumstance with a positive, long-term perspective. Welcoming a newborn to the world is an amazing experience that goes far beyond administrative tasks and lists, whether the process is through pregnancy or adoption. Thus, the ultimate goal of this guide is to help you move beyond the safety concerns, baby registry, and list of to-dos, so that you can spend less time researching your pregnancy and more time connecting with loved ones and enjoying this wonderful time of anticipation!

Now before we get to the lists, please note: the terms spouse/partner, doctor/midwife, and his or her for baby are all used interchangeably to be inclusive of all. Also, if you want the real scoop from parents who have been there and done that, look for the "Practical Tips from Real Parents" sections throughout the book. These unfiltered quotes and comments, both thoughtful and humorous, were collected through surveys and interviews conducted especially for this book. Finally, expect your *Parent's Pocket Checklist* reading experience to feel unusually fast-paced and dense, due to the concise format. However, efficiency is the goal—to inundate you with hearty advice that can be read in about three hours— sparing you 300 hours of research for your pregnancy. Here we go!

Pregnancy Timeline and To Do List

▪ First Trimester

You may not look or even feel very pregnant in the first few weeks. However, a healthy first trimester is crucial to baby's development. The brain, spinal cord, and other major organs are beginning to form, and they are at peak susceptibility to alcohol, medications, chemicals, and toxins in the environment. At just six weeks pregnant, your baby's tiny heart is beating and pumping blood, and by eight weeks, nerve cells in the brain are forming primitive pathways.

At around six weeks, the same hCG hormone (human chorionic gonadotropin) that triggered your positive pregnancy test can also make you feel queasy. The good news is that morning sickness is often considered a positive sign of an established pregnancy, although this may not offer much comfort as you pay frequent homage to your bathroom fixtures. Seventy-five percent of all pregnant women experience some type of nausea, while half experience nausea and vomiting.[1] Many women also report a heightened sense of taste and smell, which can bring on strange cravings and sensations. Don't be surprised if coffee, your must-have morning drink, suddenly becomes repulsive, and bland crackers turn into your favorite breakfast, lunch, and dinner.

Just remember that the first trimester (aside from minimizing exposure to medications and toxins) is about surviving, de-stressing, and getting plenty of rest. Frankly, you have never had a better reason to take a nap. The longer you sleep, the faster your second trimester will get here!

Weeks 1-8

Medical tips

☑ Estimate your due date with an online calculator, or if you're good at math, add seven days to the first day of your last menstrual period (LMP) and subtract three months. Note: 40 weeks is the gestation period calculated from day one of your LMP to your expected due date. The 40-week calculation includes the first two weeks of pregnancy that happened *before* a woman conceived. A full term baby is born nine and a half months from *conception* or 10 months (40 weeks) from the start of Mom's last period.

☑ Check your health insurance coverage for pregnancy and childbirth.

☑ Find an obstetrician (OB or OB/GYN), certified nurse-midwife (CNM), certified professional-midwife (CPM), or family practice doctor for your prenatal care. Make sure the practice accepts your insurance and check to see if your doctor or midwife can deliver at the hospital or birthing facility of your choice. If you desire a natural childbirth, find a practitioner who will support your choices.

☑ Schedule your first prenatal checkup, usually between six and 10 weeks. Some high-demand obstetricians may not see you until 10-12 weeks. Note: This can be an excruciatingly long wait for first time parents. Just know that OBs are in high demand and short supply for good reason. They have a difficult lifestyle, round the clock demands, and one of the highest premiums for malpractice insurance among physicians. This comes after a minimum of 12 years of school (and likely debt) required for training as a surgeon.

☑ If you have had a previous miscarriage(s) or other health issues such as diabetes, tell your doctor, and you may get an appointment sooner.

☑ Strive for a partner or spouse to attend critical OB/midwife appointments, such as the first appointment, the 20-week ultrasound, and any visits due to complications. However, requiring 100% attendance may be out of the question in light of today's work demands. If you are without a supportive partner, bring a friend or family member with you to the first prenatal visit.

☑ Expect doctor visits every four weeks, until approximately 28 weeks pregnant.

❑ Purchase or borrow a week-by-week pregnancy guide and make sure that it's up to date (i.e., not *What to Expect* copyright 1984). I consider this a "must have" for pregnancy (See: Appendix C: Recommended Books and Resources).

Financial tips

❑ Calculate how a planned maternity leave will affect your finances.

❑ Consider increasing your current life insurance coverage, or purchase life insurance (See: Financial Planning for Baby).

❑ Make sure that you and your spouse have short and long-term disability, if eligible.

☑ Research maternity options at work before telling your boss or co-workers. Investigate how maternity leave is really perceived at your firm. Friends and I have noticed that some companies boast generous maternity policies during the recruiting process; however, if a woman actually takes her full paid maternity leave, she may return to a tacitly altered career track, fewer advancement opportunities, and stolen clients. Hopefully, this is not the case for you. Check out the website, http://babygate.abetterbalance.org/, to learn more about laws in your state that apply to pregnant workers and parents' rights in the workplace.

❑ Be courageous. With good performance, consider asking for a salary raise *before* you present your maternity plan. The higher pay will help offset a longer maternity leave or reduced work schedule later, if desired.

Nutrition, health, and well-being tips

☑ If you are single and expecting, know that you are not alone—40% of children in the U.S. are born to single mothers, while 53% of births to mothers under age 30 are to single mothers. If a partner or spouse is not in your life, seek support from family and friends.[2]

❑ Try not to worry excessively about miscarriage. The majority of pregnancies result in healthy babies. Miscarriage risk lies somewhere between 10 and 25% of known pregnancies (about 15% for women under age 35 and higher for over 35), and roughly 80% of those occur during the first trimester. Once a care provider detects a heartbeat, it is estimated that miscarriage risk drops to 5-10%.[3]

❑ Begin eating as healthy a diet as possible (See: What to Eat) and head to bed early.

❑ Keep hydrated with eight to ten 12-ounce glasses of water per day. Take a reusable water bottle to work and fill it regularly.

❑ Take a daily prenatal multivitamin with 27 milligrams of iron and 600 micrograms of folic acid, as recommended by the American College of Obstetricians and Gynecologists (ACOG).[4] Most women do not get all the folic acid they need from food alone, yet it can prevent major birth defects of the brain and spine. Some researchers think that folic acid may also play a role in heart health and preventing cell changes that lead to cancer.[5]

❑ Get a prescription-level prenatal vitamin at your first doctor's visit. An over-the-counter (OTC) prenatal vitamin is better than nothing. However, there are no FDA requirements for what constitutes a prenatal supplement, and most OTC prenatal offerings are inferior to prescription ingredients.

❑ If you are nauseated, eat small meals throughout the day, since low blood sugar and stomach acid build-up can make nausea worse (See: Morning Sickness and Nausea).

Fun tips

❑ Share the early news with at least one other trusted family member or friend, in addition to your partner, for support. You might want to wait with telling everyone else until the risk of miscarriage decreases, around 12-14 weeks.

❑ Sign up for weekly pregnancy emails from Baby Center or the Bump.com, if you want to keep track of your baby's development and size. These are the fruit comparison emails that take baby from the size of a tiny seed to a plump watermelon.

❑ Start pregnancy photos to journal your experience. Try the app CineMama to document your belly bump through pictures. At the end, the app compiles the photos and makes a movie set to a soundtrack of your choice. For cool, photo announcements, try Belly Snaps, which places a banner over your photos announcing your pregnancy, the gender, or simply tracking the weeks.

❑ Be discerning when purchasing pregnancy mobile apps—47% of mobile users with one or more health apps are using a pregnancy app. This creates a market ripe for scams.

Practical Tips from Real Parents
Conception after Fertility Treatments
• •

The following tips were collected through surveys and interviews conducted especially for this book.

- If you had assistance conceiving with IVF, expect a roller coaster of emotions throughout pregnancy, especially in the first trimester.

- All of the money spent and the pain endured from the ART process, in addition to previous miscarriages, can create a deeply seeded fear of losing your pregnancy.

- I had major anxiety throughout my pregnancy after years struggling with fertility.

- If you had IVF, the difference between your fantasies about being pregnant and the actual experience can cause added stress. My husband was always reminding me not to complain, but I really just needed him to listen and acknowledge my discomfort.

❏ Take a deep breath. This is a lot of information to absorb. Just remember, knowledge can help reduce your stress and anxiety and make you more confident as a new parent.

Weeks 8-14

Medical tips

☑ Write down any questions that you may have prior to your doctor's visits. Many OBs will whisk in and out of the examining room faster than you can say, "Next patient," so be prepared.

☑ Seek to understand the purpose of various first and second trimester prenatal tests (See: Is It Safe: Prenatal Testing).

☑ If you are over age 35, expect to be designated Advanced Maternal Age (AMA). Though the term may seem similar in context to "old maid," age 35 is a statistical cutoff when chances for having a chromosomal abnormality are slightly higher than the risk of miscarrying from a diagnostic test, such as amniocentesis. It is also an insurance indicator, since some tests may be covered after age 35, but not before.

☑ Check hospital schedules for childbirth preparation and breastfeeding classes ahead of time, especially if you live in a densely populated area.

Financial tips

☑ Start buying maternity clothes, or better yet, borrow them. To extend your non-maternity wardrobe, loop a thick rubber band or hair tie through the buttonhole of your pants and cover with a long stretchy tank.

❑ Once you have exhausted your friends, garage sales, and consignment shops, try some favorite maternity brands: A Pea in the Pod, Top Shop, Motherhood, Target, Gap, Ann Taylor Loft, and Old Navy. Note: Maternity return policies are strict. Most stores require returns within 10 days with a receipt and tags for store credit. No cash refunds.

❑ For trendier maternity collections, try StellaMaternity.com, PinkBlushMaternity.com, Asos.com, OlianMaternity.com, Seraphine .com, IsabellaOliver.com, and JapaneseWeekend.com.

❑ For a special occasion, rent a designer maternity dress for up to 75% less at RentMaternityWear.com.

❑ Buy or borrow a few new bras, or extend your current ones with a $2-3 bra clip extender. Many women increase a full cup size during the first few weeks of pregnancy.

Nutrition, health, and well-being tips

☑ Stock up on natural moisturizers to pamper your skin and soothe an itchy, growing belly.

☑ Talk to your doctor about an exercise routine. Exercise modification may be required for women who have undergone fertility treatments or who have pregnancy complications.

☑ Suspend your gym membership for a few months, if you are unable to use it.

❏ Expect any of the following pregnancy-related body changes and nuisance issues.[1, 6, 7]

- ▶ **Congestion/sniffles**. Hormones cause the mucus membrane lining in your nose to swell. For relief, try saline nose drops and a humidifier.

- ▶ **Constipation**. Two major issues contribute to increased constipation during pregnancy. First, hormones relax the smooth muscles in your stomach and intestines, slowing food passage through your system. Secondly, you may not be drinking enough fluids to keep up with your increased blood flow, causing you to be dehydrated. For relief, drink plenty of water and eat plenty of fiber. Drink a cup of hot water or prune juice, if you need to get things moving.

- ▶ **Heartburn**. Increased levels of progesterone cause your muscles and muscle sphincters to relax. Therefore stomach acid is more likely to come up, especially as your growing uterus compresses your stomach. Food is also pushed through the digestive system more slowly, allowing for a backup of gastric contents. For relief, avoid spicy, greasy, and acidic foods, and try not to eat and lie down, a surefire way for anyone to get heartburn.

- ▶ **Headaches**. To minimize pregnancy headaches, control your blood sugar with frequent small meals, drink plenty of water, and try to rest. For drug-free pain relief, try a head, neck, and face massage or apply a hot or cold compress. Do not take aspirin or ibuprofen while pregnant.

- ▶ **Varicose veins (or spider veins)**. Increased blood volume and pressure from a growing uterus, especially on the large vein on the right side of your body, causes weakened veins in your legs to bulge and twist. For relief, elevate your legs often and wear support hose if you are getting varicose veins in your legs and feet.

- ▶ **Hemorrhoids**. Hemorrhoids are varicose veins on your bottom. Increased blood volume, pressure from the uterus, and straining from constipation (and childbirth) can cause these veins to bulge. Sit in a warm tub or sitz bath for relief.

- ▶ **Vaginal discharge**. A thin, milky white discharge is okay. If the discharge is yellow, green, bloody, or foul-smelling, talk to your doctor.
- ▶ **Incontinence or peeing in your pants**. We're back to relaxed muscles and increased pressure from the uterus. Panty liners can save the day after a good belly laugh or sneeze.
- ▶ **Acne/pimples**. Changing hormone levels can cause an increase in oil or sebum production. Wash face, neck, and back with a gentle natural cleanser twice a day and avoid adult acne prescriptions and treatments with salicylic acid.
- ▶ **Melasma**. This skin darkening process is often called "the mask of pregnancy," due to hormones triggering the production of melanin in skin cells. Avoid skin-bleaching creams. Some cases of melasma may clear spontaneously without treatment after pregnancy.
- ▶ **Sun sensitivity**. Pregnancy hormones cause increased sun sensitivity. Be sure to wear sunscreen.
- ▶ **Hair growth**. You may have hair growth in unwanted places due to increased hormone levels. Stick with shaving and tweezing for removal, due to lack of information on the effects of hair removal creams, electrolysis, and laser hair removal.
- ▶ **Constant pressure in your lower abdomen.** Visit the restroom often, due to pressure on the bladder and fluid imbalances. If you feel as though you can't empty your bladder when urinating, bend over while seated, lean forward to reduce uterine pressure, and get the last few trickles out.

Fun tips

- ❏ Record your baby's heartbeat at your 12-week appointment with a clever phone app, such as My Baby's Beat or Lullabeats.
- ❏ Give your partner a few nights off to hang out with friends and have a few beers, and you may receive more cheerful help around the house.
- ❏ If your partner keeps telling you that he, too, feels queasy or exhausted, he's not completely nuts. As many as 65-80% of expecting fathers experience some form of Couvade Syndrome, a psychosomatic condition better known as sympathetic pregnancy.[8]

■ Second Trimester

Hurray! The second trimester is here. Your risk of miscarriage has decreased dramatically, and you may feel more comfortable sharing your news with extended family and friends. Nausea and fatigue should also improve by weeks 13-16, as you feel more energized for work, travel, exercise, sex, and planning for baby's arrival (your house is probably a mess, too). You should also regain a normal appetite. Although, remember that you are not actually eating for two; it's more like one and a sixth, since your body needs only 300 additional calories per day (½ cup of almonds = 411 calories). This equals a weight gain of one half to one pound per week in the second trimester. The average weight gain for women who start pregnancy at a normal weight is 25 to 35 pounds, while the average weight gain for twins is 35 to 45 pounds.[4]

Weeks 14-20

Medical tips

❑ Expect triple screen testing during weeks 15-20, if offered.

❑ Expect the option of amniocentesis during weeks 16-20, if required. This is usually reserved for women with a family history of birth defects, maternal age > 35, diabetes, or exposure to a viral infection, radiation, drugs, or harmful medication use during pregnancy.

❑ Anticipate a mid-pregnancy ultrasound at week 20. Decide if you want to know the baby's gender before your appointment and tell the technician your desires.

Financial tips

❑ Lay out a maternity plan for your boss. Come to the table with a list of your contributions and negotiate the maternity leave that you desire.

❑ Research childcare options (See: Choosing a Child Care Center and Hiring a Nanny). Day care centers fill up fast (some have wait lists), and high-quality nannies meeting your scheduling requirements may be hard to find. Get your partner involved in the process.

Organizational tips

❑ Start loosely planning a baby shower so that family and friends can "save the date." Baby showers are typically scheduled six to eight weeks before your due date.

❑ Start planning the nursery. No painting or sanding for Mom. Homes built before 1978 may have lead paint. Note: Lead is a potent neurotoxin with links to miscarriage, preterm birth, and developmental delays.

Fun tips

❑ Hit the sheets! As long as your doctor gives you the okay, enjoy your second trimester energy boost and bond with your partner. Many women report stronger orgasms during pregnancy, due to increased blood flow and genital sensitivity.

❑ Keep taking pregnancy photos each week. Set up an alert on your phone for reminders. For a fun progression, take photos in the same place with signs indicating the week.

❑ Expect baby's first kicks during this time, which feel like bubbles or wings fluttering in your tummy.

❑ If you don't already know the sex of baby, have fun playing gender guessing games. Do these tricks actually work? Yes, 50% of the time.

▶ *The Carrying Game*: Look at Mom's belly. Girl = carrying high, Boy = carrying low.

▶ *The Heartbeat Game:* Girl = 140 beats per minute and higher, Boy = 140 bpm and lower.

▶ *The Sweet or Savory Game*: Girl = craving sweet foods, Boy = craving savory or salty foods.

▶ *The Ring Game*: Tie a ring, such as a wedding ring, with a string and hang it over your belly. Girl = it swings back and forth, Boy = it swings in a circle.

Weeks 20-28

Medical tips

❑ Ask for pediatrician recommendations. Doctors, nurses, doulas, midwives, and other parents are great resources. Your baby will be checked at birth by your selected pediatrician or pediatric practice.

❑ Research cord blood banking. This process allows expecting parents to store baby's umbilical cord blood as a potential source for stem cells used to treat cancers and other disorders. Your baby's cord blood can be shared for the public good or stored for family use.

▸ *Pros*: Cord blood banking could be lifesaving to your child, a sibling with a disease, or someone else using a public bank.

▸ *Cons*: Your baby may never need it. It's also not a guaranteed cure for disease, and it's expensive at $1500-3000 for collection up front, plus $100-200/month for storage.

❑ Find a doula, if desired. A doula is a childbirth assistant who can provide physical, emotional, and informational support to parents during labor and delivery. The word "doula" comes from ancient Greek meaning "woman who serves", and this person can be helpful in assisting a woman through natural birth. Hiring a doula for childbirth costs an average $400-800 or $800-3500 for a DONA certified doula in an urban area, depending on her experience (See: Childbirth Options).

❑ Expect a glucose screen test to check for gestational diabetes between weeks 26-28. This test includes drinking a yucky, sugary drink, waiting an hour, and getting blood drawn. Note: Gestational diabetes affects 18% of pregnancies. It occurs when your body is not able to produce or use all the insulin it needs to "escort" glucose (the type of sugar in your blood) into your body's cells. This is where your body turns glucose into energy.[9]

Nutrition, health, and well-being tips

❑ Think daily about your iron intake. Foods high in iron include lean beef, chicken, fish, lentils, spinach, and fortified cereals. You will need plenty of iron to make hemoglobin, the protein in red blood cells that carries oxygen to both Mom and baby. By the third trimester, expect to have your juices flowing with up to 50% more blood volume.[7]

❑ Expect more rapid weight gain during the second trimester and don't be surprised if you have at least one whopper of a weigh-in at the doctor's office during this period.

❑ Work on your marriage or relationship during pregnancy. Even if there is no trouble on the horizon, stormy waters may lie ahead, especially in the intimacy department. Studies show that new parents have about a third of the alone time they had before having children.

Organizational tips

❑ Update or write a will, including specifications for your child's inheritance and guardianship.

❑ Send out baby shower invitations.

❑ Register for baby gifts with your partner. Take an experienced mom with you who can help you cut out the fluff, or at least consult an experienced parent before adding items in the store or online (See: Baby Registry).

Fun tips

❑ Take a babymoon now before your feet and back are aching. You will want to stay closer to home in the third trimester.

❑ If you are having a bad day, search "awkward pregnancy photos" in Google images and have a good belly laugh.

∎ Third Trimester

You are in the home stretch! However, be prepared. The third trimester can be very physically demanding. Expect backaches (due to a growing belly and two pounds of extra breast weight), knee aches (due to weight gain), swollen feet (due to fluid retention), difficulty sleeping (thanks to your belly, heartburn, baby's acrobatics, and frequent urination), and other lovely side effects of growing a human being inside of your body. Despite these minor distractions, take a few moments to spend quality time with your loved ones and reflect on this amazing process.

Weeks 29-35

Medical tips

❑ Expect doctor/midwife visits every two weeks from 28-35 weeks.

❑ Prepare your birth plan and ask questions about labor and delivery (See: Birth Plan). Watch online videos of births to get a realistic sense of natural birth vs. epidural vs. C-section deliveries.

Nutrition, health, and well-being tips

❑ Enjoy your baby shower! Don't let family and friend dynamics stress you out.

❑ Expect back pain, not just from your belly and weight gain, but also because the ligaments supporting your abdomen are becoming more stretchy and pliable for childbirth.

❑ Expect your belly to itch as the skin stretches and expands. Moisturizing creams, lotions, and oils can help soothe dry, stressed skin.

Organizational tips

❑ Send thank you notes for baby shower gifts. Buy a big box of cards to have on hand for gifts that you receive after birth.

❑ Purchase any baby items still needed, returning duplicates and non-essential items. Use merchandise credit from returns to buy essentials, such as feeding and health supplies.

❑ Complete a childbirth class, preferably with your spouse or a partner.

❑ Pre-register for your hospital or birth center. Take a tour of the labor and delivery unit, if possible.

❑ Pack a hospital bag (See: Hospital Packing).

❑ Read up on baby care now. You will be too tired to do this after baby is born.

❑ Read up on breastfeeding now and line up support with a lactation consultant or a breastfeeding nonprofit group in your area, such as La Leche League.

❑ Read up on natural childbirth, if desired. The term natural birth implies a goal of no drugs and no interventions. Educate yourself and your support team about natural birth, be sure to write a birth plan, and strongly consider using a doula to help get you to the finish line without drugs or an epidural.

❑ Get baby's car seat installed and inspected. Watch online videos for installation for your brand and model.

Fun tips

❑ Wash baby's clothes and linens in a dye and fragrance-free detergent. Do not remove tags from clothes that may not be worn, such as newborn dresses, sweaters, jeans, etc. You can resell, re-gift, or donate them later.

❏ Schedule newborn photos before baby is born, especially if you have a popular photographer in mind.

❏ Buy a baby memory and photo book and fill out the pregnancy sections while the memories are still fresh. Take it with you to the hospital and record details of baby's birth.

❏ Check out an app, such as Full Term or Contraction Master, to help time contractions.

❏ Go out to eat, go to the movies, and enjoy time out with family and friends before you have to pay a babysitter $15 an hour.

Week 35-delivery

Medical tips

❏ Expect weekly doctor or midwife visits until delivery.

❏ Stay close to home, since you are generally no longer safe to fly at 35 weeks, and you never know what could happen.

❏ Expect a Group B strep test (GBS) between weeks 35-37, which is just a vaginal swab.

❏ Talk to your doctor or midwife about delayed cord clamping. Instead of immediately clamping the umbilical cord, studies have shown that delaying the clamping by two to three minutes allows iron-rich, stem-cell rich, and oxygen-rich blood to be pumped to baby after birth.[10]

❏ Call your health insurance provider and ask about the requirements for adding your baby to your policy.

❏ Select your pediatrician. Baby will need to be checked right after birth.

Nutrition, health, and well-being tips

❏ Expect interrupted sleep during the final weeks of pregnancy, due to frequent bathroom trips, back pain, leg cramps, heartburn, baby's kicks, and general discomfort. Sleep on your left side with a pillow between your legs. This keeps the uterus and baby's weight off your liver, which sits on the right side of your abdomen.

❏ Try not to push too hard in the final weeks. You want to keep that bun in the oven to full term, if possible. Baby's eyes, lungs, skin, and other systems are still developing after 35 weeks.

❏ Find some time to stretch (especially on all fours for the lower back), breathe deeply (to calm yourself and prepare for contractions), and meditate or pray about your upcoming labor and delivery.

❏ Expect false labor pains in the final weeks before delivery, also known as Braxton-Hicks contractions. These contractions are an infrequent tightening of the belly that typically stops or lessens after you change activity. Real labor contractions are more regular, more frequent, and more painful, and they increase in frequency and intensity with time.

❏ Prepare for labor and delivery with positive psychology. Remind yourself that labor is "helpful pain" and "useful pain" for allowing you to meet your child. Try to limit using words about childbirth that instill fear.

❏ If your due date has passed and you are opting for natural birth with no induction, try these classic natural labor inducing techniques: go for a walk, get a massage, stimulate your nipples (to produce oxytocin), have sex if you are cleared for it (sperm contains prostaglandins, which can thin and dilate the cervix), eat spicy food (unless you have terrible heartburn), or try acupuncture or acupressure, if cleared by your doctor.

Organizational tips

❏ Write an "If I go into labor tonight" plan for work and home. Pre-designate individuals to cover your duties at work, walk your dog, or take care of an older sibling in the middle of the night.

❏ Make an email list of friends and family. Use this list for an electronic baby announcement. Fill in your baby's height and weight after birth.

❏ Email yourself a list of phone numbers to call shortly after birth, such as the number for adding baby to your insurance policy, starting maternity leave at work, a dog walking company, etc.

❏ Finalize baby names with your spouse/partner. The Social Security web site is a favorite source for baby names. Other popular name sites are babynames.com, babynamewizard.com, and behindthename.com (for name etymology and history).

❏ Keep your baby name a secret until birth, unless you want to hear everyone's opinions about it.

❏ Before baby arrives, sit down and write out a rough list of assigned chores and household duties with your spouse or partner. Balance the list until you both feel a sense of equality.

❏ Before baby arrives, have a discussion about the spiritual direction of your family. If you and your spouse do not share religious beliefs, if one is religious and the other is not, or if you were raised with different religious backgrounds, the subject will come up once you have children, especially if one parent wants the child to be baptized, dedicated, or christened.

❏ Buy some roomy pajamas or a nursing-friendly nightgown, if you do not want to wear hospital gowns.

❏ If you do not already own them, buy some large, cotton granny panties for your postpartum recovery and stock your home with natural maxi-pads. Avoid chemical-heavy pads with odor-lock protection to avoid chemical burns from extended use.

❏ If you plan to breastfeed, buy some nursing bras, nipple cream, and nursing pads (See: Baby Registry: Breastfeeding Supplies).

❏ Cook and freeze meals for after delivery. Clean out your fridge to make room for meals delivered after baby.

❏ Have a friend set up a meal schedule for you on takethemameal .com or a similar website. Email the link to any church groups, service organizations, or close family and friends in the area.

❏ Look on Groupon, LivingSocial, or other deal sites for a half-price cleaning service to deep clean areas of your home that may not receive attention in the next few months.

Fun tips

❏ Check out a book at the library that has *nothing to do* with having a baby.

❏ Take any older siblings on a "special date" before the baby arrives. Go get ice cream together. Remind them how special they are to you. Have a sibling gift picked out to celebrate baby's arrival.

❏ Write a note or make a short video telling your baby how you feel about him or her in the weeks before birth. This could be fun to read when your child is older or watch on your phone when your toddler is screaming in the grocery store.

❏ Baby is considered full term at 37 weeks, so be ready!

Is it Safe?

· · · · · · · · · · ·

Unlike books written by a single obstetrician, midwife, or pediatrician, this guide compiles "Is It Safe?" information from a multitude of respected medical sources, adding practical applications and interesting supporting facts along the way.

When I was in the Navy, launching a 72,000-pound aircraft from the deck of a floating nuclear power plant in the middle of the ocean was not exactly what most would call a safe exercise. We asked ourselves, "Is it safe?" daily with danger lurking around every corner. It was our job to constantly assess and mitigate risks without being paralyzed by fear and anxiety about our environment. A pregnant woman may find herself in a similarly precarious position.

I will be the first to admit that pregnancy safety can be difficult to discuss with just the right balance. On one hand, no one wants to stress out an expecting mom, causing her to worry about every single thing that she eats, breathes, and puts on to her skin; and truthfully, the *individual* risks of eating a cold deli sandwich or using a face cream with salicylic acid are probably very low. On the other hand, this is not your mother's pregnancy. Today, moms-to-be have to be the EPA, USDA, and FDA, as the laws that regulate over 80,000 new and existing chemicals in our environment are ineffective and out of date.* What does this mean for an expecting couple? With current legislation, government programs and

---

* The primary law for chemical safety, the Toxic Substances Control Act (TSCA), called *toss-ka* by people in the know, was passed in 1976. It provides the U.S. Environmental Protection Agency (EPA) authority to regulate new and existing chemicals used in commerce. When TSCA was enacted, all existing chemicals were grandfathered into the system and considered safe for use.

Did You Know?

Why Babies are so Vulnerable to Toxins

Babies and young children, whether in the womb or swaddled in a blanket, are not little adults. Adults have tight connections between their blood, brain, and cerebrospinal fluid (CSF). This is called the blood-brain barrier. However, embryos and newborns have immature, permeable, and "leaky" connecting points, making them critically susceptible to drugs, toxins, and chemicals in the environment. These chemicals can disrupt and alter the way our genes work together, causing developmental defects.[12] This vulnerable group also does not have the ability to metabolize, detoxify, and get rid of toxins, as an adult does, because the kidney and liver systems are still developing throughout gestation and after birth.

labels are *not* protecting your unborn child, and who knows what these chemicals are doing to your developing fetus's body and brain *in combination* with one another?

Over time, we have learned that toxins do pass through the umbilical cord during pregnancy. Just as nutrients and fluids from a mother's body are transported to baby, everything else from the environment flows there too. In a 2004 umbilical cord study, doctors found a total of 287 industrial chemicals circulating through the bodies of newborn babies (through analysis of cord blood), including mercury, fire retardants, and pesticides. Of the 287 chemicals, 217 were known to be toxic to the brain and nervous system, 180 were identified as cancer-causing, and 208 were cause for birth defects or abnormal results in animal testing.[11]

Doubts about Pregnancy Safety

Early in my first pregnancy, I knew that certain foods and chemicals were bad or off-limits, but I didn't really understand the potential long-term consequences of my choices. Others new to the pregnancy scene may have similar doubts or misgivings, such as:

1. I wasn't planning on smoking or drinking whiskey, but aren't modern parents a little bit *too* paranoid about pregnancy dos and don'ts?
2. I don't want to be one of those crazy helicopter parents. I had a childhood full of unsafe things, and we turned out okay.
3. I was born into a world full of chemicals, and my doctor says that I'm healthy.
4. Haven't they already done away with DDT, lead, and all the really bad stuff?
5. My obstetrician hasn't said very much about environmental toxins.
6. Isn't baby wrapped up in a protective bubble called the placenta anyway?

After six years spent researching these topics, I want to share a few things with you as a mom.

1. **Protecting your unborn child from environmental toxins, infections, and diseases should never be confused with paranoia.** If someone wants to makes fun of you for being cautious, then so be it. Decisions that you make during pregnancy can have lifetime consequences for your child.
2. **Being over-protective of your body while pregnant should not be confused with an over-protective parenting style, such as helicopter parenting.** The globalization of food production and the manufacturing of goods that has occurred in the last 10-15 years requires parents to think twice about the food they eat and the products they buy. You'll have plenty of time to worry about over-parenting later.
3. **The world has changed since you were in utero.** Due to extraordinarily low production costs in China and other countries, it is cheaper for food to be grown and goods to be shipped halfway around the world than to be grown or made down the street. That's why a toddler in Washington State is likely to be sipping on a juice box with apples from China (85% of apple juice in the U.S. is imported with the vast majority from China), while farmers here in the U.S. are maximizing crops with chemicals and GMOs. The problem is that a developing fetus or young child cannot process the chemicals used on those foods, as adults do, and the developing brain and nervous system are particularly vulnerable.

4. **DDT, lead, and other chemicals may have been banned for certain uses in the U.S. However, these substances still linger in the water, soil, and older buildings, and they are readily used overseas.** For example, DDT is used today to fight malaria in tropical areas, while paint with higher levels of lead is one-third the cost of paint with lower levels of lead in China. Search "lead paint recalls" to see just how prevalent this neurotoxin is in favorite toys and children's products on the shelves today.[13]

5. **Your obstetrician may not have discussed a long list of environmental toxins with you for various complicated reasons.** Based on a survey of obstetricians, she is likely to be limited on time. She may also sense that you are already anxious, and she does not want to cause more anxiety, especially with questions she is not prepared to answer, due to uncertainty about the evidence. She likely wants to discuss environmental health more openly with her patients, but does not have extra time to dig into the research. She also silently worries about what might happen to her throughput if she starts the conversation about toxins with all of her patients.[14]

6. **Not too long ago, scientists thought that the placenta shielded a baby from toxins like a big invincible bubble** (the placenta is a blood-filled structure that attaches to the wall of the uterus, while the umbilical cord arises from it and attaches to baby.) Today, we know that alcohol, caffeine, nicotine, medications, and most toxic metals have the ability to readily cross the placenta, enter the fetal bloodstream, and harm unborn babies.[15]

Are you convinced yet? In light of the loose regulation of toxins used in our food and everyday products and rapidly increasing rates of autism, attention-deficit hyperactivity disorder (ADHD), dyslexia, diabetes, cancers, and other childhood diseases, I recommend the same conservative approach to safety in pregnancy that we used in Naval Aviation: "If there is a doubt, there is no doubt." Here is a comprehensive checklist that begins by asking "Is It Safe?"

■ Alcohol

❑ No. The American College of Obstetricians and Gynecologists (ACOG) and the American Academy of Pediatrics (AAP) agree that pregnant women should avoid alcohol. If teetotaling is not possible, try a few occasional sips of wine. Bottom line: Don't waste your time and energy quarreling over whether sips, or even a small glass of wine, will hurt your baby. The underlying issue is that if a respected syndicate of physicians, such as ACOG or AAP, gave the green-light to "seldom sips of alcohol," it would likely lead to more ingestion.

■ Coffee/Caffeine

❑ Limit to one cup per day or less than 200 mg of caffeine, including coffee, tea, soda and chocolate. ACOG maintains that moderate caffeine use of less than 200 mg per day and miscarriage are not linked.[16]

❑ Calibrate your cup. Not all brews are the same.
  ► Starbucks venti 20 oz. cup has 415 mg.
  ► Starbucks grande 16 oz. cup has 330 mg.
  ► Starbucks tall 12 oz. cup has 260 mg.
  ► 20-oz. bottle of Diet Coke has 78 mg.
  ► 8-oz. cup of black tea has 40 mg.

❑ Consider cutting out caffeine altogether.
  ► A study of 60,000 pregnancies in Sweden found that babies' birth weight decreased 21 to 28 grams and gestation period lengthened by five hours for every 100 mg of caffeine consumed per day.[17]

■ Unpasteurized or Fresh-squeezed Juice

❑ Do not drink fresh-squeezed juices from restaurants, juice bars, or farm stands. This seems counter-intuitive at first, but fresh juices are not pasteurized to protect against harmful bacteria, such as salmonella and E. coli. Bacterial infections can cause serious illness in those with weakened immune systems, such as pregnant women, the elderly, and young children.[18]

∎ Sushi

❑ Do not eat raw sushi or shellfish, which can harbor parasites or bacteria. You can eat cooked sushi or vegetarian rolls; however, stick to cooked seafood low in mercury, such as wild salmon and occasional shrimp. The tuna used in sushi tends to be very high in mercury.[4]

∎ Fish

Not all fish are the same. While you want to avoid fish with high levels of mercury, eliminating it altogether is a mistake. Fish are loaded with omega-3 fatty acids that help your baby's developing brain and vision, especially in the third trimester. Therefore, FDA is continually looking into how to update their fish consumption advisories for pregnant and breastfeeding women, notably by including minimum recommendations for safe fish in addition to maximum amounts. Note: For a printable, wallet-sized reference card for eating fish, visit The Natural Resources Defense Council link at http://www.nrdc.org/health/effects/mercury/walletcard.pdf or Purdue University's website Fish4Health at http://fn.cfs.purdue.edu/fish4health/Walletcard.html.

❑ **Avoid:** shark, swordfish, king mackerel, fresh tuna (bigeye, ahi), tilefish, mahi-mahi, grouper, amberjack, orange roughy, and fish from contaminated waters.

❑ **Limit to 6 oz. per week:** canned albacore tuna and freshwater fish caught by family and friends.

❑ **Limit to 12 oz. per week:** shellfish, canned light tuna, smaller ocean fish, farm-raised fish, and store-bought freshwater fish.

❑ **Safely eat:** wild salmon, sole, flounder, haddock, halibut, ocean perch, pollack, cod, and trout.

Did You Know?
That Sounds Fishy!
• • • • • • • • • • • •

Today, more than 90% of our fish is imported, yet less than 1% is tested for fraud, such as mislabeling and fish substitution. Between 2010 and 2012, the ocean environmental group Oceana conducted one of the largest seafood fraud investigations to date, collecting over 1200 samples in 21 states. DNA testing found that one-third of the U.S. samples were mislabeled: grocery stores mislabeled 18% of samples, restaurants 38%, and sushi venues had a 74% fraud rate. Substitution of seafood is particularly alarming for pregnant women, since tilefish and other species on the "FDA Do Not Eat" list were labeled and sold as halibut and other "Safer to Eat" fish. Bottom line: Avoid eating fish from questionable sushi venues and unknown markets. Stick to seafood found in reputable national chains, such as Whole Foods, or trusted mom-and-pop fish markets with whole fish, which are more difficult to swap.[19]

Note: *Consumer Reports* issued new guidance in August 2014 for light canned tuna, indicating that while this fish is generally safe, occasional spikes of high levels of mercury have led the non-profit to advise women to skip all canned tuna throughout their pregnancy.

■ Cheese

Due to a suppressed immune system and other factors, pregnant women are 20 times more likely to contract listeriosis, a bacterial, food-borne illness from eating unpasteurized soft cheeses, unpasteurized dairy products, hotdogs, and lunch meats unless cooked.[20]

❑ *Safely eat:* Most cheese sold in the U.S., including soft cheeses, are made from pasteurized milk (mozzarella, cottage cheese, cheddar, etc.). The pasteurization process kills the listeria organism.

❑ *Do not eat:* Imported soft cheese or cheese from raw milk, such as Brie, Camembert, Greek Feta, Montrachet, Neufchatel, goat, and queso fresco, may contain listeria. Listeria can also be found in unpasteurized semi-soft cheeses, such as blue, Asiago, Gorgonzola, Havarti, Muenster, and Roquefort.

■ Hot Dogs and Deli Meats

❑ Thoroughly cook hot dogs or deli meats, or heat to a steaming hot temperature in a microwave, to avoid listeria and other pathogens. This means that if your Costco hot dog just came out of the steamer, it should probably be okay for listeria. A Kirkland Signature hot dog does contain 20% of your daily salt intake and sodium nitrite.

❑ Limit nitrates and nitrites. Nitrates and nitrites are used to preserve coloring and prevent spoiling in cured meats, such as ham, bacon, and hot dogs. When cooked with high heat or broken down in the stomach, nitrites form nitrosamines, which may cause cancer. Particularly vulnerable groups to nitrates and nitrites are pregnant women and young children.[21-23]

■ Pâté or Meat Spreads

❑ Do not eat pâté or refrigerated meat spreads to minimize risk of listeria.

■ Raw Eggs

❑ Do not eat raw eggs in cookie dough, batter, homemade Caesar dressing, and homemade desserts, including tiramisu, mousse, and meringue, if you want to be completely safe from salmonella.

▪ Peanuts

There is a good reason for the confusion on this issue. The American Academy of Pediatrics (AAP) flip-flopped its position on eating peanuts during pregnancy in recent years. In 2000, the AAP warned that pregnant women should *not* eat peanuts or tree nuts while pregnant. In 2008, the group reversed its position, explaining there is not enough evidence to prove that avoiding peanuts and other allergenic food products while pregnant reduces allergies, eczema, and asthma. A 2014 study supports the claim that early allergen exposure (eating peanuts while pregnant) increases tolerance and lowers risk of childhood allergy.[24]

❑ Talk to your doctor about eating peanuts, especially if food allergies are prevalent in your family. If there are no allergy concerns, the AAP advises that if you are pregnant or lactating, you do not have to avoid foods such as milk, eggs, and peanuts, since no protective benefit against food allergy has been found.

▪ Leftovers

❑ Heat leftovers until steaming to kill bacteria. Do not ask for a doggie bag at a restaurant, unless you know that you're heading straight home.

▪ Artificial Sweeteners

❑ Choose foods and beverages without artificial sweeteners. While there isn't clear evidence linking artificial sweeteners and pregnancy, artificial sweeteners, including saccharin (Sweet 'N Low), aspartame (Nutrasweet, Equal), sucralose (Splenda), and stevia (Truvia), prime the body for sweet tastes, promoting the consumption of more sweets to satisfy cravings. Opt for water, seltzer, or milk instead. Note: To further clarify the "artificial" nature of these sweeteners, saccharin is derived from coal tar, aspartame is made from methanol and converts to formaldehyde after digestion,

Practical Tips from Real Parents
Exercise
• • • • • •

- Prepare for labor and delivery like you are working up to a big race or big game, and you may be pleasantly surprised how your body reacts. I did this to better prepare for my second birth after the first one kicked my tail.

- My favorite pregnancy exercise was to take my phone outside and do laps around the neighborhood while talking to friends and family. Stay close to home, though, because you may need to make a pit stop.

- Prenatal yoga is the best pregnancy exercise. It helps you stretch, focus, de-stress, and prepare for labor. This is a good time to try yoga for the first time, too, because you don't have to deal with snooty or super skinny yogis.

sucralose is chlorinated sugar, and even stevia often requires unnatural agents to reduce its bitter taste. Greater consumer awareness of these sweeteners may explain why diet soda sales are in a nosedive.

■ Exercise and Pregnancy

❑ *Exercises to do:* Swimming, walking outdoors or on a treadmill, cycling on a stationary bike, pregnancy yoga, pregnancy calisthenics, and stretching routines. Stretching on all fours will relieve back pain and pressure, especially during your third trimester.[7]

❑ *Exercises to avoid:* Waterskiing, diving/jumping into pools, horseback riding, downhill skiing, cross-country skiing >10,000 feet, scuba diving, bicycling on wet pavement or downhill paths (where a fall is likely), sprinting, or any high impact sports that could cause injury to Mom or baby.

❑ *Jogging:* Jogging is typically permitted with your doctor's approval, as long as you are not a high risk pregnancy, such as preeclampsia, placenta previa, bleeding, etc. It is generally recommended that you keep the distance to under two miles per day on level terrain.

❏ *Mountain Biking:* It depends. A benign trail ride may be okay early in pregnancy, but avoid bumpy, downhill rides with a risk of falling.

❏ *Weightlifting:* Low impact weight training can be a great way to stay fit during pregnancy. However, most doctors recommend that you use lighter weights (5-10 pounds). You may not want to lift while lying flat on your back, as your uterus rests on the vena cava, restricting blood flow.

■ Air Travel

"No later than" flying rules vary from airline to airline, and some domestic and international carriers require a doctor's certificate or medical clearance between 25 and 35 weeks. Talk to your doctor before traveling.

❏ Ask for a "pat down" through airport security, especially if you travel frequently or have doubts about scanners. TSA claims that x-ray machines and body scanners are safe for pregnant women since the kind of radiation you are exposed to doesn't penetrate the body very much. However, there is no guarantee against machine malfunctions, and there is a safer alternative.

❏ If you fly pregnant, choose an aisle seat to facilitate frequent bathroom visits. Wear loose clothing and avoid tight pants. Stand and stretch often.

❏ Program your doctor or midwife's phone number into your cell phone, just in case.

■ Seat Belts

❏ Always wear a seat belt. Put the lap strap under your belly and across the hips. The shoulder strap should go between your breasts and to the side of your belly.

■ X-Rays

❑ Tell your doctor and dentist that you are pregnant, even if it is obvious, and avoid all routine x-rays for dental and diagnostic work.

■ Smoking and Secondhand Smoke

❑ *Smoking:* Most people know that smoking causes cancer, lung disease, heart disease, and other major health problems. Smoking while pregnant adds to the list, potentially causing miscarriage, problems with the placenta, prematurity, increased risk for sudden infant death syndrome (SIDS), and increased risk for birth defects, such as a cleft palate or cleft lip.[25]

❑ *Secondhand smoke:* Secondhand smoke contains over 7000 chemicals. Hundreds of these chemicals are toxic, and roughly 70 are believed to cause cancer. One study shows that women exposed to secondhand tobacco smoke have an increased risk for adverse pregnancy outcomes, including stillbirth, miscarriage, and ectopic pregnancy.[25, 26]

■ Medications (talk to your doctor before taking any medications)

My rule of thumb: do not to take any medications, prescription or OTC, unless you absolutely have to take them to stay healthy during pregnancy with a doctor's approval. Some medications may be required to prevent harm to you and your baby (i.e., for epilepsy, asthma, high blood pressure, etc.). For some women, OTC or prescription medications may be required to treat infections during pregnancy, such as a yeast infection, urinary tract infection, or sexually transmitted disease. Talk to your doctor about certain drugs, such as terbutaline (used to stop premature labor), valproic acid (used to control seizures), and antipsychotics and mood stabilizers.[27]

❏ *Pain relievers:* **Avoid aspirin, naproxen, and ibuprofen while pregnant, including Advil, Aleve, Motrin, and Bayer.** Studies have shown that aspirin and other non-steroidal anti-inflammatory drugs may increase the risk of miscarriage by up to 80%.[6] Acetaminophen (Tylenol) is generally the preferred OTC pain reliever during pregnancy for occasional use; yet two separate studies in 2014 (one aggregating over 64,000 pregnancies) linked acetaminophen use during pregnancy with higher risk for asthma, ADHD, and other behavioral disorders.[28, 29]

❏ *Cold medicines:* Talk to your doctor about medicines for cold and flu symptoms.

❏ *Allergy medicines:* Continue allergy shots with your doctor's approval, but do not begin new medications.

❏ *Herbal medicines:* Do not take herbal medicines unless prescribed by your doctor since not enough is known about their safety.

■ Household Cleaning Products

❏ Go green! Phase out toxic cleaners. Make sure there is good ventilation in your cleaning area and wear gloves to protect your skin. Avoid mixing chemicals, such as ammonia and bleach, which can produce toxic fumes.

■ Household Herbicides, Insecticides, and Pesticides

❏ Buy organic foods in key food groups, wash food thoroughly, and avoid using chemical sprays to kill insects and rodents inside and outside of your home.[30]

❏ Take your shoes off when you enter your home. Place a shoe rack by the door.

❏ Avoid common household weed killers, such as Monsanto's Roundup.

Did You Know?

Glyphosate

• • • • • • • •

Monsanto's glyphosate-containing herbicide, RoundUp, has been making headlines, due to its underestimated toxicity.[31] RoundUp is a common household weed killer and the most widely used herbicide on wheat and soy crops in the U.S. Farmers use RoundUp not only to kill weeds but also to speed up the dry down process for wheat, such as reaching 20% moisture for harvest. Glyphosate has been strongly linked to birth defects and non-Hodgkin's lymphoma, in addition to other diseases. Levels of glyphosate are now ten times higher versus decades ago, due to GMO, herbicide-resistant crops.[32]

■ Changing the Cat's Litter Box (or gardening in soil with cat feces)

❑ Have someone else change the litter box, and keep your cat indoors. Cats can become infected with toxoplasmosis as they ingest infected insects, birds, and rodents. Cats transmit this parasitic infection through their feces, which can cause birth defects, especially if contracted in the early stages of pregnancy. Also, garden with gloves if there is a chance of contacting cat feces in the soil.

■ Skin Care and Skin Care Products

❑ Know that topical ingredients do get absorbed into the bloodstream. Agents or creams that injure the thick, outer layer of skin called the stratum corneum, such as strong acids, are absorbed quickly and more readily.

❑ Avoid Retin-A/Retinol/retinoids (found in ROC Retinol Correxion, L'Oreal Revitalift, Neutrogena Age Intensives, and Oil of Olay

Pro-x), tetracycline, and products containing salicylic acid and beta hydroxy acid/BHA (most OTC acne washes and creams).

❏ Avoid prescription acne medications, similar to Accutane (the generic name is isotretinoin, sold under the trade names Amnesteem, Claravis, and Sotret).

■ Facials

❏ Avoid Botox and spa facials that use unknown chemical ingredients, or peeling agents such as glycolic acid.

■ Manicures and Pedicures

❏ Bring your own instruments from home if you are serious about reducing infection risk.

❏ Ask your technician to be gentle or skip these altogether if you are worried about contracting nail fungus, especially with pregnancy pedicures. Pregnancy conditions–such as restricted blood flow to the feet, a suppressed immune system, and increased nail bed damage caused by swollen feet stuffed into small shoes–increase vulnerability to fungus.

■ Coloring Your Hair

❏ While the American College of Obstetricians and Gynecologists (ACOG) suggests that minimal hair coloring during pregnancy is probably okay (only small amounts of dye are absorbed through the skin), schedule color appointments after your first trimester. If you must color, consider getting highlights, as opposed to full color, to reduce overall chemical exposure. If you are worried about salon chemicals, but early stray grays are driving you crazy, try a henna-based hair dye found in natural stores.[20]

Hot Tubs and Saunas

❑ Avoid hot tubs and saunas while pregnant. Studies show that water >105°F can be damaging to developing cells and embryos. A study of over 1,000 pregnant women in California showed a twofold increased risk of miscarriage associated with the use of a hot tub or whirlpool bath after conception.[33]

Hot Baths

❑ Keep bath water to < 100°F, or around your own body temperature. Avoid baths that raise your body temperature above 102-103°F.

Massage

❑ Request a masseuse trained in prenatal massage, and ask for a special maternity table. If a table is not available, make sure that you are propped up on your left side for circulation.

Alcohol-based Hand Sanitizers

❑ Prioritize washing hands with soap and water over hand sanitizers. The use of alcohol-based sanitizers has been questioned for pregnant women since alcohol may be absorbed through the skin. If used sparingly, this should not add up to detectable amounts.

Triclosan/Anti-bacterial Soaps

❑ Be cautious using too many anti-bacterial soaps and toothpastes with triclosan. Not only is triclosan linked with bacterial resistance to antibiotics, but FDA is also reviewing triclosan for possibly altering endocrine function, hindering an enzyme linked to the metabolism of estrogen. Estrogen plays a critical role in fetal brain development and gene regulation.[34]

■ Scented Feminine Hygiene Products and Douches

❑ Avoid douching, feminine sprays, and scented sanitary napkins because they can irritate the vagina and increase the risk of urinary tract or yeast infections.

■ Thong Underwear

❑ Buy cotton underwear that you feel good in and skip the thongs (cue in Sisqó). Thong underwear is linked to a higher risk of urinary tract infections and bacterial vaginosis, and thongs can also irritate hemorrhoids. If you must wear thongs, try a cotton maternity variety and sleep in regular underwear. If you are prone to yeast infections, stick with moisture-absorbing cotton.

■ Sleep Position

❑ Try to sleep on your left side to maximize blood flow, and avoid sleeping on your back after four months. Back-sleeping causes your uterus to press against your inferior vena cava, which returns blood from your lower body to the heart. The constriction can lower blood pressure and cause hemorrhoids, varicose veins, and swelling in the feet and ankles. If you wake up "feeling tingly," simply roll over to your left side.[35]

Practical Tips from Real Parents
Sleeping While Pregnant
• • • • • • • • • • • • • • • •

- I had crazy insomnia while I was pregnant, all three trimesters. I would immediately get up to check work emails, or watch Netflix on my iPad, when I should have been listening to soothing music or doing something calming. Try your best to relax and get rest at night.

- Getting up to go to the bathroom several times each night is really annoying. Try to cut back on liquids in the evening, and make sure the path to the bathroom is clear before you go to bed.

- I could not have survived without my Snoogle! My husband was less than thrilled to haul that giant thing with us on vacation, but it kept me comfortable.

- Eat your larger meal in the middle of the day, or else expect heartburn to keep you up at night.

- Stretch before you go to bed if leg cramps are waking you.

- You may want to wear a thin maxi pad to bed, especially in the third trimester. Every time I rolled over my belly pushed on my bladder.

▮ Vaccinations

For pregnant women
Diseases such as rubella and German measles present serious risks to a fetus in the first trimester, and, ideally, women should be up to date with vaccinations *prior* to becoming pregnant.

❑ *Vaccines:* Talk to your doctor about vaccine safety during pregnancy, particularly with shots administered during the first trimester.

❑ *Flu shot:* Flu is more likely to lead to serious illness in pregnant women, and contracting flu during pregnancy can increase your risk for miscarriage, premature birth, and low birth weight.[36] Also, a flu shot may protect your baby after birth. In a 2011 study, babies with mothers who had a flu shot while pregnant were nearly 50% less likely to be hospitalized for the flu as infants than babies whose mothers were unvaccinated.[37] If you get the flu shot, be sure to request the shot, not the nasal spray, which is a live virus and not appropriate for pregnant women.

■ Prenatal Testing (included due to risks of miscarriage from invasive tests)

Prenatal tests help identify health problems for both a mother and her unborn child. For Mom, they can detect blood type, gestational diabetes, anemia, STDs, and other pregnancy complications. For baby, prenatal testing can identify the chances of having a birth defect, chromosomal abnormality, or fetal abnormality, such as heart problems. Keep in mind that a screen test indicates a possibility of a problem, while a diagnostic test provides results with more certainty and accuracy.

❑ *As early as Week 10:* **Noninvasive prenatal testing** (NIPT) is a sophisticated blood test that analyzes fetal DNA in the maternal bloodstream to determine risk for chromosomal abnormalities. NIPT is typically offered to high-risk pregnancies only. Research is underway to determine how this emerging technology can be used for others receiving prenatal care (i.e., noninvasive prenatal screening generated $200 million in U.S. revenues in 2013, yet growth estimates place the industry at $5 billion by 2018). Note: The decision of whether to change current recommendations for NIPT from high-risk pregnancies to *all* pregnancies is complex, requiring more evidence for costs, false-positive rates, ability to obtain a result, and overall performance for detecting abnormalities.

❑ *Weeks 11-14:* A **nuchal translucency screening** (NT) is a non-invasive test that can help your doctor assess a baby's risk for Down syndrome and other chromosomal abnormalities and heart defects. NT screening uses ultrasound to measure the nuchal fold at the base of baby's neck, since a fetus with an extra chromosome may have more fluid in this area. This test can be combined with blood work

Going Deeper
Prenatal Testing
• • • • • • • • • • •

Prenatal testing is a touchy subject. Some parents elect not to pursue prenatal testing because they do not want to put their baby at risk, or their religious or moral beliefs are clear about carrying a baby to full term. Others choose to proceed with prenatal testing for various reasons: because certain testing is already covered by their insurance (due to maternal age, etc.), to gain clarity about whether their child has Down syndrome or a chromosomal abnormality, to have an option of intervention, to begin preparing for a child with special needs, or to help identify hospitals and resources needed for a complicated pregnancy and delivery.

for more accurate results, and it is notorious for false positives and negatives.

❑ *Weeks 10-12*: **Chorionic villus sampling** (CVS) is an invasive diagnostic test that draws a small sample of the placenta, and it is only performed if baby is at risk for genetic abnormalities. CVS may be recommended to families with high risk for inheritable disorders or immediately following a suspicious NT screen. The results detect chromosomal abnormalities and genetic disorders with high levels of accuracy (98-99%). Ask your doctor about the risk of miscarriage with CVS testing, as a large gap exists between historical estimates and current estimates, ranging from one in 100 to one in 1000. Note: It is likely that CVS miscarriage rates are higher than amniocentesis because CVS is performed earlier in pregnancy. After a miscarriage is recorded, there is no way to know whether the actual procedure caused a miscarriage.

❑ *Weeks 15-18*: **Amniocentesis** is an invasive diagnostic test that may be performed for women who are 35 years or older, have a higher-than-normal risk for genetic problems, or who have had a suspicious screen test. This test is nearly 99% accurate for neural tube defects and close to 100% accurate for genetic abnormalities. For years, mothers have agonized over whether to perform amniocentesis, due to risk of miscarriage (estimated between one and 300 and one in 500, although new research indicates risks as low as one in 1600). Many innovations, such as the use of ultrasound, have increased the safety of amniocentesis.[38]

❏ *Weeks 16-22:* The **maternal serum alpha-fetoprotein** (MSAFP) or **multiple marker screening** is routinely offered in the second trimester if you are under 35 (older expecting moms typically receive an earlier screen). Blood drawn in the "triple screen" measures the level of alpha-fetoprotein and the hormone levels of estriol and HCG. When a hormone marker called inhibin-A, a substance made by the placenta, is added, the test is called a "quad screen." The quad marker significantly boosts detection of Down syndrome.

Toxins Suspected of Causing Autism, ADHD, and Other Neurodevelopment Disabilities (NDDs)

. . . .

Autism, ADHD, and other neurodevelopment disabilities (NDDs) affect about 10 to 15% of births today, with one-third of those cases attributed to genetic causes.[39] This means that environmental factors are likely influencing the remaining 60-70%, to include environmental chemicals interacting with genetic susceptibilities. To better understand just how prevalent these chemicals are in our bodies, a 2011 nationally representative study of 268 expecting mothers found certain PFCs, PCBs, phenols, PBDEs, phthalates, PAHs, perchlorates, and organochlorine pesticides in 99-100% of women sampled.[40]

However, before we dive into another science-heavy section, I would like to help set the stage for this checklist. From the moment I started writing this book, I have struggled with how to present the material. My goal is not to dilute vital information, but with an estimated average 8th- to 9th- grade reading level for American adults, any discussion with fifteen letter words is going to make 99% of us tune out. I have been reading about these toxins for years, and nearly every chemical pamphlet and fact sheet is written over my head.

Yet this checklist ranks near the top of "all things modern parents should know," and the long names of these chemicals must be listed so that we know what to avoid. So please bear with me. I can't change the fact that the elements of the periodic table were named after Russian scientists, Greek names for astronomical objects, and cities around the

The Worst offenders

To focus on the worst of the worst toxins, avoid lead, mercury, pesticides, and endocrine-disrupting chemicals, such as BPA and phthalates.

world, but I can help you cut down your chemical exposure by explaining where to find it and how to avoid it. Here are the top chemicals suspected of causing autism, ADHD, and NDDs from the experts at The Mount Sinai Children's Environmental Health Center, with the support of the National Institute of Environmental Health Sciences and Autism Speaks. This list has been expanded to include action items, simple language, and supporting research.[41, 42]

❑ **Lead**
- ▶ *What is it?* Lead is a heavy metal and powerful neurotoxin that has been shown to cause brain damage in developing babies.
- ▶ *Where do we find it?* Lead can be found in the paint in homes, buildings, and day care centers built before 1978 and in old plumbing. Lead dust is the #1 cause of lead poisoning, and it is not always visible to the human eye. Babies and young children get exposed to lead when they put something with lead dust into their mouths.[43]
- ▶ *How do I avoid or minimize it?* Do not sand, paint, or renovate an old home while pregnant. Consider lead testing if your home was built before 1978. Do a thorough cleanup after all remodeling projects with wet mops, wet cloths, and a HEPA vacuum (a high-efficiency air filter removes very fine particles from the air that pass through the filter.) Use a dust sampling kit to test for lead dust after the cleanup. Drink filtered water if you are concerned about lead leaching from older pipes. Avoid shopping at bargain stores for baby toys, such as a dollar-type store. Researchers note that bargain stores have the highest amounts of lead and arsenic in their toys and toy jewelry.[44]

❑ **Methylmercury**

▸ *What is it?* This organic compound is created by coal-powered industrial plants and ends up in our rivers, lakes, and oceans.

▸ *Where do we find it?* Methylmercury is found in fish and shellfish. A fetus is exposed to mercury in the womb, due to a mother's consumption of fish. The developing fetal nervous system is significantly more sensitive to mercury, especially during early pregnancy. Impacts on cognitive thinking, memory, attention, language, and fine motor skills have been seen in children exposed to mercury in the womb.[45]

▸ *How do I avoid or minimize it?* Avoid seafood with the highest levels of mercury while pregnant. Avoid handling and disposing of mercury-containing products while pregnant, such as thermometers, fluorescent light bulbs, and tilt-switches.

❑ **Polychlorinated biphenyls (PCBs)**

▸ *What is it?* PCBs are older industrial chemicals used in hundreds of products produced before 1979, including electrical products, insulation, adhesives, caulking, paints, carbon copy paper, and engine coolant. The EPA classifies PCBs as probably causing cancer, and they are also linked to endocrine disruption, developmental disabilities, and decreased immune functions.

▸ *Where do we find it?* PCBs do not break down in the environment. Instead, they filter into the soil and water and slowly accumulate in animal fat and fish skins and ultimately in us.[46]

▸ *How do I avoid or minimize it?* PCBs collect in animal fat and fish skins, so trimming these can reduce exposure. Eat wild salmon. Studies show that PCBs can accumulate in farm-raised salmon, due to smaller feed fish. Steer clear of older fluorescent lights that may still have older transformers or ballasts with PCBs. Keep young children from touching, peeling, and chewing older caulk.[47]

❑ **Organophosphate pesticides**

▸ *What is it?* Many of these pesticides were developed as chemical warfare agents during World War II, so it should be no surprise this group of pesticides is highly toxic.

Organophosphate pesticides (OPs) cause a range of problems when children are exposed during pregnancy and in
early childhood, such as reduced memory, mental and emotional problems, and higher risk for ADHD. OPs disrupt the
nervous system by interfering with an enzyme that regulates
nerve impulses and acts as an important chemical regulator
of brain activity.

▶ *Where do we find it?* We find OPs, such as chlorpyrifos, the
most widely used insecticide in the U.S., on conventional
crops (especially cotton, almonds, oranges, and apples),
feed crops (especially corn), and in other non-crop settings,
such as golf courses, greenhouses, and buildings for struc-
tural pest control. OPs are specifically used to control cock-
roaches and pests in city apartments.

▶ *How do I avoid or minimize it?* Prioritize organic fruits and
vegetables. Eat a variety of fruits and vegetables from different stores and sources. Wash fruits and vegetables under
running water and peel away skins. In homes with pests,
clean up food crumbs and seal cracks and crevices as your
first defense.

❑ **Organochlorine pesticides**
▶ *What is it?* Organochlorine pesticides, solvents, and spray
fumigants, known by names such as DDT and chlordane,
have largely been banned in the U.S. and Europe, due to
health and safety concerns; yet they are widely used in developing countries, especially for fighting malaria. Because of
their chemical makeup, organochlorines break down very
slowly and remain in soil, water, and ultimately in the fatty
tissues of our bodies. Organochlorine pesticide exposure
is associated with several chronic diseases and cancers,
including Parkinson's, neurological disorders, birth defects,
and abnormal immune function.[48]

▶ *Where do we find it?* Organochlorine pesticide remnants
can still be found in agricultural storage facilities and the
environment. Endosulfan, a DDT-era insecticide banned
in 2010 and phasing out until 2016, is one of the last OCs
used on fruits and vegetables (apples, blueberries, strawberries, potatoes, etc.) The EPA classifies Endosulfan in its

most extreme category (highly acutely toxic) because small amounts are lethal in lab studies.[49]

- ▶ *How do I avoid or minimize it?* Prioritize organic fruits and vegetables. Eat a variety of fruits and vegetables. Wash fruits and vegetables under running water and peel away skins.

❏ **Endocrine disruptors (ECDs), such as phthalates and bisphenol A (BPA)**

- ▶ *What is it?* ECDs are chemical toxins that act like hormones, tricking the body into over-responding, responding at the wrong time, or blocking natural reactions.
- ▶ *Where do we find it?* ECDs are found in BPA (food and soda can linings, water bottles, and receipt paper), phthalates (pronounced THAL-ates, which are in plastics, cosmetics, vinyl tile, and air fresheners), and flame retardants (clothing, furniture coverings, computers, and mattresses).[50]
- ▶ *How do I avoid or minimize it?* Limit the use of canned goods. Always reheat foods in glass, not plastic containers. Avoid plastics, but if you must use them, avoid the 3, 6, and 7 recycle symbols, and look for symbols 2, 4, and 5. Be wary of hand-me-down plastic toys, bottles, teethers, and feeding products made before 2009. Buy cosmetics and personal care products with safer ingredients. Avoid air fresheners and products with "fragrance" as an ingredient (phthalates are used to help to stabilize chemicals and make fragrance oils last longer.) Check for use of flame retardants on clothing, furniture, and baby products.

❏ **Automotive exhaust**

- ▶ *What is it?* Vehicle emissions contain volatile organic compounds (VOCs), oxides of nitrogen, particulate matter, and carbon monoxide. One study showed that having a mother living within 1000 feet of a freeway while pregnant doubles the likelihood of having a child with autism.[51]
- ▶ *Where do we find it?* Exhaust levels are highest next to busy highways or in densely populated areas.
- ▶ *How do I avoid or minimize it?* Try to avoid living next to a busy highway.

❑ **Polycyclic aromatic hydrocarbons (PAHs)**

▶ *What is it?* PAHs are organic compounds that exist naturally in fossil fuels, such as coal, crude oil, and natural gas. They are released into the air as carcinogens, or cancer-causing chemicals, by the incomplete burning of fossil fuels.

▶ *Where do we find it?* PAHs are present in fossil fuel products, and PAH levels may be 10 times greater in urban areas than rural areas. Around the home, PAHs are found in burned meat, anti-dandruff shampoos, cigarette smoke, mothballs, and coal-tar driveway sealants.

▶ *How do I avoid or minimize it?* Eat less charbroiled meats, avoid cigarette smoke, and use nontoxic alternatives to mothballs, such as cedar chests, vacuuming often, and plant-based deterrents. Remove your shoes before entering your home, especially if you have contact with heavy oils, asphalt, or roofing tar.[52]

❑ **Brominated flame retardants (polybrominated diphenyl ethers or PBDEs)**

▶ *What is it?* These compounds work to inhibit combustible materials, such as a sofa, from igniting (thanks to heavy lobbying by the tobacco industry in the 1970s). PBDEs get into our lungs through dust and into our blood through ingestion and skin contact. Mothers participating in research studies have been shocked to learn they had PBDEs in their breast milk. PBDEs are linked to cancer, autism, infertility, and other neurological and developmental problems.

▶ *Where do we find it?* These chemicals are found in mattresses, furniture foam, motor vehicles, TVs and computers, and coatings on fabrics.[53] In 2011, a study of 101 widely used baby products found that 80% of them contained flame retardants.[54] PBDE levels have doubled in people every three to five years for the past three decades.

▶ *How do I avoid or minimize it?* Throw away ripped items with foam padding inside and watch for PBDE dust when pulling up old carpet. New foam items are not likely to contain PDBEs; however, foam padding or furniture produced before 2005 should be inspected carefully. Use a vacuum fitted with a HEPA filter to reduce PBDE dust.

❑ **Perfluorinated compounds (PFCs)**

▶ *What is it?* PFCs, or non-stick chemicals, are widely used to make products resistant to stains, grease, and water. Teflon and Scotchgard are two of the most recognized brand names of PFCs. PFCs break down very slowly in the environment and bind to organic tissue, including those that make up human blood and the brain. PFCs have been linked to several types of cancer.

▶ *Where do we find it?* We find PFCs in stain-resistant carpets and furniture, grease-resistant food packaging (fast food containers, pizza boxes, and microwave popcorn), non-stick cookware, dental floss, clothing, and shampoo.

▶ *How do I avoid or minimize it?* Check personal care labels for the words "fluoro" or "perfluoro" (dental floss, cosmetics, moisturizers, and eye makeup). When you start seeing scratches in your cookware, replace it with cast iron or untreated stainless steel. Choose clothing, carpeting, and furniture without stain-resistant treatments.[55]

Additional Neurotoxins

Dr. Philip Landrigan at Mount Sinai School of Medicine in New York and his colleague, Dr. Philippe Grandjean at Harvard School of Public Health, have studied industrial chemicals for over 30 years. In 2014, these scientists sounded the alarms calling for the urgent formation of an international clearinghouse for industrial chemicals to fight this "silent, global pandemic."[39]

The list of neurotoxins was also updated to include:

❑ **Arsenic**

▶ *What is it?* Arsenic occurs naturally in the environment (in rocks, air, soil, and water) and as a by-product of agricultural and industrial activities. Arsenic is perhaps less known for its neurological nastiness than as one of the most prominent environmental causes of cancer mortality in the world. Arsenic has been linked to lung, skin, and bladder cancers, heart disease, stroke, and diabetes. However, it can also interfere with brain development and cause behavioral problems.

▶ *Where do we find it?* This odorless, tasteless potent poison is found in small amounts in our food and water.

▶ *How do I avoid or minimize it?* Widespread high concentrations of arsenic are found in the West, Midwest, parts of Texas, and the Northeast. Get your water tested if you drink from a well, especially in New England (Maine to Massachusetts) or the Midwest (Michigan and Minnesota), which are areas with high natural levels of arsenic in rock, or if you live in an area with mining or big agriculture (central valley California, Western states), if you live near metal smelters where metal is made, or if you live near a garbage incinerator. Dr. Landrigan and other groups also recommend avoiding or limiting rice consumption, especially rice from Texas and Louisiana, noting that the Gulf Coast areas treated cotton crops a century ago with arsenic pesticides.

❏ **Toluene**

▶ *What is it?* Toluene is a colorless, flammable liquid.

▶ *Where do we find it?* Toluene is added to gasoline to improve octane ratings. It is also used to produce benzene and other household products and solvents, such as paint, paint thinner, gasoline, rubber cement, nail polish, and detergents. Solvents have been linked to hyperactivity and aggressive behavior.

▶ *How do I avoid or minimize it?* If you smell fumes from these products, leave the room. Don't deliberately sniff it. Avoid exposure in the workplace, such as printing and painting.

❏ **Manganese**

▶ *What is it?* Manganese is a naturally occurring substance that can cause damage to the brain at high levels. Excessive manganese levels are linked with diminished intellectual function (ADHD and reduced IQ) and impaired motor skills (Parkinson's disease).[56, 57]

▶ *Where do we find it?* Manganese is a normal part of air, water, soil, and food. As a trace element found in people's diet, manganese in small amounts is essential to keeping your organs healthy, including the brain. However, high concentrations can be harmful. Pregnant women, infants and children are exposed to manganese mostly through diet (cereals, leafy vegetables, fruit, and fruit juices), including breast milk and formula. Vegetarians who consume foods rich in manganese, such as grains, beans, and nuts, and heavy tea drinkers may have higher than normal manganese levels. Manganese inhalation can also be toxic.

▶ *How do I avoid or minimize it?* Check your well water for manganese levels, especially if you are pregnant. Filter your water. Avoid soy formulas with high manganese levels.[58] Do not feed baby soy or rice milk beverages in the place of infant formulas.[59] Limit exposure to factories with welding or manganese products, mining activities, and automotive exhaust.

❑ **Fluoride**

▶ *What is it?* Fluoride compounds are salts that occur when the element fluorine combines with rocks or soil.

▶ *Where do we find it?* Fluoride is found in toothpaste and drinking water. Although helpful in small doses for dental health, too much fluoride can lead to tooth and bone lesions. An analysis of 27 studies on high levels of fluoride (mostly in China) concluded that high concentrations of fluoride can cause adverse effects on the brain.[60]

▶ *How do I avoid or minimize it?* Watch fluoride levels in your water. Keep young children from ingesting toothpaste by smearing small amounts on their toothbrush and keeping tubes out of reach.

❑ **Tetrachloroethylene**

▶ *What is it?* This is a chemical used for dry-cleaning and metal degreasing.

▶ *Where do we find it?* When you bring clothes home from the dry cleaners, tetrachloroethylene (perchloroethylene or PERC) is released in small amounts into the air. It can also be found in drinking water.[61]

▶ *How do I avoid or minimize it?* Dry-clean your clothes without the use of PERC. If you cannot find a PERC alternative, air out recently dry-cleaned clothes. Avoid living in an apartment directly above a dry-cleaning facility.

Chemicals in Cosmetic and Personal Care Items

· ·

Beauty may be skin deep, but the chemicals in your personal care products are likely to go deeper—into your bloodstream and body. Many consumers are surprised to discover the FDA does *not* review the safety of cosmetics and personal care products before they go to market, other than color additives. Instead, the agency has authorized the industry to police itself through a Cosmetics Ingredient Review (CIR) panel. To note, this panel has declared just 11 ingredients as unsafe since it was established in 1976, and its recommendations for restricting personal care ingredients are not binding to companies.[62] In contrast, the European Union has banned over 1,000 ingredients from use in cosmetics and personal care products. What does this mean for Americans? Well, for starters, in the same way that Mars, based in McLean, VA, markets M&M candies with artificial dyes in the U.S. (dyes linked to hyperactivity), while using vegetable and plant-based dyes for M&M's in Europe, American beauty companies sell same-label cosmetics that are safer overseas than the products made for customers back home. Talk about irritating!

With such a loosely regulated industry, it is becoming clear that we should look more closely at ingredient labels and ask ourselves a few questions:

- What is happening to my body as my skin absorbs an average of nine personal care products per day, containing 120 chemicals or so, day after day, and year after year?

- Then what happens to those chemicals when they get washed down the drain and sent into our water system?

To help you think about some of these issues, here is a list of some of the worst chemical offenders in beauty and personal care. [63]

❑ **Antibacterials (triclosan)**
   ▶ *What is it?* Triclosan is currently under review with the FDA over potential long-term health risks, such as unanticipated hormone effects and contributions to resistant bacteria. Triclosan also contaminates the environment. After triclosan is washed down drains, it is converted to dioxin when exposed to sunlight in an aqueous environment. It can also combine with chlorine in tap water to make chloroform, a probable carcinogen.[34]
   ▶ *Where do I find it?* Triclosan is found in toothpaste, soaps, and hand sanitizers, such as Colgate Total toothpaste, Softsoap liquid hand soap, Dial liquid soap and bars, Clearasil Daily Face Wash, and Bath & Body Works antibacterial soaps.
   ▶ *How do I minimize or avoid it?* Use natural soaps without the antibacterial label. Try a natural toothpaste, such as Tom's of Maine or The Natural Dentist.
❑ **Coal tar**
   ▶ *What is it?* Coal tar is a thick brown or black liquid that forms as a by-product when coal is processed. Since coal tar has been used for the treatment of psoriasis and other skin diseases for over a century, it has been grandfathered into the system. Coal tar is known to increase skin sensitivity to sunlight.
   ▶ *Where do I find it?* Dyes with a coal tar base are used in dandruff shampoos (Neutrogena T/Gel Shampoo, Psoriatrax Anti-Dandruff Tar Shampoo), permanent hair dyes (salon and drugstore dyes made by Loreal, Revlon, Clairol, and others), mouthwash (FD&C Green 3), and toothpaste (FD&C Blue). The EU banned coal tar in 2004. Much of the evidence linking hair dyes with cancer has come from studies of salon workers.

- ▶ *How do I avoid or minimize it?* Check labels on hair dyes, skin creams, and dandruff shampoos. Look for these ingredients: Coal tar solution, tar, coal, carbo-cort, coal tar solution USP, crude coal tar, estar, impervotar, KC 261, lavatar, picis carbonis, naphtha, high solvent naphtha, naphtha distillate, benzin B70, and petroleum benzin.

❑ **Diethanolamine (DEA)**

- ▶ *What is it?* Diethanolamine (DEA) is a chemical that can adversely affect hormones and cell functioning and development. The EU has banned DEA in cosmetics.
- ▶ *Where do I find it?* DEA is used in shampoos and soaps to increase lather. Ethanolamines are also found in lotions, shaving creams, ointments, eyeliners, mascaras, blush, foundations, and sunscreens.
- ▶ *How do I avoid or minimize it?* Avoid labels with MEA, TEA, and DEA and anything that ends in –ethanolamine. Worry less about mascaras with DEA and more about lotions that remain on the skin and shampoos lathered in close proximity to your brain.

❑ **1,4-Dioxane**

- ▶ *What is it?* 1,4-dioxane is a cancer-causing byproduct of a process called ethoxylation, which is a shortcut companies take to make soaps and shampoos milder and less irritating to the skin. 1,4-dioxane is on the state of California's list of chemicals known to cause cancer, and it is banned for use in cosmetics in Canada. The Environmental Working Group (EWG) estimates that 97% of hair relaxers, 57% of baby soaps, and 22% of the more than 25,000 products in the Skin Deep database may be contaminated with 1,4-dioxane.
- ▶ *Where do I find it?* 1,4-dioxane is found in products that make suds, like shampoo, bubble bath, and liquid soap.
- ▶ *How do I avoid or minimize it?* 1,4-dioxane should not be in cosmetics and personal care products certified under the USDA National Organic program. Avoid labels with sodium laureth sulfate and ingredients written as PEG, -xynol, ceteareth, and oleth.

❑ **Formaldehyde**
  ▸ *What is it?* Formaldehyde is a probable human carcinogen that can be added to products as an ingredient or released from formaldehyde-releasing preservatives (FRPs).
  ▸ *Where do I find it?* Formaldehyde is found in products such as baby bath soap, nail polish, and hair dyes, as a contaminant or a break-down product. Vulnerable groups are infants, salon workers, and nail salon workers.
  ▸ *How do I avoid or minimize it?* Avoid labels with formaldehyde, quaternium-15, DMDM hydantoin, imidazolidinyl urea, diazolidinyl urea, sodium hydroxymethylglycinate, and 2-bromo-2-nitropropane-1, 3-diol (bromopol). Look for "toxic-trio-free" nail polish (formaldehyde, toluene, and DBP). Avoid keratin-based hair straighteners in hair salons, such as Brazilian Blowout. These products were found to contain up to 12% formaldehyde. Even Jennifer Aniston attributed a recent short hair chop to a "bad Brazilian."

❑ **Fragrance and phthalates**
  ▸ *What is it?* These endocrine disruptors mimic the action of our natural hormones, and they can cause reproductive and developmental harm.
  ▸ *Where do I find it?* Phthalates are often hidden under the term "fragrance" in beauty products. Look for phthalates, such as dimethyl phthalate (DMP), diethyl phthalate (DEP), and dibutyl phthalate (DBP), in hair spray, perfumes, deodorant, nail polish, and almost anything with fragrance.
  ▸ *How do I avoid or minimize it?* Use fragrance-free products.

❑ **Lead and mercury**
  ▸ *What is it?* Lead is responsible for making color lipsticks last. The longer it lasts, the more lead it contains. Also, the FDA generally does not allow mercury in drugs or cosmetics; although, mercury has been found in excessive levels in many beauty and skin products made overseas and sold in local ethnic stores.
  ▸ *Where do I find it?* Brands of lipstick or lip-gloss, such as Clinique, Maybelline, Revlon, and Cover Girl, are found to be lead positive. Lead can also show up in products that

have hydrated silica, such as toothpaste. Mercury has been found in soaps, cosmetics, and skin care products in stores that tend to cater to Latino, African-American, Asian, and Middle Eastern communities.

> ▶ *How do I avoid or minimize it?* Choose organic or natural cosmetics that do not contain lead and mercury (See Baby Registry: Just for Mom).

❑ **Nanoparticles**

> ▶ *What is it?* Nanoparticles are tiny particles within lotions and makeup that could cause cell damage.
> ▶ *Where do I find it?* Nanoparticles of zinc oxide and titanium oxide can be found in cosmetics and sunscreens. There is reasonable evidence that normally harmless skin ingredients, such as titanium dioxide, may cause damage if introduced to the body in nanoparticle size; especially concerning are smaller nanoparticles with a pre-existing skin condition, such as recent exfoliation or a cut in the skin.
> ▶ *How do I avoid or minimize it?* Choose products that are free of nanoparticle-size ingredients, especially sunscreens.

❑ **Parabens**

> ▶ *What is it?* Parabens are common preservatives that prevent bacteria growth. Parabens became controversial due to their weak estrogenic effects in animals studies. Estrogen disruption is linked to breast cancer and reproductive issues.
> ▶ *Where do I find it?* Parabens are found in about 85% of cosmetics.
> ▶ *How do I avoid or minimize it?* Check for methyl-, ethyl-, propyl-, butyl-, and isobutyl- paraben. Choose paraben-free brands, such as Burt's Bees, Aveda, Dr. Hauschka, and Josie Maran Cosmetics.

❑ **Petroleum distillates (PDs)**

> ▶ *What is it?* Petroleum distillates are solvents made from crude oil. They are used as inexpensive moisturizers in cosmetics and personal care products. The EU restricts or prohibits petroleum distillates as possible human carcinogens.
> ▶ *Where do I find it?* PDs are found in mascara, eye shadow, foundation, wart remover, and foot-odor powder.

▶ *How do I avoid or minimize it?* Check for the terms "petro-leum" or "liquid paraffin" in products.

❑ **P-Phenylenediamine (PPD)**

▶ *What is it?* P-Phenylenediamine is widely used as a dye, and it is associated with allergic reactions.

▶ *Where do I find it?* PPD can be found in 307 hair coloring and bleaching products in EWG's Skin Deep database. PPD can cause irritation and damage to the nervous system and lungs.

▶ *How do I minimize or avoid it?* Scan a product's barcode with the Skin Deep mobile app before purchasing home hair coloring products.

❑ **Hydroquinone**

▶ *What is it?* Hydroquinone, banned from cosmetics in the EU, is one of the most toxic ingredients still used in personal care products today, with links to cancer, organ toxicity, allergies, and immune system toxicity.

▶ *Where do I find it?* Hydroquinone is found in skin lighteners, facial and skin cleansers, facial moisturizers (under-eye treatments), hair conditioners, and nail glue.

▶ *How do I minimize or avoid it?* Hydroquinone is heavily marketed to women of color in skin lighteners. Avoid labels with hydroquinone, tocopheral acetate, tocopheral, tocopheral linoleate, and other ingredients with the root "toco."

Morning Sickness and Nausea

· ·

Morning sickness, though typically not harmful to you or your baby, can sincerely affect your quality of life, especially in the first trimester. To start, the term "morning sickness" is often a misnomer, since nausea and vomiting can last the entire day. Morning sickness also typically peaks at a time when many women are trying to hide or remain private with their pregnancy, especially at work. If you find yourself in this position, know that nearly half of all women who experience nausea in pregnancy feel complete relief by 14 weeks. Until then, try a few of these tips and tricks for nausea relief.

❑ Eat small meals throughout the day. Don't skip meals.
❑ Take note of what foods and smells are triggers for queasiness, such as raw meat, garbage, greasy foods, or strong body odor, and avoid them.
❑ If you can't avoid an offending smell, pack decoys in your purse: citrus lotion for your hands, a pleasant herb pouch with lavender or mint, or a small washcloth with a dab of lemon oil.
❑ Keep crackers at your desk at work and by your bed. Eat a few before you get out of bed each morning. Favorite picks: one serving of Trader Joe's 12 Grain Mini Snack Crackers has 10% of the daily value of iron. For a gluten-free option, try Food Should Taste Good Brown Rice Crackers made from brown rice flour, sesame seeds, flax seeds, amaranth, and quinoa or crackers made from chickpea flour.
❑ Try acupressure wristbands, such as Sea Bands used for seasickness.

Try these food suggestions for nausea:

- Bland foods: chicken soup, broth, plain baked potato, potato chips, pasta
- Whole grains: toast, bagels, brown rice, oatmeal
- Cold foods: sandwiches, raw veggies and hummus, avocados, cheese
- Fruits and vegetables: cold applesauce, pears, citrus, potatoes
- Ginger: ginger ale, ginger tea, ginger snaps, Gin-Gins candy
- Crackers or pretzels, with peanut butter or almond butter for protein
- Lemons: sniff them, slice them and put them in water
- Peppermint: decaf tea, mints
- Popsicles: Italian ice, real fruit bars, frozen fruit, homemade yogurt and fruit pops
- Lollipops or hard candy: Preggie Pops, Preggie Pop drops, B-natal candy
- Beverages: sparkling water, water with electrolytes: SmartWater, Vitamin Water, 365 brand

❏ Put gentle pressure on your wrist (in the groove between the tendons below the top crease of your wrist).

❏ Put a cool compress on your neck.

❏ Drink a cold Gatorade or freeze beverages with electrolytes in ice cube trays for hydration. Suck on frozen fruit or a healthy frozen yogurt bar.

❏ Take a prenatal vitamin daily for adequate vitamin B6, which is linked to relief of pregnancy nausea. If you suspect that the iron in your prenatal vitamin is making you sick, talk to your doctor about a slow-release option.[64]

❏ If the size of your prenatal vitamin is too big to swallow (calcium is a bulky mineral), talk to your doctor about a smaller pill.

❏ Avoid sitting in front of a computer monitor outside of work. Unnoticeable monitor flickering can make some women nauseous.

❏ Drive rather than riding as a passenger in the car.
❏ Wear loose clothing. If your pants or skirts are tight around the belly, it may make your nausea worse.
❏ Finally, if you just need to "let it go" and you want to look chic doing it, don't leave home without a designer barf bag from morningchicness.com.

What to Eat While Pregnant

· ·

A healthy diet includes lots of fruits and vegetables, lean proteins, and whole grains (though types and amounts of the latter are debatable). During pregnancy, you can fine-tune a basic healthy diet by adding foods that contain essential nutrients for your developing baby, such as lean protein, iron, calcium, folate, DHA, and other vitamins and minerals.

If you are vegan or vegetarian, talk to your doctor or midwife, or consult a registered dietician. You may need supplemental protein and supplemental vitamins B12 and D.

Essential Nutrients for Pregnancy

❑ Protein
  ▸ Your developing baby's cells are growing at a rapid pace. Every cell in the human body is made up of protein.
  ▸ *Food sources:* cottage cheese, boneless/skinless chicken breast, fish, lentils, milk, peanut butter, quinoa (pronounced keen-WAH), beans, and eggs
❑ Iron
  ▸ Your body needs about 50% more iron when you are pregnant, primarily to make hemoglobin, the protein in red blood cells that carries oxygen to your organs and tissues. Boost iron intake by pairing vitamin C-rich foods with iron-rich foods, such as mandarin oranges with edamame, red peppers with spinach, and tomatoes with broccoli.

- *Food sources:* iron-fortified cereal, beans, spinach, lean beef, duck, poultry, quinoa, pumpkin seeds, tofu, lentils, black-strap molasses, and edamame (cooked soybeans)
❑ **Calcium**
  - Baby needs calcium to build strong bones and teeth. If you do not consume enough calcium, your body will take it from your bones, which can lead to osteoporosis later.
  - *Food sources:* milk, yogurt, cheese, ice cream, salmon, spinach, broccoli, edamame, roasted almonds, fortified cereal, and fortified orange juice
❑ **Vitamin B9 (Folate)**
  - Folate helps prevent neural tube defects, which are serious problems with the brain and spinal cord.
  - *Food sources:* fortified cereal, spinach, beans, lentils, asparagus, broccoli, avocado, peanut butter, oranges, and dark leafy greens
❑ **Vitamin B6**
  - This vitamin helps produce protein for new cells, form new red blood cells, and boost immunity.
  - *Food sources:* fortified cereal, garbanzo beans, baked potato with skin, lean beef, and chicken breast
❑ **Vitamin B12** (found naturally in animal sources)
  - This vitamin helps make DNA, the genetic material found in all cells, and it plays a role in healthy brain and nervous function. Vitamin B12 also produces red blood cells and helps your body convert fats and carbohydrates to energy.
  - *Food sources:* wild salmon, lean beef, lamb, chicken
  - *Vegetarian sources:* milk, yogurt, eggs
  - *Vegan sources:* Kellogg's All-Bran cereal, General Mills Multi-Grain Cheerios, vitamin B12 fortified soy milk and other B12-fortified foods
❑ **Vitamin C**
  - Vitamin C is not stored in the body, so you'll need a fresh supply for your immune system and for baby's growing body.
  - *Food sources:* oranges, kiwi, strawberries, mango, pineapple, grapes, bell peppers, tomatoes, asparagus, broccoli, spinach, and cauliflower

❏ **Vitamin D**
  ▸ Vitamin D is essential to building baby's bones and teeth.
  ▸ *Food sources:* milk, low-mercury fish, asparagus, eggs (in the yolk), vitamin D fortified orange juice, and vitamin D fortified soymilk
❏ **Docosahexaenoic Acid (DHA)**
  ▸ Omega-3 fatty acids support healthy brain and eye development.
  ▸ *Food sources:* wild salmon and fortified eggs (safest food sources during pregnancy)

What is the "Pregnancy Diet?"

Several authors have coined variations of the phrase, but if you hear this term, it is more than likely a reference to the pregnancy "daily dozen" diet from *What to Expect: Eating Well When You're Expecting.* Please reference the book for more in-depth analysis and recipes.[18]

❏ **Calories:** roughly 300 extra calories daily
❏ **Protein:** three servings daily
❏ **Calcium:** four servings daily
❏ **Vitamin C:** three servings daily
❏ **Green and yellow vegetables and yellow fruits:** three to four servings daily
❏ **Whole grains and legumes:** six or more servings daily
❏ **Iron-rich foods:** some daily
❏ **Fat and high-fat foods:** approximately four servings daily (depending on your weight gain)
❏ **Salty foods:** in moderation
❏ **Fluids:** at least eight glasses daily
❏ **Prenatal vitamin supplements:** a pregnancy formula taken daily

Tips for Pregnancy Nutrition

❏ **Talk to your doctor before taking any supplements other than a prenatal vitamin.** For example, if you don't drink milk, and you

Did You Know?
Pregnant and Gluten-Free
• • • • • • • • • • • • • • • • •

Popular books, such as bestsellers, *Wheat Belly* by cardiologist William Davis and *Grain Brain: The Surprising Truth about Wheat, Carbs, and Sugar–Your Brain's Silent Killers* by neurologist David Perlmutter, have helped spearhead a mainstream gluten-free movement, maintaining that gluten and excess carbohydrates lead to inflammation in our bodies and brains. Non-celiac pregnant women on a gluten-free diet should talk to their doctor or midwife. (Note: celiac disease is a digestive and autoimmune disorder that can damage the lining of the small intestine.) Many gluten-free products are made with unenriched grains and starches that are loaded with calories and short on vitamins and minerals.

- **If you are diagnosed with celiac disease, talk to your doctor.** Expect to maintain a healthy gluten-free diet during pregnancy. Strive to breastfeed your infant through baby's gluten introduction, as it may decrease his or her chance of acquiring celiac disease.

- **If you are on a gluten-free diet "just because", talk to your doctor.** Without proper monitoring, a gluten-free diet can leave you depleted of B vitamins, iron, calcium, zinc, and fiber. For example, breads made with tapioca, rice, and other gluten-free flours are typically not fortified. Fortified breads and cereals are some of the top sources of B vitamins for women in the U.S. This group needs vitamin B_9, also known as folic acid or folate, to prevent birth defects.

- **To maintain a gluten-free diet, focus on good sources of gluten-free foods to boost potentially deficient areas.**
  - *Sources of gluten-free fiber:* beans, quinoa, ground flax seeds, berries, sweet potatoes with skin, nuts, kale, chia seeds, broccoli, and prunes
  - *Sources of gluten-free iron:* beef, poultry, liver, soybeans/edamame, lentils, green peas, spinach, and amaranth
  - *Sources of gluten-free calcium:* milk, hard cheese, yogurt, fortified milks (almond, soy, etc.), and green leafy vegetables

> ▸ *Sources of gluten-free B vitamins:* meats, leafy greens, nuts, seeds, beans, quinoa, GF oatmeal, brown rice, and enriched products (Rice Chex, etc.),
>
> ▸ *Sources of gluten-free zinc:* poultry, beef, liver, dark turkey meat, pecans, pumpkin seeds, beans, and brown rice

take a calcium supplement, you may not know that calcium supplements from natural sources, such as oyster shell or bone meal, can be high in mercury.

❑ **Take a prescription-level prenatal vitamin with DHA.** While popping a gummy bear may seem like an easier option than swallowing a horse pill, some prenatal gummy brands, such as Vitafusion PreNatal, do not contain iron, calcium, thiamin, or riboflavin. DHA and other vitamin and mineral levels are also lower than recommended daily values.

❑ **Take your prenatal vitamin with orange or fruit juice.** Vitamin C enhances the absorption of iron into the bloodstream.

❑ **Take your prenatal vitamin at a different time than calcium supplements** or TUMS to get the full benefit of each.

❑ **Drink plenty of water.** If plain water is too bland, add slices of lemon, lime, cucumber, or watermelon to enhance flavor. Consider trying an infusing water bottle, such as a BPA-free Infuser bottle, or a stainless steel Aquazinger water bottle.

❑ **Try a breakfast cereal that really packs a punch, containing 100% of the Daily Value for folic acid *and* iron *and* vitamin B12,** such as General Mills Total and Total Raisin Bran, or Kellogg's Product 19 and All-Bran Complete.

❑ **If you eat meat, prioritize lean cuts of beef and pork** since they contain choline as well as protein.

❑ **If you eat canned tuna, choose canned light tuna over white, albacore tuna,** which is higher in mercury. FDA limits canned light tuna to 12 ounces per week and albacore to six ounces per week for pregnant women.

❑ **Skip canned goods for tomato sauces in glass bottles or soups in BPA-free Tetra Paks.**

❑ **For canned goods, stick to brands without BPA,** such as Eden Foods, Amy's, and some Trader Joe's canned products, such as tomatoes, corn, tuna, and beans (except baked beans).

❑ **For snacks, choose a fruit, vegetable, protein, or calcium food:** a hard-boiled egg, an orange, a banana, trail mix, Greek yogurt with flaxseed sprinkles, cottage cheese cup, string cheese, veggie sticks with edamame hummus, a small box of fortified cereal, a Larabar or Kind bar, apple slices with peanut butter, nuts, or seeds.

❑ **For lunch**, try a mashed avocado-chickpea sandwich, leftover slices of lean beef and sliced red peppers, pre-cooked lentils on a bed of quinoa, or hit a local salad bar and load up on vegetables and lean protein.

❑ **For desserts**, try a glass of chocolate low-fat milk (using an organic syrup such as Trader Joe's Organic Midnight Moo), a cored and baked apple with raisins and cinnamon, a frozen fruit and yogurt smoothie, a fresh fruit salad with honey and diced mint leaves, natural ice cream, or a square or two of dark chocolate.

❑ **For cooking oils and salad dressings**, use heart-healthy canola, flaxseed, and olive oils.

❑ **For trips to the supermarket, shop for whole foods around the edges of the store.**

❑ **Try a helpful nutrition app. Fooducate** and **ShopWell** both have built-in bar scanners that read ingredient labels and provide nutritional food scores for packaged foods. Fooducate adds funny warnings, such as "Look out! Not 100% whole grain" or "Contains controversial artificial colors," while ShopWell personalizes and adjusts nutritional scores based on your diet and food preferences, such as gluten intolerance, dairy intolerance, diabetes, etc.

❑ **Finally, don't let "nutrient eating" lead to over-eating.** In the time leading up to my first pregnancy, I was consumed with an intense job hardly thinking about nutrition. I gained 30 pounds in my first pregnancy. During my second pregnancy, I was writing a book about pregnancy and obsessing over my nutritional intake. My pregnancy weight gain was 50 pounds with a healthy diet. Looks like I covered all of those important nutrients and then some!

Pregnancy Nutrition Books

There is perhaps no better time in life to read a book about nutrition than while pregnant. Unlike books on breathing techniques and childbirth, which address a process that could be over in hours, nutritional advice can benefit you and your family for life. Here are some of my picks for the best pregnancy nutrition books:

Best for Easy Reading

❑ *What to Expect: Eating Well When You're Expecting* by Heidi Murkoff and Sharon Mazel

Best for Sample Menus and Recipes

❑ *Eating for Pregnancy: The Essential Nutrition Guide and Cookbook for Today's Mothers-to-Be* by Catherine Jones and Rose Ann Hudson (a culinary school graduate and perinatal nutritionist/registered dietician team)

Best for Nutrition Nuts

❑ *Expect the Best: Your Guide to Healthy Eating Before, During, and After Pregnancy* by Elizabeth Ward (spokesperson for the American Dietetic Association)

Best Vegetarian

❑ *Your Vegetarian Pregnancy: A Month-by-Month Guide to Health and Nutrition* by Holly Roberts (vegetarian and OB/GYN)

Best Vegan

❑ *The Everything Vegan Pregnancy Book: All you need to know for a healthy pregnancy that fits your lifestyle* by Reed Mangels (coauthor of the American Dietetic Association's position paper on vegetarian and vegan diets and food guide for vegetarians)

Practical Tips from Real Parents
Eating and Nutrition
• • • • • • • • • • • • •

- Don't be lazy about taking your prenatal vitamin. Take it at the same time each day. Set an alarm on your phone if you tend to forget things.

- If your prenatal vitamin is making you sick, take it with food. You can also cut it in half.

- Be aware that some prenatal vitamins contain stool softeners because of the extra iron. I couldn't stand having sticky poo all the time (I'd rather be constipated), so you may want to check the label on your prescription before your doctor orders a nine month supply.

- Try not to let pregnancy justify eating junk food or too much food. I kept telling myself "Well, I'm going to get fat anyway," and guess what? I did.

- Don't drink too many juices while pregnant. I did this to cut out diet soda however the calories and sugar add up. My doctor attributed much of my 60-pound weight gain to my liquid intake.

- If you get carried away with eating mid-pregnancy, don't diet to make up for it in the third trimester. Simply eat a healthy diet and work off the extra pounds after baby arrives.

- Don't eat sugar or bread right before your 28-week, one-hour glucose test (for gestational diabetes), or else risk a "false positive" and a follow-on three-hour test. Talk to your doctor about whether to fast or not. If you do eat, eat eggs for breakfast well before the test.

Pregnancy Grocery List

. . . .

This grocery list has been compiled using multiple nutrition books and online sources. The **most nutrient-dense choices for pregnancy** are listed at the top of each food group (left to right).

Colorful vegetables *(select a few and mix them up each week)*

- ❏ sweet potatoes
- ❏ bell peppers
- ❏ broccoli
- ❏ avocados
- ❏ winter squash

- ❏ tomatoes
- ❏ artichokes
- ❏ carrots
- ❏ cauliflower
- ❏ beets

- ❏ green peas
- ❏ asparagus
- ❏ brussel sprouts
- ❏ summer squash
- ❏ parsley

Dark green, leafy vegetables

- ❏ spinach
- ❏ kale

- ❏ swiss chard or collard greens

Colorful fruits *(select a few)*

- ❏ blueberries
- ❏ blackberries
- ❏ raspberries
- ❏ strawberries

- ❏ cantaloupe
- ❏ kiwi
- ❏ papaya
- ❏ mango

- ❏ bananas
- ❏ oranges
- ❏ grapefruit
- ❏ apples

- ❏ cherries
- ❏ pineapple
- ❏ watermelon

Dried Fruits

- ❏ apricots
- ❏ raisins
- ❏ figs

Whole grains

- ❏ quinoa
- ❏ fortified cereal (Total, All-Bran)
- ❏ oatmeal
- ❏ 100% whole wheat bread
- ❏ whole wheat tortillas or pitas
- ❏ whole grain or protein-fortified pasta
- ❏ brown rice
- ❏ whole grain crackers
- ❏ baked chips

Beans

- ❏ lentils
- ❏ soybeans/ edamame
- ❏ chickpeas/ garbanzo
- ❏ black beans
- ❏ pinto beans
- ❏ kidney beans

Lean meats and proteins

- ❏ beef (95-98% fat free)
- ❏ pork
- ❏ chicken breast
- ❏ lamb
- ❏ tofu

Dairy products

- ❏ low fat Greek yogurt
- ❏ skim milk, with vitamin D and DHA
- ❏ soy or almond milk (with calcium)
- ❏ cottage cheese
- ❏ string cheese
- ❏ cream cheese

Fish and seafood *Mayo Clinic safe seafood list*
8 to 12 ounces, approx. 2 meals per week

- ❏ salmon (wild U.S.)
- ❏ anchovies
- ❏ herring (Atlantic)
- ❏ sardines
- ❏ trout
- ❏ shrimp (wild North American)
- ❏ pollock
- ❏ canned light tuna
- ❏ canned salmon

Eggs

- ❏ eggs fortified with omega-3 acids

Nuts, Seeds, and Popcorn

- ❏ walnuts
- ❏ almonds
- ❏ pumpkin seeds
- ❏ sunflower seeds
- ❏ ground flax seeds
- ❏ popcorn
- ❏ peanut butter (natural)

Beverages

- ❏ calcium-fortified orange juice
- ❏ 100% fruit juice
- ❏ sparkling water (glass bottle)
- ❏ natural or organic ginger ale

Baking and Condiments

- ❏ whole wheat flour
- ❏ organic ketchup
- ❏ all fruit, low sugar preserves

Financial Planning for Baby

· ·

❑ **Set aside at least three months living expenses for emergencies** and then add three months more, if you can.

❑ **Add your child to your life or health insurance policies.** Typically, you have 30 days to do this with your employer after a major life change.

❑ **Research childcare options based on your income and expenses.** Use web-based calculators to examine your family budget, with and without the expense of childcare, in order to assess the feasibility of one parent staying at home or the impact of a potential job loss.

❑ **Create a budget using budget software or an online tool.** Don't forget to include baby expenses. For a free, web-based personal financial tool that plugs into your banks, credit cards, investments, and retirement accounts, showing you where your money goes, try Mint.com or the Mint app.

❑ **Purchase life insurance for you and your spouse or increase current coverage.** Consider purchasing a term insurance policy, which is cheaper than permanent insurance and has a death benefit without an investment account attached. A 20- or 30-year premium term policy, which is convertible to permanent insurance in the future, is adequate. With a routine physical and a medical questionnaire, you can lock in rates for the next 20 to 30 years.

❑ **Consider disability insurance.** While supporting your child, you will need to guarantee income if you can't work.

❑ **Make a will.** Half of all Americans and 70% of adults under age 34 do not have a will. Dying without a will means that you have no say about who gets your bank accounts, real estate, jewelry, cars, and other property after you die. Your assets will be tied up in what is called "probate," an expensive and lengthy legal process that could last months or years, depending on the complexity of the estate. If you *and* your spouse die without a will, the state will choose a guardian for your child and decide how your money and property are to be divided. If you have family assets that you would like to be passed directly to a child, and not to your spouse, a trust should be established.

❑ **Take advantage of all child tax deductions, credits, and savings programs**. Talk to an attorney for tax advice. Looking into these types of tax savings programs could save you thousands of dollars.

▶ **Dependent exemption.** When you add a child to your family, you can add a tax exemption called a "dependent exemption" to your personal exemption (or exemptions, if you are filing jointly). The dependent exemption reduces your taxable income, and the amount you save depends on your tax bracket—the higher your bracket, the more you save up to a phase-out income.

▶ **Child Tax Credit.** The popular $1000-per-child tax credit, provided your income is below a certain threshold ($55,000 married filing separately, $75,000 single, or $110,000 married filing jointly) is complex but worth checking out. The child tax credit was enacted in 2013, and it offers parents a reduction of their tax bill dollar for dollar, if they qualify.

▶ **The Child Care Credit.** The child care credit provides a tax credit for the first $3000 of child care expenses, including day care centers, nannies, and even day camps during the summer break.

▶ **Dependent Care Flexible Spending Account (FSA).** Check to see if your employer offers a Dependent Care FSA, which lets you set aside a portion of your paycheck tax free to pay for child care expenses. This also lowers your taxable income. There are typically limits to the amounts that can be contributed.

▶ **Medical Flexible Spending Account (FSA).** This FSA lets you set aside a portion of your wages tax free for out-of-pocket medical expenses, such as co-payments, deductibles, some drugs, and other qualifying expenses. FSAs are available through many employer-based health plans. The major disadvantage is that you must spend what you put into the account.

❏ **Get started on college savings**. Set up a fund that you, grandparents, and relatives can contribute to early on, if budget allows. For a baby born in 2015, the College Board college cost calculator estimates that in 18 years, the cost of tuition, fees, room, and board for four years of private college will add up to $657,011 (using a 7% cost inflation rate). The cost of out-of-state public college will amount to $509,029. In-state public college will cost $295,308, and four years of in-state community college, $172,293.*

❏ **Don't be afraid to ask for a salary raise** *before* **baby's arrival.** Despite advancements in education for women, female full-time workers still make 77 cents for every dollar earned by men, a wage gap of 23%.[65] Some of that gap is likely explained by differences in college majors and types of jobs, such as science, technology, engineering, and math or STEM jobs vs. lower paying jobs in education and healthcare. Yet outright discrimination in pay, promotions, and hiring is also a likely contributor. When negotiating your salary, consider these tips:

▶ Keep a detailed record of your specific achievements and accomplishments.

▶ Know the market value of your salary for your region.

▶ Know your company's compensation policies.

▶ Initiate a meeting and then let your employer talk first, or risk naming a price lower than a potential offer.

▶ Don't say "yes" immediately to an offer.

▶ Don't settle for "no." If your salary is non-negotiable, ask for other benefits, such as a bonus, vacation time, flextime at home, profit sharing, etc.

▶ Be polite and professional, but be bold. If you really want something, you have to ask.

---

* Note: The national average tuition cost has inflated 6-7% each year for the past 30 years. Total cost estimates based on national averages are calculated by the College Board's Trends in Pricing. To update costs, visit http://www.collegesavings.org/collegeCostCalculator.aspx.

20 Tips for a Greener Pregnancy

· ·

Just a decade or two ago, being green meant that you were probably wearing Birkenstocks and living a "crunchy," "granola," or "alternative" lifestyle. Today being green has become decidedly mainstream, thanks to a rising generation of parents and consumers who are informed, Internet-savvy, and seeking eco-friendlier options for everyday life. Being green takes on a whole new meaning when you are pregnant, too, as you strive to protect not only the environment but also your unborn child.

❑ **Even if you have never considered being green in your entire life, be green while you are pregnant.** Your baby is affected by everything that goes into your body, including gases and fumes.[11]

❑ **If you desire a hospital-free birth and have a low-risk pregnancy, consider using a midwife at a nonhospital birth center**. As long as you are in close proximity to emergency support, a birth center may be more open to your requests for a natural labor and delivery.

❑ **Let a doula help**. Some studies show that having a doula present during birth can reduce invasive or sometimes unnecessary medical interventions, such as pain medications, Pitocin to induce labor, or premature C-sections.[66]

❑ **Worry more about daily green practices and less about natural birth.** Strive for a natural birth, if desired. However, everyday activities during pregnancy, such as eating organic foods, minimizing exposure to toxins, using greener products, and avoiding alcohol, cigarettes, and medications, are far more likely to impact your baby than the decision of whether to have an epidural or not. Studies show that baby's health is about the same whether a mother chooses an epidural or natural birth, with statistically similar blood pH levels, Apgar scores, and meconium levels in the bowels.[67]

❏ **Pick a green-leaning pediatrician.** How do you treat ear infections? What is your policy for antibiotics? Read the practice website and assess how green your pediatrician may lean.

❏ **Recycle and re-use secondhand baby gear, maternity clothes, and baby clothes that are outgrown quickly.**

❏ **Check food labels and ingredients carefully.** Prioritize organic whole foods during pregnancy, especially meat, eggs, and dairy. Eat ocean-friendly, sustainable seafood (different from mercury in seafood), which can be found in the Monterey Bay Aquarium Seafood Watch Pocket Guide for your region. Read infant formula labels.

❏ **Consider slowly replacing the family's linens with organic cotton.** Conventionally grown cotton accounts for more than 25% of global insecticide use and 10% of total pesticide use.[68]

❏ **Use as many natural beauty and personal care products as possible.** Focus your dollars on products that remain on your skin, such as creams and lotions, or on products that are used on your head, such as shampoo.

❏ **Beware of personal care products with phony "green" labels.**
  ▶ **Hypoallergenic:** Manufacturers can use this word without proving their claim.
  ▶ **Natural:** This word is meaningless and can be applied to any personal care product.
  ▶ **Organic:** This can be used as a label in personal care even if only 1% of the content is organic.
  ▶ **Fragrance free:** This implies that a product has no scent or odor. Even if there is no scent, other substances can be added to mask the odor of other ingredients.
  ▶ **Unscented:** This generally means that no ingredients have been added to mask odors. Confused? Good. Beauty companies want you to be. Bottom line: "fragrance-free" products may still have essential oils or fruit/flower extracts added, which can contain allergens, just like natural and synthetically blended "fragrances."

❏ **Check skin and personal care product ingredients online.** These databases can help you learn more about the current safety of personal products.
  ▶ The Campaign for Safe Cosmetics at www.safecosmetics.org
  ▶ Skin Deep product guide at www.cosmeticsdatabase.com
  ▶ NIH Household Products at www.householdproducts.nlm .nih.gov

❏ **Skip any toxic home renovations that could uncover lead dust in your home.** Test old paint with a DIY lead testing kit or have a professional inspection of your home. Older Venetian blinds can also have lead.

❏ **Limit bottled water and install a water filtration system in your home, or use a high-quality filtering carafe.** Filtered tap water is your best choice for hydration. Two studies in 2008 found an alarming number of pollutants in bottled water, including industrial chemicals, bacteria, and radioactivity.[69, 70]

❏ **Reduce indoor pollutants.** Change your sheets once a week, vacuum carpets and furniture, and dust and clean regularly with a wet cloth. For mold, fix leaks and eliminate sources of moisture. Use an exhaust-vent while cooking on a gas stove or range. Have a contractor tune up any furnaces, flues, chimneys, and gas appliances. Install a carbon monoxide detector. Consider an air purifier for your home. Grow air-purifying plants: Areca palm, Lady palm, Bamboo palm, rubber plant, Chinese evergreen, Gerbera daisy, and Janet Craig.[71]

❏ **Use green gardening and landscaping techniques.** Compost garden and household waste. Use natural fertilizers and plant foods, such as TerraCycle or eco-brands at Lowe's or Home Depot. Plant organic and heirloom seeds. Get green gardening tips from www .joegardener.com or watch recorded episodes of *Growing a Greener World*, an award-winning public TV program on green living, organic gardening, and farm-to-table cooking.

❏ **Use green methods of indoor pest control.** Use a cordless vacuum to sweep up crumbs (Dyson vacuums are worth every penny) and caulk around showers and sinks. Use sticky pads to catch critters indoors rather than using sprays and toxins.

- ❑ **If you live in an area with limited access to green products, try online retailers.** For natural food, health and beauty, pet, and household products, try Amazon's VineMarket.com or AbesMarket. com. For sustainable home goods, try BranchHome.com or Bambeco.com. For organic home gardening supplies, try OliveBarn. com.
- ❑ **Vote with your dollars.** Choose organic foods and eco-friendly products. When the competition goes up, prices will come down.
- ❑ **Be skeptical of established green brands and curious about new labels.** Once a brand or product has established a loyal customer base, executives will scale back the product's cost by reducing or eliminating the most expensive ingredients. Newer green products and smaller brands must differentiate themselves from the big guys, and they can't do that with cost. Quite often, they differentiate themselves by offering purer, healthier products.
- ❑ **Plant a tree in honor of your baby.** One tree can absorb up to 48 pounds of carbon dioxide per year, which adds up to one ton by the time your child is 40 years old. For more comprehensive green tips, read *Raising Baby Green: The Earth-Friendly Guide to Pregnancy, Childbirth, and Baby Care* by Alan Greene (author), Jeanette Pavini (contributor), and Theresa Foy DiGeronimo (contributor).

Choosing a Child Care Center

· ·

If you work outside the home, your choice of child care may be one of the most important decisions that you make for your child. This decision should be thought of as a fluid situation that may change, though, depending on your circumstances. For example, during pregnancy you may select a day care center near your office and register for a future time period. However, if your baby is born prematurely or has other health issues, you may want to wait a few months before introducing baby to this center, especially during cold and flu season.

Before we begin with our child care center checklist, let's discuss some pros and cons of different child care options.

Child Care Center (Day Care)

Pros: state regulated, possibly accredited beyond state requirements (National Association for the Education of Young Children or NAEYC), extra resources for toys and supplies, other children to play with, accountability, additional safety, higher supervision of caregivers

Cons: a strict schedule requires precise drop-off and pickup times (i.e., incurring fees for every minute late), potential overstimulation, lack of peaceful sleeping options, germs and more germs, other children may adversely affect your child

Average Cost: $380 to $1564 a month for babies and toddlers, depending on your location*

Home Day Care

Pros: usually less expensive than other options, home environment, smaller group than a day care center, other children to play with, usually more flexibility with drop-off and pickup times

Cons: no backup if the care provider gets sick, less stringent accountability and licensing, safety standards may be lower, more germs than a nanny, closed during holidays and vacation time, TV may be used excessively for younger children who can't tattle

Average Cost: $300 to $1000 a month for babies and toddlers

Nanny

Pros: more convenient than day care, flexibility in scheduling, peaceful sleep in familiar surroundings, consistency with one caregiver, one-on-one attention (interactive conversation with an adult), a nanny may care for a sick child when a day care center would require backup care

Cons: nanny supervision is low, a baby or toddler cannot communicate indiscretions, dependence on one person, need for backup care, the extra expense and paperwork of being an employer (nanny taxes, paying for sick time and vacation time, etc.)

Average Cost: $2167 to $3033 a month for babies and toddlers

Now let's proceed with how to choose a child care center, but don't worry, the Hiring a Nanny checklist is coming up next.

---

* Source for child care costs: National Association of Child Care Resource and Referral Agencies (NACCRRA)

Start Early

❑ Start researching child care as early as possible. This process may take time.

Assess Child Care in Your Area

❑ Begin your search by talking to friends and co-workers in the area.

❑ Call local experts, such as a local Child Care Resource and Referral agency (CCR and R), if desired.[72]

❑ Search "day care" or "child care" and your city online to find centers, or register for an online child-care service such as Care.com or Sittercity.com. Find an accredited child care center in the NAEYC searchable database at http://families.naeyc.org/find-quality-child-care.

❑ Assess whether your family qualifies for any child-care financial assistance.

❑ Obtain information about complaints and licensing violations.

When your list narrows, assess your child-care options with the following questions:

Child-to-Staff Ratio and Group Size

❑ How many children are being cared for in the child-care program for your age group? Double-check real vs. aspirational numbers. Visit during working hours to crosscheck.

❑ How many teachers or caregivers are present? State minimums exist for each age group (i.e., one home caregiver is limited to caring for two infants.)

❑ What is the turnover rate for teachers/staff?

Supervision and Security

❑ Are children supervised at all times?

❑ Is supervision consistent during meal time and nap time?

❑ How do the caregivers discipline children?

❑ If the center is a home day care, are children taken out of the house? Does the provider walk or drive?

❑ Are there security cameras at the front desk to monitor visitors coming in and out?

❑ What is the pick-up and drop-off policy?

Director Qualifications

❑ Does the director of a child care center have at least a bachelor's degree in a child-related field?

❑ How long has the director worked in child care? (At least two years of experience is preferable.)

❑ Does the director understand children well?

❑ Is this someone whom you would like to work with on a regular basis?

Lead Teacher Qualifications

❑ Does the lead teacher in a child care center have a bachelor's degree in a child-related field?

❑ Has the teacher worked in child care for at least two years?

❑ What is the level of interaction between teachers and parents?

❑ Is there regular communication between teachers and parents?

Hand-washing and Diapering

❑ Do all caregivers and children wash their hands often (i.e., when children walk into the classroom, before eating, and after using the bathroom or changing diapers)?

❑ Is hand-washing consistent for older children who may be around your baby?

❑ Is the place where diapers are changed clean?

❑ Do caregivers keep a hand on the child while changing his diaper?

Eating and Sleeping

- ❑ What is the feeding schedule and meal policy?
- ❑ Is the program willing to use and warm breast milk?
- ❑ Does the center or home day care provide snacks and meals? At what age? What is the cost?
- ❑ If food is brought from home, is the center willing to heat it?
- ❑ Is each child able to sleep according to their own rhythms, or is a schedule set by the center?
- ❑ Where will my child sleep?

Immunizations

- ❑ Is your child up-to-date on all of the required immunizations?
- ❑ Does your state have a standard medical entry form for child care centers? What other information do you need to gather from your child's pediatrician for entry?
- ❑ Does the child-care program have records proving that the other children in care are up-to-date on all required immunizations? Ask about the number of exemptions.

Hazardous or Toxic Substances

- ❑ Are hazardous or toxic substances kept away from children (cleaning supplies, rodent traps, pest sprays, gardening supplies, etc.)?
- ❑ Has the building been checked for dangerous substances like radon, lead, carbon monoxide, and asbestos?
- ❑ Is poison control information posted? Are teachers trained for poison incidences?

Emergency Plan

- ❑ Does the child-care program have an emergency plan if a child is injured, sick, or lost?
- ❑ Does the child-care program have a food allergy plan?

❑ Does the child-care program have a standard process about who to contact in an emergency?

❑ Consider leaving your cell number on your child's check-in sheet each day, in addition to forms filled out for day care entry.

Fire/Emergency Drills

❑ Does the child-care program have a plan in case of a disaster like a fire, tornado, flood, blizzard, or earthquake? National emergencies?

❑ Does the child-care program do practice drills once every month?

Child Abuse and Accountability

❑ Have all caregivers had background checks?

❑ Can caregivers be seen by others at all times, so a child is never alone with one caregiver?

Medications

❑ Does the child-care program keep medication out of reach from children?

❑ What is the medicine policy? Policy for applying diaper cream and sunscreen?

❑ Are the caregivers trained, and the medications labeled, to make sure the right child gets the right amount of the right medication at the right time?

Staff Training/First Aid

❑ Have caregivers been trained to keep children healthy and safe from injury and illness?

❑ Do they know how to do basic first aid and CPR?

❑ Have they been trained to understand and meet the needs of children of different ages?

❑ Are all child care staff, volunteers, and substitutes trained on and implementing infant back sleeping and safe sleep policies to reduce the risk of SIDS (sudden infant death syndrome)?

❑ When infants are sleeping, are they on their backs with no pillows, quilts, stuffed toys, or other soft bedding in the crib with them?

Playgrounds

❑ Is the playground regularly inspected for safety?

❑ Does a fence surround the playground?

❑ Are the soil and playground surfaces checked often for dangerous substances and hazards?

❑ How old is the equipment?

❑ Is the equipment the right size and type for the age of children who use it?

Cost-Benefit Analysis

❑ If a child care center is significantly more expensive than its competitors, why?

❑ Do you have a back-up plan if your child is sick? How much will that cost per hour?

❑ Do you have a list of priorities for your child care needs? What are your child's health considerations?

❑ Is it worth paying more to have your child at home with a nanny, or do you prefer the accountability and structure of a day care center?

❑ Is home day care a better option to balance cost and size of a large day care center?

Other Considerations

❑ How is TV used in the day care?

❑ What is a typical day in the day care center?

❑ Are you allowed to observe the prospective day care center, or home day care, during working hours? Assess overall impression,

Practical Tips from Real Parents
Day Care and Child Care Centers

• •

- If possible, choose a day care center near your work. Late fees can add up if you have to commute through traffic, or if you are habitually late.

- Make sure that you read the fine print with late fees for pickup. One day care we considered was $5 per minute late (after a five minute grace period). This seemed excessive at first, but now I understand why. The parents, including myself, were always running late.

- Home day care can be good or bad for baby's first year. In an environment with just a few children, your baby will probably get more attention and more sleep than in a commercial day care center. However, you have to constantly assess how other children coming into the home are affecting your child.

- With home day care, be mindful of males living in and passing through the home. No one wants to think about this stuff, but child sexual abuse offenders are 90 to 95% male.

- Expect lots of colds the first year in day care. Babies put everything into their mouths, and it is impossible for workers to keep your child from getting sick.

- If your baby has a perpetual diaper rash, put together a rash kit and provide explicit instructions for baby's diaper care.

- If your child seems unusually unhappy at drop-off or pickup, don't discount this reaction. There may be a problem.

- Don't be afraid to speak up or change your child care center if you think something is wrong.

happiness of the children, and level of speaking engagement with the children.

❑ Have you talked with other parents with children currently attending the prospective child care center?

❑ Do caregivers respect the culture, languages, and values of the families in the center?[73]

Hiring a Nanny or Babysitter

. . . .

A few years ago, a friend and his expecting wife shared how thrilled they were to have selected a nanny for their unborn child who would teach their baby three different languages. Seriously, whose toddler isn't trilingual these days? I withheld any sarcastic comments. However, it really bothered me; this intelligent, well-meaning couple may have unknowingly selected the wrong caretaker for their child. Above all other qualifications, a good nanny or babysitter should have:

- **Knowledge of child development**
- **Self-control** and
- **Emotional maturity**

She should understand why children behave the way they do, and she must be able to calm and soothe an upset child. She should understand that safety comes first and be familiar with the repetitive, unpredictable nature of caretaking. Languages spoken, academic degrees, and other societal measures of achievement are not at the core of what it takes to love and nurture a child. Moreover, children need consistency. If a nanny is only able to work a few months while taking classes for a short time, she may not be a good fit for a long-term job.

Getting Started

❏ **Start early.** The process of hiring a nanny requires time and effort. It may take two to three months to conduct a search without an agency.

❏ **Do not rush the process.** Anyone can call himself or herself a nanny. There is no regulating agency that licenses or monitors nannies; therefore, your effort in screening individuals is key to discerning caretakers that can be trusted with your child.

❏ **Assess your budget for a nanny agency.** Agency fees can range from $1200-5000. Some busy, working parents find this service to be worth the money, while others find the fee to be prohibitively expensive.

❏ **If you decide to use an agency, call several different ones and ask to speak with the director.** Read the small print before you sign any contract.

❏ **For self-searchers, get organized.** Label all emails and forms with a "Nanny Search" header or filter. Keep a notebook to log phone calls and notes.

❏ **Try an online nanny and babysitting service.** If you are using an online service to find your nanny, such as 4nannies.com, Care.com, or Sittercity.com, search for online promotion codes and reduced first month rates. Care.com is my favorite online service.

Self-Search: Advertising the Position

❏ **Post your job with an online service and browse candidates in your area.** Contact anyone who fits your profile, even if the availability does not match up completely.

❏ **Ensure that your job posting establishes clear expectations.** This should help filter candidates. Consider the following questions:
  ▶ How many days per week? Hours?
  ▶ Will you request occasional overtime, or overnights for work travel?
  ▶ How many years of experience are required?
  ▶ Is proximity to your home required?
  ▶ Does your candidate have reliable transportation?

- ▶ What specific duties are expected, especially if housekeeping is included? Cooking, cleaning, laundry?
- ▶ Are driving duties expected? Do you require a clean driving record?
- ▶ Is health insurance provided?
- ▶ How much paid vacation time is provided?

❏ **If you are uncomfortable with an online search, post ads at a local college, church or synagogue, or on a local mom's group list-serve.**

❏ **Protect your personal information** by not including your home phone or address until you have narrowed candidates. Establish a separate email address for your search, if desired.

❏ **Request that candidates leave their name, phone number, years of experience, and other qualifications on your cell phone or email.**

❏ **Conduct a quick Internet search to assess each candidate.** Eliminate those with unsavory Facebook profiles, photos, tweets, etc.

❏ **Call your list of candidates with a standard set of questions.**

❏ **Set up interviews only with those who answer the questions to your satisfaction.** Verify the hours and days required and a short job description before confirming an in-person interview.

Self-Search: Conducting Background Checks

❏ **Collect identification information for each applicant.** Remember, this is standard procedure for any job application, and a full-time nanny is going to be with your child daily. You do not need to collect this information for a simple babysitting job.

- ▶ Birth certificate or Social Security card
- ▶ Valid driver's license
- ▶ Home phone, address, and cell number
- ▶ Character references (no family members)
- ▶ Work references (addresses and phone numbers, no friends or family)
- ▶ CPR certificate, if required
- ▶ Proof of a physical exam from the last two years, if required
- ▶ Resume and cover letter

❏ Make copies of IDs and crosscheck references.

❏ Consider visiting the home of references to ensure that kids are present.

❏ **Conduct a criminal background check.** Check for aliases and numerous addresses in a short period of time. Conduct background checks with a healthy dose of skepticism. Many candidates will provide misleading information, overestimate qualifications, and supply friends and family as references.

Interviewing

❏ **Make a list of your priorities**, such as years of experience, experience with infants, clean driving record, irons, cooks, cleans, etc. Seek the best candidate for your priorities.

Interview Questions – Personality Assessment (applies to both nannies and babysitters)

❏ Can you tell me about your childhood?

❏ Tell me about your past experience nannying or babysitting. What were the ages of the children?

❏ Do you enjoy working with children?

❏ What do you find most challenging about nannying?

❏ Please explain any gaps in work history.

❏ What is your child-rearing philosophy?

❏ What is your view on disciplining children as a nanny?

❏ How would you handle the following situations:
  ▶ What if our infant has a high fever?
  ▶ What if our infant has colic and will not stop crying?
  ▶ What if our daughter swallowed a coin and was choking?
  ▶ What if our son fell down the stairs?
  ▶ What if our toddler son bites, or hits, the baby?

❏ Are you flexible and able to roll with it, or do you prefer structure and planning ahead?

Interview Questions – Job Assessment

❑ Are you willing to do light housework?

❑ Are you willing to iron? Fold clothing?

❑ Are you willing to cook? Take care of our pet?

❑ Are there household activities that you will not do?

❑ Are you willing to take our baby on walks outside regularly?

❑ How many children are you comfortable supervising?

❑ How flexible is your schedule, if we need to leave early, get home late, or travel overnight?

❑ What is your driving record?

❑ Are you willing to abide by household rules for TV watching and media use while on the job?

When your nanny, or babysitter, arrives at your home

❑ Consider a trial period, observing your prospective nanny and evaluating whether you are ready to enter into a contract together.

❑ Make sure that you have your nanny's personal information on file: address, cell phone number, and email.

❑ Post information for all members of your family.

❑ Post your home address and phone number, in case of emergency.

❑ Determine the best way to reach each other during the day, or in the case of an emergency.

❑ Post numbers for the pediatrician/pediatrician's office, schools, and a close friend, family member, or neighbor that could assist in case of emergency.

❑ Ensure that both you and your nanny have a signed work agreement, including agreed upon pay, work hours, and expected duties.

Nanny Taxes

Here's the scoop on nanny taxes. You will have some friends who choose to pay their nannies in the clear (filing taxes), and you will have some friends who choose to pay their nannies under the table (paying cash). Be assured this topic will never be discussed at playgroups or dinner parties. Moreover, some expecting parents may not understand that workers must prove eligibility to work in the U.S. before filing taxes (employees affirm this by filling out a form called an I-9.) So to help you navigate this tricky topic, especially for full-time nanny positions, let's discuss nanny taxes.

Pros: By paying taxes, you will not have to worry about the IRS or legal troubles, especially if you are an aspiring CEO or public official. Paying employer taxes allows your nanny to receive benefits that other professional workers enjoy, such as Social Security income, Medicare, disability, and unemployment benefits.

Cons: Your nanny will make roughly 15% less than her hourly rate, and you will pay 10% more for taxes and other costs. The paperwork is complicated, completing regular filings to your employee, the IRS, and state government. Note: You can hire companies, such as HomePay or Home-Work Solutions to do the hard work for you, or use DIY online subscription services, such as QuickBooks or NannyPay.

Practical Tips from Real Parents
Hiring a Nanny or Babysitter

- Your baby is hard-wired to want and need you, and they are going to cry for you. Loudly. This is the toughest part about leaving a child with someone else.

- If you are a working mother without family in the area, know that you will be delicately handling a nanny relationship for years to come, and it's not easy.

- There is no perfect nanny. No one can be expected to take care of your child exactly as you do.

- Micro-managing your nanny can have horrible consequences. Pick your battles.

- Treat your nanny well. This is a business relationship, but it is also a personal relationship that you do not want to jeopardize.

- Do not try to undercut your nanny's pay, vacation time, or talk down to her. Treat her professionally, and invest in her as part of your family.

- Be careful with hiring nannies for children between ages zero and three. When children are older, they can tell you what they did all day.

- Nanny cams are legal in all 50 states, even without consent, as long as it is not in a bathroom or a private place, such as an au pair's bedroom. However, we found that we didn't have time to watch our nanny cam footage (to actually catch something), and if you don't trust your nanny, then you probably shouldn't hire her anyway. Note: Some states protect against using audio in recordings.

- Be sure to explicitly state rules about phone use at home, while driving, and at the park, especially once baby is mobile. Set hard and fast rules about TV and screen time, and don't keep convenient junk food around the house, or else that is what your nanny will feed your child.

- If your nanny has other children, your relationship may be in constant conflict, especially when you are late, because she has to make provisions for her own children.

- A nanny with her own children will be out of work more often, requiring back-up care. On the other hand, someone who is significantly older may not have the energy to chase an energetic toddler, and teenagers are on their phones constantly. Take your pick.

- Many nannies will want to care for your child along with their own child or children. Just know that a nanny's own active toddler may consistently wake your newborn, while a nanny's newborn may keep your older baby or toddler from going outside, to the park, etc. due to their nap schedule. Make sure that you receive a discount for this inconvenience.

- If you live in an urban area, you will notice that nanny pricing is all over the map. Super affluent households throw normal wages through the roof in certain cities.

- Set your rules and schedule very clearly up front to avoid seeming like a micro-manager later, such as rules for healthy foods, diapering, TV, cell phone use, tummy time, learning activities, outside time, discipline, safety, etc.

Childbirth Options:
Delivering Your Baby

· · · · · · · · · · · · · · · · · · · ·

The best childbirth option is the one that ends with a safe delivery, a healthy mom, and a healthy baby.

Parents and moms-to-be have more options than ever before for delivering their baby. Do you want a natural delivery in a home-like setting? Or do you prefer having the security of modern medicine in a hospital setting? Deciding which type of childbirth experience that you desire is a very personal decision, although some factors, such as a high-risk pregnancy or insurance coverage, may limit your choices. Let's walk through the pros and cons of several childbirth options.

Location of the Birth

■ Hospital

Pros: Complete medical intervention is available, a NICU may be available for baby, insurance typically covers the birth, and you can stay overnight and rest. Many hospitals now offer private rooms and family-centered care, allowing your partner and your baby to stay with you.

Cons: Ambience is less home-like, privacy is limited, birth positions may be restricted, and effort may be required to have a natural birth (interventions are more likely to be pushed in a hospital setting.)

You may not want to have a hospital birth if:
- You are a woman with a low-risk pregnancy who desires a natural birth in your home or a home-like setting.
- You are a woman with a low-risk pregnancy who has prepared for a natural birth and senses that your closest hospital may offer resistance to your childbirth plan.

▮ Birthing Center

Pros: Birth centers offer a higher chance of achieving a natural birth, and they provide a home-like setting with larger beds, soft chairs, birthing tubs, balls, and other equipment to help you feel comfortable. Most centers are located near a hospital (some are physically located in a hospital), and you will typically go home the same day as giving birth.

Cons: Insurance may not cover the costs if the center is not accredited, and you will have to travel to a birthing center just like a hospital. You are sent home the day of giving birth, which can be difficult without help. You must also prepare for a transfer to a hospital, if complications arise (7-12% is the average transfer rate for a birth center.)

You may not want to have a birthing center birth if you:
- Have a pregnancy complication, such as preeclampsia (pregnancy induced high blood pressure), diabetes, etc.
- Are pregnant with multiples
- Do not have insurance that covers your birth center, and you cannot afford the out of pocket cost

■ Planned Home Birth

Pros: A planned home birth gives you the ability to give birth in a familiar and comfortable setting, and the ability to wear what you want, eat food, and walk around your home freely. At home, you will have no time constraints, more privacy, and more control over labor positions and the birthing process. Home births also cost less than hospitals and birthing centers.

Cons: The risk for infant death with home births is two to three times higher than hospital births (though still low overall). You must plan for a hospital transfer in case of emergency, and life-threatening problems can arise without notice. Homebirths are illegal in some states, although unassisted births without a certified professional midwife are legal. Not all insurance companies cover home births.[74]

A health care provider may caution against a planned home birth if you:
- ❏ Are pregnant with multiples
- ❏ Previously had a C-section
- ❏ Have a pregnancy complication, such as preeclampsia or preterm labor
- ❏ Have diabetes, hypertension, or a chronic medical condition
- ❏ Have a baby not in a head-down position

Note about home births: The American College of Obstetricians and Gynecologists (ACOG) and American Academy of Pediatrics (AAP) affirm that hospitals and birthing centers are the safest place for births in the United States, while respecting the right of women to make a medically informed decision about delivery. ACOG does not support the provision of care by lay midwives or other midwives who are not certified by the American Midwifery Certification Board.[75, 76]

Types of Delivery

■ Vaginal Birth

Pros: Vaginal birth is the natural way with a generally quicker recovery and shorter hospital stay. In this type of delivery, women participate more actively in the birth process, which can lead to a sense of accomplishment. Baby is also less likely to have respiratory problems and is exposed to beneficial bacteria in the birth canal, while Mom has a decreased risk for hemorrhage, blood clots, or complications. Breastfeeding is typically easier after vaginal birth.

Cons: For some women, the risk of perineum tearing with a vaginal delivery may cause fear and anxiety. Baby also risks oxygen deprivation, due to cord compression or other problems, and baby may experience trauma through the birth canal. Women who deliver vaginally also have a higher risk for incontinence and pain with intercourse in the weeks after delivery, especially with a tear.

■ Cesarean-section (C-section)

Pros: A scheduled C-section can provide a greater sense of control, knowing when baby will be born, and reduce anxiety about labor pain and delivery. A C-section reduces the risk of oxygen deprivation and birth trauma to baby. It also lowers risk for women with STDs or infections (herpes, HIV, hepatitis, and HPV). Though C-sections are major surgeries, they are very common, representing one-third of U.S. births.

Cons: Risks from complications with surgery are higher than the risks associated with a vaginal birth. A C-section may also have a longer recovery, increased risk of maternal blood loss, increased risk for infant mortality, increased risk for respiratory issues, and a lower APGAR score (designed to test baby's physical condition right after delivery). C-sections are more expensive than vaginal births, and breastfeeding may be more difficult. Bowel functions may be uncomfortable, and internal scar tissue may affect future deliveries.

Pain-Management

■ Epidural

What is it? An epidural provides continuous pain relief to the lower body while allowing a woman to be fully conscious. Between 50 and 70% of women giving birth at hospitals use epidural anesthesia.

Pros: An epidural provides very effective pain relief during labor and delivery, and the medication is localized, which means that you remain alert. Only a tiny amount of the medication reaches baby, unlike certain narcotics, and once in place, an epidural can be used for an emergency C-section or to have tubes tied after delivery.

Cons: You may lose sensation in your legs (depending on the dose and stage of labor), and you will be required to have an IV, blood pressure monitoring, and fetal monitoring. An epidural can slow labor, and you may need a catheter. One in 100 women report a bad headache, which can result from spinal fluid leakage, which is a good reason to remain as still as possible when the needle is placed.

A health care provider may not allow this type of pain relief if you:
- Have extremely low blood pressure
- Have a blood infection, bleeding disorder, or skin infection near the insertion
- Have experienced a previous allergic reaction to local anesthetic

■ Natural Birth

What is it? Labor and delivery with no drugs or interventions

Pros: Natural techniques are non-invasive, leaving little potential for harm to you or your baby. There is no loss of sensation, and many women feel empowered by feeling and controlling more of their birth experience. Techniques learned for managing pain, such as meditation, breathing exercises, and self-hypnosis may help manage stress and pain for a lifetime.

Cons: Natural pain-management techniques do not eliminate pain like an epidural, and a prolonged labor or complication may alter expectations for natural birth. Additional time and energy are required to educate and prepare the mother and her support team for a natural birth.

■ Childbirth with a Doula

What is it? A doula is a person who is trained and experienced with childbirth. A doula provides continuous physical, emotional, and informational support during labor and delivery.

Pros: Research shows that the presence of a doula at birth reduces the incidence of C-sections and requests for pain medications, reduces the need for Pitocin (a labor-inducing drug), forceps, and vacuum extraction, and reduces negative feelings about one's own childbirth experience. Doulas can advocate for you with other care providers and help you and your partner remember everything from childbirth class.

Cons: A partner may feel secondary in helping with the birth process, and doulas can be expensive ($400-800 average, or up to $800-3500 for a DONA certified doula, depending on experience). Most insurance companies will not cover the cost of a doula. Some hospital staff members may also feel threatened by a doula questioning their practices or standards of operation.

Who can benefit the most from a doula?
- A woman opting for natural childbirth, a first-time mom, a single mom, or a woman who did not have a positive previous birth experience

Practical Tips from Real Parents
Natural Birth
• • • • • • • • •

- Get a solid natural birth education before the big day. Seek out books and classes that explain how labor and birth work and how to manage the pain. It gets intense, so you need to understand what you are getting into.

- Be sure that you are 100% into natural birth. Don't go into it thinking that you'll just try it. That's like training for a marathon and then asking for someone to pick you up at mile 13.

- Pick nurses, doctors, and midwives who are into natural births. Some people are and some people aren't—find care providers who will support your decision.

- Hire a doula, if you really want to guarantee success.

- If your husband balks at hiring a doula, be persistent. Have him talk with other couples and see that doulas are worth the money. Also, if the cost is just too much, you may be able to request a doula-in-training for free, paying expenses for gas, parking, etc. Doulas trying to get certified might be happy just to gain additional birth experience.

- Stay at home as long as possible. If your contractions are consistently less than five minutes apart and getting stronger then call your midwife. If you check in and you are still not dilated, go home.

- Eat and drink at home before you come to the hospital.

- Try hypnotherapy (deep breathing, mental relaxation, and focused imaging) to help you get through labor.

- Dim the lights, listen to some music, and try to relax.

- Don't obsess about timing your contractions. My husband went "app crazy" trying to record contractions, and it really was more of a distraction than helpful.

- Learn how to relax and become a "wet noodle." Breathe through your diaphragm.

- Get a massage. Your doula will tell you that touch can provide powerful reassurance from your partner. I just wanted him to feel like he was doing something useful.

- Use a bouncy ball or birthing ball to take pressure off your legs and allow you to move without using too much energy. Ask for a telemetry-monitoring unit to keep you mobile.

- Hop in a shower or a birthing tub to help with the pain. The water will help relax your muscles.

- Use hot and cold packs to distract you and help relax tight muscles in your back, neck, or forehead.

- Get up and move around during labor. Changing positions will help minimize your discomfort. The pain is worse lying down.

- Staying upright and leaning forward will reduce pressure on pelvic nerves and help baby's head to remain pressing down on your cervix.

Birth Plan

· · · · · · · · · · ·

A birth plan is a document created by you that outlines your desires for what kind of childbirth you would like and how you would like your baby cared for after birth. Many women write a birth plan after they have talked with their care provider and have researched what their hospital or birth center offers in terms of routines and care. I also recommend writing out your own plan rather than checking off a generic template. Your plan will have more credibility behind it if you write it yourself. Finally, keep the tone friendly and flexible. If you use forceful language or present your plan in a confrontational manner, don't expect to make too many friends on the hospital or birth center staff. Childbirth is a dynamic process, and your health and baby's health are the most important considerations for any birth plan.[77, 78]

The following list is provided to help you think through some of your childbirth decisions. More comprehensive birth plans can be found online.

Keep It Simple
Birth Plans
· · · · · · · ·

The key to an effective birth plan is to keep it short and sweet—less than one page.

Name/Due Date/Midwife or Doctor/ Doula/ Birth Center or Hospital:

Important health issues, fears, or concerns:

Special considerations or religious requests:

Before labor begins, I prefer:

❑ To go into labor naturally and not be induced, as long as baby and I are healthy
❑ At least 10 to 14 days to pass after my due date before inducement
❑ To use natural induction methods first
❑ To use natural induction methods only

During the first stage of labor, I prefer:

Support

❑ Partner present during labor and birth
❑ Support from a doula
❑ Other family members present

Vaginal Exams

❑ No vaginal exams until I go into labor
❑ Limited vaginal exams
❑ No membranes to be broken, unless there is an emergency

Environment

❑ Wear my own clothes
❑ Lights dimmed
❑ Music playing (of my choice)
❑ Silence
❑ Medical students and residents may/may not perform medical procedures

❑ Medical students and residents may/may not attend my birth
❑ To stay hydrated with fluids and ice chips
❑ To eat and drink, as approved by my doctor
❑ A saline/Heparin lock (a type of vein access used for a low risk mother)

Labor augmentation

❑ Prefer natural methods
❑ Pitocin is okay (Pitocin is the synthetic version of the natural hormone, oxytocin, which causes uterine contractions.)
❑ Prostaglandin gel is okay (contains the hormone prostaglandin to help soften and thin out the cervix)
❑ No amniotomy (artificial rupture of membranes), unless necessary

Pain Relief, Natural Methods

❑ Support from a partner or doula
❑ Relaxation, breathing, and visualization
❑ Hypnotherapy
❑ Shower, bath, or jacuzzi
❑ Distraction techniques
❑ Birth ball
❑ Massage
❑ Acupressure
❑ Focal point
❑ Hot/cold therapy
❑ Pelvic rocking

Pain Relief, Drugs

❑ Do not offer medication during labor
❑ Classic epidural
❑ Walking epidural (not available at all hospitals)
❑ Analgesics or narcotics

During the Second Stage of Labor or pushing, I prefer:

Positions

- ❏ No stirrups or footrests
- ❏ To avoid supine positioning (on my back)
- ❏ To use a squatting bar, birthing chair, or birthing stool
- ❏ To use people for support of my legs
- ❏ To deliver in a birthing tub

Pushing technique

- ❏ Push spontaneously (I do not want to be told when to push)
- ❏ Push, as directed by a doula or staff
- ❏ Prolonged breath-holding, as directed by a doula or staff
- ❏ Push without time limits, as long as baby and I are healthy

Delivery

- ❏ To avoid forceps
- ❏ To avoid vacuum extraction
- ❏ Use a mirror to see head
- ❏ Touch the baby's head as it crowns
- ❏ Who will catch the baby (doctor, partner, or Mom assisting and pulling on to chest)

Perineum

- ❏ No episiotomy
- ❏ Use of warm compresses, oil, and massage
- ❏ Natural tearing okay
- ❏ Episiotomy with local anesthesia okay

If a C-section is deemed necessary, I prefer:

- ❏ To make sure all other options are exhausted
- ❏ To have my partner with me
- ❏ To have the screen lowered to see the baby come out
- ❏ To have baby stay with my partner at my side after initial checks

Once the baby is born, I prefer:

Birth

- ❑ To wait two to three minutes until the cord stops pulsating
- ❑ To have my partner cut the cord
- ❑ To bank the cord blood
- ❑ To have baby placed on Mom right away

Placenta

- ❑ For the placenta to be born spontaneously without Pitocin/oxytocin
- ❑ To be given/not given routine Pitocin after the placenta is born
- ❑ Retain my placenta

Breastfeeding

- ❑ No supplementation is to be offered
- ❑ I request a lactation specialist

Newborn Care

- ❑ Baby rooming-in with me, unless there is an emergency
- ❑ Partial rooming-in, with baby sent to the nursery at night for Mom's rest
- ❑ Delay routine procedures, such as cleaning, ointment in eyes, etc., for bonding and breastfeeding
- ❑ Circumcision will/will not be performed, if we have a boy

Practical Tips from Real Parents
Birth Plan
• • • • • •

- Make sure that you run a rough draft of your birth plan by your doctor. He or she may need to modify your requests for clarity and safety.

- Think about your birth plan in two parts: Plan A for what you would like to happen for a normal labor and delivery and Plan B for what you desire should complications arise.

- Print your birth plan on brightly colored paper so that everyone can find it. Put a nice thank you post-it on the paper, so that nurses and staff might actually read it.

- Print several copies of your birth plan for your partner, doula, nurses, and others.

- My midwife told me to steer clear from stating that certain procedures were "unacceptable" or "forbidden." You can write "unless medically necessary" to show that you understand that deviations from your plan can happen.

- Birth plans are not just for women wanting to give birth naturally. If you want an epidural, remember to voice any other concerns, such as the desire to avoid an episiotomy, use of forceps, a vacuum extraction, etc.

- The process of writing the birth plan and learning about what might happen during labor and delivery can be more useful than the plan itself.

Packing for the Hospital

· ·

You will want to have a basic hospital bag packed at 35 weeks. However, do not worry if you arrive at the hospital without your bag. Friends and family can always bring requested items later.

Packing List for Mom

- ❑ **Practical nursing nightgowns or loose pajamas**. Make sure to bring pajamas that you don't mind getting stained. Nightgowns may be most comfortable because you don't have to worry about a waist-band around your belly, especially with a C-section incision.
- ❑ **Nursing or maternity bras.** You may want to wear these with visitors. Otherwise, I would go bra free for easy nursing.
- ❑ **Large, cotton, granny panties.** Bring these for supporting after-birth pads, if you do not want to wear the hospital-issued mesh underpants. You will be bleeding after birth, as your uterus heals and remaining tissues detach from the uterine wall, regardless of whether you had a C-section or vaginal delivery.
- ❑ **A comfy bathrobe.** Wrap this over your nightgown for walks around the maternity ward or birth center.
- ❑ **Socks.** You can wear hospital non-skid socks, or bring your own.
- ❑ **Flip-flops.** These are for the shower and for wearing home in warm weather, if your shoes are uncomfortable.
- ❑ **Slippers with tread**. Bring these for walks down the hallways.
- ❑ **Sanitary pads.** The hospital will provide pads for you; however, you may prefer smaller pads after the first few days.

❑ **Toiletries.** Bring your own travel-sized shampoo, conditioner, deodorant, toothbrush, toothpaste, body lotion, lip balm, hairbands, and contact lens case and solution, as desired.

❑ **Makeup bag.** You may not be interested in your appearance right after birth, unless you want to dab on some concealer and eyeliner for family photos, but it feels great to have a shower and apply makeup for your departure.

❑ **Hair dryer, flat iron, hair cream, wraps, or other hair accessories.** Whatever you need to feel beautiful, bring it.

❑ **Nipple cream.** You may receive a small sample tube in the hospital. However, if you desire a special, non-lanolin cream, then bring your own.

❑ **Nursing pads.** These are for colostrum leakage, and I recommend washable ones. Hopefully, you will be home before your milk comes in, which is typically three to five days.

❑ **Nursing pillow with slipcover.** Have someone bring your Boppy®-type nursing pillow after your delivery. This pillow should keep baby elevated from your tender abdomen and pelvic region.

❑ **Going home outfit.** Don't forget that your uterus will still be enlarged after birth, causing you to look five or six months pregnant. Your legs may also be swollen from fluids, so avoid tight jeans or pants.

Packing List for Baby

❑ **Newborn one-piece suits or kimono-style shirts.** At least two, if you want baby to wear something other than a hospital-issued shirt.

❑ **Baby socks.** At least two pair, although a tight swaddle can take care of cold feet, too.

❑ **Newborn hat or skullcap**, if desired. Good luck getting a hat to stay on your baby's head.

❑ **Swaddle blankets.** These can be used for swaddling baby and for your trip home.

❑ **Burp cloths.** Bring several of these for nursing and for family to use while holding baby.

❑ **Going home outfit.** Choose a comfortable playsuit or sleeper and wrap him or her in a cute blanket for photos.

Packing List for Dad

❑ **Changes of clothes.** Bring these in a carry-on sized suitcase or gym bag.

❑ **Toiletries.** Bring your toothbrush, toothpaste, shaving cream, razor, hair gel, comb, etc.

❑ **Pillow from home and a blanket, if not already provided.** Hopefully your hospital room will be equipped with a place for Dad to sleep. Be sure to select linens that are colorful to keep them out of the hospital laundry.

General Packing List

❑ **iPod, MP3, or CD player with headphones and speakers.** Your favorite tunes should help you relax during labor and your recovery. Some parents also play white noise for baby to drown out alarming hospital sounds.

❑ **Books and magazines.** This is not the time for *War and Peace* or *The Economist*. As you approach your due date, pick up a selection of lighter reading.

❑ **An iPad, tablet, or laptop computer.** Hopefully you will get a room with a window, and most hospitals and birth centers offer free Wi-Fi.

❑ **Digital camera and video camera.** Don't forget chargers, batteries, and extra memory cards. Discuss appropriate camera angles during delivery (i.e., "No below the waist shots, please.")

❑ **Digital watch,** preferably with a second hand for timing contractions, or use a phone app.

❑ **Hospital registration forms.** Hopefully you have already pre-registered online or through a birthing class.

❑ **Birth plan,** if you have one (See Birth Plan). Be flexible when the big day arrives.

❑ **Insurance cards.**

❑ **Your drivers' licenses.** Please check hospital and state requirements for baby's birth certificate. If a child's parents are unmarried at birth, legal paternity must be established. Paternity is important to protect both a parent's and child's rights for creating a support order, establishing health insurance through an employer, and protecting benefits if the child's father dies, such as Social Security, veteran's benefits, or assets left in a will.

❑ **Car seat**. Make sure the car seat is installed and checked.

❑ **Cell phones and chargers**. Do not forget these items. You will be eager to keep in touch with family and friends.

❑ **Cash.** For parking, vending machines, Starbucks for Dad, and other hospital cafeteria items.

Optional items

❑ **Gift for an older sibling**, if he or she will be visiting you in the hospital. I recommend a trip with Mom to the hospital cafeteria, or simply a walk down the hallway, to assure your child that you are okay. Talk to him or her about how special it is to be a big brother or sister.

❑ **Your favorite pregnancy book or birthing technique guide**, if you want to reference it during labor.

❑ **Tennis balls, massage oil, or lotion** for back massage, if desired.

❑ **Lollipops and hard candies** to soothe a dry mouth. Sugar-free candy will not make you as thirsty.

❑ **A couple of reusable shopping bags to bring home extra supplies,** such as baby's suction bulb, extra pads, mesh underpants, a perineum-bottle, diapers, creams, etc.

Practical Tips from Real Parents: Just for Dad

. . . .

You are not going to find dude talk and stereotypes in this book. Involved fathers bring positive benefits to children that no one else can *exactly* duplicate. Dads who take interest in their children positively affect their children's cognitive ability, psychological well-being, and social behavior. Fathers who treat the mothers of their children with respect and who deal with conflict rationally and appropriately are likely to raise boys who know how to treat women respectfully. Girls who are loved and appreciated by their fathers see how they should be treated and are more likely to engage in non-abusive relationships with men. Let it be said: children need their fathers, and moms need support.[79]

Now, on to our practical tips collected from the book's survey and written just for Dad. Expect this collection of advice to be witty, honest, and straight to the point!

- Expect your wife or partner to be completely nuts throughout pregnancy.

- Expect your wife to be the center of attention throughout pregnancy. Then expect your baby to be the center of attention after birth. Notice that you, the father, are never the center of attention.

- Offer foot and back rubs freely during pregnancy and your wife will want to have sex with you more.

- Your wife is going to nag you endlessly about moving to a bigger house, and then your baby will sleep in your bed until he is three.

- My wife obsessed about moving out of our apartment into a home in the suburbs because we were going to host grandparents and need extra bedrooms for the children. Now she misses the city. Go figure.

- Don't renovate the house while you are expecting and don't even think about smoking, including celebratory cigars.

- That pregnancy-nesting thing is for real. My wife was Swiffering the walls before baby arrived.

- Don't wait until the last minute to find a day care, nanny, or babysitter. Your wife or partner is going to freak out when she goes back to work anyway, but it helps to have found someone who is vetted early.

- Don't worry too much about losing your social life with a newborn. Babies are fairly portable for restaurants and such. Toddlers are a different story.

- I'm here to tell you: you're not going to get laid as much after baby, but a little understanding will go a long way. It does get better.

- Try to help out more around the house. In the first few months of pregnancy, the smells of cleaning products will make her sick, and by the last few months, bending over the bathtub is rough.

- When the dishes start to stack up in the sink, especially in the first trimester, it's time to get your lazy, selfish butt off the couch and do the dishes.

- My wife snored like a bear when she was pregnant, which was funny at first. After several months, I decided that I better get to bed first.

- Some days you might regret even getting pregnant, especially if your wife is uncomfortable and whining all the time. Just support her and know that one day you will not even know what life looks like without your child.

- Agreeing on a baby budget can be tough. However, you need to have the conversation. Set rules for purchases, too, especially baby clothes (you don't need any). Get involved with the baby registry process if you want to have a say in what you are spending.

- Don't be surprised if agreeing on a name for your baby is really hard. You may have your heart set on a family name, while your wife says "no way" because it reminds her of some silly guy or girl in grade school.

- Come up with ground rules if you anticipate a fight over naming the baby, such as "Dad names a boy, and Mom names a girl."

- Mothers-in-law can be tricky during pregnancy. My mom did not agree with us having our baby with a midwife and doula instead of a doctor. She always had snarky comments to make about natural birth, how much we were spending on baby products, etc. She nearly drove my wife crazy.

- Tell your significant other to relax about her baby shower. Families live apart today, so just try to be happy with whoever shows up.

- Take a birthing class together.

- Expect the birth plan to go out the window. My wife wanted a natural birth with our firstborn, and she freaked out when she had to have a C-section. Now we have a healthy kid in elementary school. A healthy baby and mom are all that really matters.

- Don't sweat it if your wife yells at you during labor. Just stay by her side and focus on her and a healthy delivery.

- Be in charge of installing the car seat. Watch a few YouTube videos and just do it before your wife hits the panic button.

- Educate yourself and your family on postpartum depression. Understanding is half the battle.

- Catch up on your favorite action movies. Your home theater system will not be entertaining loud explosions once baby arrives.

- Parenting requires on-the-job training for Mom and Dad. Remember that everyone is learning as they go along.

- Get involved with baby planning during pregnancy, and you won't feel so left out after baby arrives. You don't have to obsess over details, but just show that you care.

- Just remember, though you may be in a support role during pregnancy, you are not the backup parent.

- Correct your wife when she asks you to babysit. You don't babysit your own child.

- It is easy to wonder if your baby even needs you through pregnancy and the newborn phase, but just wait. Your time is coming, and sometimes dads have a way of being more patient and forgiving later when it comes to children making messes, stress, or just knowing how to calm everyone down.

- Hanging out with my kids is so much more rewarding than work. I wish I had understood that when my children were young.

- Remember that you get to set your own rules for fatherhood. You don't have to be just like your dad.

- When you are thinking about being a dad, write down all the men who were positive role models in your life: your own dad, a grandfather, an uncle, a coach, a teacher, etc. Now emulate the characteristics that you appreciated for your own child.

Practical Tips from Real Parents: Moments and Days after Birth

· ·

To help you survive the days and weeks after birth, I have compiled some helpful practical advice from parents who were willing to share honest tips about the birth experience and the weeks thereafter.

In the heat of childbirth

- Don't be surprised if your water breaks before you start labor. My water broke at work at 35 weeks, and I was shocked.

- If your labor progresses more rapidly than you expect, have your husband call 911, and they can talk him through the whole process.

- Don't worry if you keep passing gas while pushing. It happens. I was completely mortified, and the nurses hardly seemed phased.

- Know that it's completely normal to throw up while giving birth. I had projectile vomit in the final stages of labor, and my best friend threw up when the doctors started pulling on her stomach to get her baby out during a C-section.

- There aren't many moments in life when you can say, "It's really okay to poop yourself." I did poop myself while pushing, and my baby did the same thing as soon as she was born. No big deal.

- If you are uncomfortable with multiple doctors or nurses in training watching your C-section, tell you doctor beforehand.

- I became really uncomfortable when my body went numb for my C-section. I wanted to panic, but just breathe and stay calm.

- My baby's shoulders got stuck, which made my delivery more exciting than I would have hoped. Just know the pain and suffering melts away as soon as you hold baby in your arms.

- I was overwhelmed with tears of joy when my daughter was born. I couldn't believe how much I loved her.

for the moments and days after childbirth

Bonding Tips

- Embrace your first bonding moments with baby through skin-to-skin contact and cuddling, if possible.

- Talk to baby as soon as she enters the world. She may not be able to see very well, however she will recognize your voice.

- Don't worry if you aren't able to bond with baby right after birth, due to Mom or baby's health. Bonding has occurred throughout pregnancy through smells and sounds in the womb.

- If you have a C-section and baby is healthy, ask if your partner can hold baby next to you as you get sewn up.

Recovery Tips

- Expect to leave the hospital with no shame left in your being. I had male residents and nurses looking at my hoo-ha during our first meeting. It took my husband months to get that far.

- Expect the nurses to come in and offer a massage. It's actually the worst massage ever, as they knead your belly like bread dough and try to get your uterus to contract and shrink.

- I was so wiped out after labor and then an emergency C-section that I hardly could pay attention to my baby.

- You may start to wonder if you are ever going to poop again during the first few days after birth. Every hour the nurses will ask you, "Have you passed gas?"

Baby Care Tips

- Try not to stress too much over baby's appearance. Newborns can be funny looking with a cone-shaped head, unruly hair, birthmarks, redness, rashes, bruising, baby acne, scratches, and other marks. Most of these are due to Mom's hormones and the birth process.

- Newborns have other funny quirks, too. Their eyes are crossed (this should go away in two to three months), their skin sometimes peels, they get startled easily, and they get the hiccups a lot. This is all normal.

- I am a labor and delivery nurse, and I often see parents treating their newborn like a porcelain doll. Don't worry about moving baby or changing her diaper. Just get in there and get the job done.

- If possible, try to breastfeed within an hour after birth. This process may feel really awkward if your lower body is still numb from an epidural. You may need help supporting the baby.

- If your baby is having problems latching on at first, don't worry. Talk to your nurses about getting a lactation specialist to work with you and try to be patient.

Visitor and Photo Tips

- Take pictures of baby right after birth. He or she will be covered in all kinds of blood and sticky stuff, but your kids will love looking at these gooey pictures later.

- Send out a mass email with a photo when the baby is born. The joyful news will spread in seconds, and then hopefully everyone will leave you to rest.

- Accept visitors only when you're ready.

- Put a little bit of makeup on and take family photos in the hospital, even if you are not feeling very photogenic. You will cherish these pictures forever.

Preparing to Go Home Tips

- Enjoy your quiet, intimate family time in the hospital. This seems to go away once you get home, especially if you have older children.

- Rest, rest, rest! There is no shame in sending baby to the hospital nursery, or putting a do-not-disturb sign on your door after the first night.

- I thought I would shrink back down to my normal size faster, but I looked six months pregnant in my going home photos. Note: This is due to uterus enlargement and fluid retention.

- Prepare your pets for baby. Bring a baby blanket home for your pet to smell, or sleep with, prior to baby's homecoming.

BABY REGISTRY

Baby Registry: What You Need to Know and What to Buy

· ·

The following product recommendations are the result of a comprehensive, independent research process, synthesizing hundreds of reviews from books, online baby stores, parent surveys, and our own personal experience. The following endorsements have been made without payment, fee, or receipt of any product. Please note: we have done our best to provide accurate information, however prices and products are subject to change.

Buying baby gear can be daunting for a first time parent, and purchases add up quickly. Therefore, it is imperative to begin this section knowing that **you do not need everything on this list** (besides, unless you are Ivanka Trump, you cannot afford all of this stuff, even with generous gift-givers.) The intent of this guide is to provide many different options for different types of parents with a diverse set of needs and wants, depending on budget, space in the home, climate, lifestyle, etc. Also, the vast majority of items can be found in gently used condition for significantly less at garage sales, consignment sales, on Craigslist, or—your best option—as hand-me-downs.

This doesn't mean that you can't have fun shopping for baby. Just go into the registry process with your eyes open. Having a baby is big business. Retailers salivate over pregnant women and expecting couples. Who is about to have her daily routine upended? Whose shopping habits are in major flux, and who might be so exhausted in the next year that she buys everything at one store? As soon as an expecting mom goes to

Walmart or Target and purchases cocoa butter, organic milk, and ginger ale, instead of conventional milk, coffee, and bleach, like she used to buy, corporate statisticians will forever target her, based on their expecting mommy algorithms. From this point onward, she can expect coupons, mail fliers, web advertisements, and all types of conscious and sub-conscious consumer cues to bombard her life, signaling her to "buy, buy, buy" for baby. Giving contact information or using a credit card at a maternity store, like Motherhood or Pea in the Pod, is also a surefire way to sound the baby alarms.

Now that you understand that you don't need every baby product under the sun and that everybody wants your money, let's discuss the pros and cons of a few popular baby registry options.

Retailer Options: Popular Baby Registry Stores and Online Offerings

▮ Babies R Us (BRU)

Pros: Every expecting parent needs a brick and mortar store for touching, feeling, and testing big budget items, and it is nice to return items to a physical store. Babies R Us also has a large inventory, locations around the country, and an okay Rewards program with coupons. With BRU, you can also add items to your registry online.

Cons: Prices are 10-20% higher on everything. Baby gifts labeled as online-only must be returned to a physical store; if they are mailed back, the purchaser receives the credit. Online-only product returns require a packing slip or gift receipt.

Completion Discount: A physical "10% off baby registry completion" coupon should arrive in the mail approximately two weeks prior to your due date. The coupon excludes diapers, formula, furniture, BRU gift cards, and other special orders. Remember to register for items that you wish to receive the completion discount on before making your final purchase.

■ Target (TGT)

Pros: This store is very convenient for gift givers and any gift cards or merchandise credit will be easy to use on store offerings beyond baby.

Cons: The selection of baby items in-store is limited, and some parents complain that customer service is lacking. The return policy requires a gift receipt or a printed Gift Purchase Log, which stamps your gift giver's item at the time of purchase.

Completion Discount: A physical "15% off baby registry completion" coupon should arrive in the mail approximately six weeks prior to your due date. Using a Target RED card can take off another 5%. Download the Target app to your phone and add items to your baby registry without waiting in the customer service line.

■ Buy Buy Baby (BBBY)

Pros: This store, owned by Bed Bath and Beyond, contains a large selection of floor-to-ceiling baby merchandise, including designer strollers and high-end baby products that BRU does not carry. They also accept non-expired 20% off BBBY store coupons (with many brand restrictions), and they are generally willing to price-match a competitor on identical items. I would rate their customer service as excellent, too.

Cons: The biggest drawback for this option is limited store locations nationwide, forcing some gift givers to buy online. Prices for items are also typically higher because the store offers convenience, a large number of items, and a baby registry service.

Completion Discount: A "10% off all remaining items" coupon should be sent in the mail roughly four weeks prior to your due date for in-store use, and a separate coupon code will be emailed to you for use online.

∎ Amazon (AMZN)

Pros: This online-only option is mostly lower in prices, convenient, and tax-free in a few states. Shipping is free on qualified baby items over $25. Amazon also offers a universal registry, allowing items to be added to your registry from outside websites. The return policy includes a free prepaid mailing label to print and return eligible items for a full refund within 90 days of delivery. Returns outside of 90 days will deduct shipping costs.

Cons: Many parents complain about multiple trips to the UPS store and printer issues making the return process frustrating. Amazon also has no way of regulating third party purchases from your gift givers, as third party members may have different return policies.

Completion Discount: The Amazon 10% completion discount code should be emailed to you, and it begins 60 days prior to your entered baby arrival date and expires 90 days after the date with a $5000 cap on your one-time order (a maximum $500 discount). Read the fine print. The completion discount only applies to eligible baby items that are fulfilled by Amazon (e.g., Tuck's medicated pads for your postpartum recovery may not qualify, while Earth Mama Angel Baby Mama Bottom Balm does). To receive a 15% completion discount, you must be an Amazon Mom member at the time you redeem your registry completion discount and the primary registrant. Amazon Mom is a free membership program that offers discounts geared toward parents of young children. The hallmark of Amazon Mom is a 20% discount on diapers and wipes, which are auto-delivered to your door with a recurring "subscribe and save" order. The downside is that you must remember to change sizes as baby grows, or else lose your savings by having too many leftover too-small diapers.

■ Walmart (WMT)

Pros: Walmart is nearly impossible to beat on pricing. Much of the country shops at Walmart for groceries and everyday items, so it may make sense to have your baby registry here.

Cons: Because Walmart sells such huge volumes of products, such as 30% of all diapers sold in the U.S., the executives in Bentonville have enormous power over suppliers. They are notorious for twisting the arms of manufacturers into drastic cost-cutting measures, which means lower prices *and* lower-quality baby products for you. It is common practice for name-brand companies to make cheaper versions of their products to be sold only in big-box stores like Walmart. For this reason and poor reported customer service, I would take my baby registry elsewhere, unless Walmart is your only choice.

Completion Discount: There is no completion discount at Walmart.

■ Universal gift registry online

Pros: This option allows you to register for gifts on different web sites, combining products from Amazon, Etsy, IKEA, Land of Nod, etc. Popular companies that offer a universal baby registry are **BabyList, Kaboodle, MyRegistry, TheBump**, and **Wishpot**. Web-based companies change rapidly; however, **BabyList** is currently at the top of the class, receiving excellent reviews for its crisp design and easy-to-navigate user interface. BabyList also offers creative registry items and solutions for things you really need, such as allowing people to pool money for a doula or cloth diaper service, or to offer a homemade meal after birth.

Cons: Dealing with multiple return policies with a universal gift registry can be a pain. For creative or modern gifts, such as a doula, expect at least one snarky relative to consider a cash-like gift coupon as tacky. For this reason, I would not select the "Donate to Baby's College Fund" option, as it tacitly implies money-grubbing. However, a healthy, homemade meal is a pretty good deal for any tired new parent.

■ Baby Registry Product Considerations

Now that we've covered some options for your registry, let's get into the meat of the matter— narrowing down these products. Before you zap too many items into your virtual cart, I recommend asking a few pertinent questions (the answers will help you decide on the price range and quality required for each product.)

1. What are the safety considerations for this product?
2. How long will this product be used? Months or years?
3. How often will this product be used? Daily or occasionally?
4. What are my priorities and lifestyle needs?
5. What baby registry items can I do without?

Note: Prices are subject to change. For example, if a car seat or stroller is listed online for significantly less than the MSRP/List price for the manufacturer, it is probably a previous year or discontinued model.

Baby Gear

■ Car Seat

This is a very important piece of baby gear, so prioritize your budget to buy a new seat, if possible. If you are budget constrained, ask loved ones to pool gifts together. Only use a newer model car seat, if you are borrowing one from a trusted friend or family member.

Keep It Simple
Prioritizing Big Budget Items
• • • • • • • • • • • • • • • • • • •

If you add up the average cost for baby's first year, using moderate-ly-priced baby registry items and day care, you can expect to exceed $10,000. If you hire a full-time nanny and select top-of-the-line baby gear and eco-friendly products, you can expect to top $20,000/year. Moral of the story: you have to cut costs somewhere. Costly baby gear, which may only last a few months, is a good place to start. To help you prioritize, or cut out, some of the most expensive items in your baby registry, I asked hundreds of parents to rank the following baby gear items, in order of importance (excluding a car seat and crib, which are perhaps the most important items).

1 is most important and 10 is least important

1. Stroller
2. Baby carrier (Ergobaby, Baby Bjorn)
3. Portable crib (Pack 'n Play)
4. Baby swing
5. Bouncer seat
6. Activity mat or play gym
7. Stationary entertainer, ExerSaucer, or Jumperoo
8. Baby sling or wrap
9. Bumbo seat
10. Doorway jumper

Types of Car Seats

1. **Infant seat or rear-facing convertible seat**. Infants should ride in a rear-facing infant seat (also called an infant carrier), or a rear-facing convertible seat, after birth. The AAP recommends that children ride rear-facing until age two.

▶ **Infant seat**. A convenient handle on the infant seat lets you transport baby from a base that stays in the car to a stroller or to your home without disturbing naptime.

▶ **Rear-facing convertible**. This is a larger-sized seat that stays in your car and will accommodate a child for a longer period of time than an infant carrier (until he weighs between 40 and 70 pounds). "Convertible" implies that the seat can start off facing backward and later be converted, or turned around, to face forward. If your baby rides in an infant seat after birth, a convertible is the seat that she will transition to when she exceeds the maximum weight or outgrows the height limit of the infant seat.

2. **Booster seats**. Booster seats are for children who have outgrown a forward-facing harness seat in height or weight, yet are not big enough to use an adult seat belt.

3. **Seat belts.** Children who have outgrown their booster seats (usually around 4'9" in height and eight to 12 years old) should ride with a seat belt in the back seat until at least 13 years of age.

Car Seat Installation

Infant Base Installation with LATCH
(Lower Anchors and Tether for Children)

1. Before you begin, read your car seat instruction manual and your vehicle's owner manual for car seat installation carefully. Dad is not allowed to skip these steps!

2. Watch a car seat installation video online for your car seat model on YouTube.

3. Place the car seat base in the back seat of your vehicle. Select the center or right outboard side since a side impact is more likely to happen on the driver's side (pulling into traffic rather than a right turn).

4. Locate the lower anchors in your vehicle. These are thick, open hooks, which are typically buried between the seat back and rear seat cushion.

5. Attach the lower straps with hooks on the car seat base to the lower anchors. Make sure the straps aren't twisted.

6. Press down firmly on the car seat base and tighten the straps. I like to get inside the car and press my knee or foot down firmly inside the base while tightening the straps or center-pull strap.

7. You should not be able to move the car seat base side-to-side or front-to-back more than one inch.

8. Check that your seat is at the correct recline angle. Babies must ride in a semi-reclined position to keep the airway open. Most seats will have a built-in angle indicator, such as a carpenter's level bubble, to help.

9. Attach the infant carrier to the base. Make sure that baby's straps are at or below shoulder level.

Infant Base Installation with a Seat Belt

1. Before you begin, read your car seat instruction manual and your vehicle's owner manual. Pay special attention to how to "lock" the seat belt.

2. Watch a car seat installation video online for your car seat model.

3. Place the car seat base in the back seat of your vehicle.

4. Thread the seat belt through the belt path making sure that nothing is twisted.

5. Buckle the seat belt.

6. Lock the seat belt (another child could wrap a loose belt around his or her neck.)

7. Press down firmly on the car seat base and tighten. You can also have someone else pull the seat belt strap tightly while you put your weight on the base.

8. Make sure your car seat base is installed at the correct recline angle.

9. Attach the infant carrier to the base.

Infant Car Seat Buying Tips

❑ **Buy an infant seat.** I recommend buying an infant seat, rather than a convertible seat, due to better fit and convenience. Many rear-facing convertibles also have a five-pound minimum weight limit, and baby's shoulders must be at or above the lowest harness slot. A convertible seat may be too big if you deliver early or have a small baby. Also, infant car seats are convenient since most brands detach from

Safety Alert!
Car Seats
• • • • • • •

❑ **Make sure that you install and use your car seat properly.**
Read the instruction manual, as well as the car seat section in
your car's manual. If you have any doubt, find a car seat inspection station near you at http://www.nhtsa.gov/apps/cps/index.
htm. The National Highway Traffic and Safety Administration
reports that three out of every four car seats are not used
correctly.[80]

❑ **Avoid these common car seat mistakes.**

▸ *Are the LATCH (Lower Anchors and Tethers for Children)
anchors buried between the seat back and cushions?* Few
automakers put the lower anchors out in the open. Take
a deep breath and keep digging for those small metal
bars that will keep your child's seat secure.

▸ *Is the seat too loose in the car, or able to move one inch or
more?* Put your knee in the seat with all of your weight
and pull up on the straps. Use your arm if your infant seat
is too small. Lock the seat belt, if required.

▸ *Can't get your infant seat to stay at a 45-degree level?* Use
a tightly rolled up towel or cut a swimming pool noodle
and place it under the seat where baby's feet rest.

▸ *Is your baby's harness too loose?* If you can pinch the harness fabric, tighten the straps to a snug fit.

▸ *Is the center clip out of position?* The retainer clip should
rest across your child's breastbone, although it can move
out of position when removing baby from the seat.

❑ **Keep your child rear-facing until age two.** A 2007 study
found that children under age two are 75% less likely to die or
be severely injured if they are rear-facing, while another study
cites that one-year-olds are five times less likely to be injured
in a crash if they are in a rear-facing seat. Children younger
than two have relatively large heads and small necks, and the
force of a front-facing crash in a front-facing seat can cause
spinal cord injuries.[81]

❏ **Place your car seat in the center of the back seat.** Child occupants seated in the center have a 43% less risk of injury than children seated on either outboard side.[82]

❏ **Don't use a car seat for all of baby's naps.** The AAP warns that babies sleeping in a seated position can receive significantly less oxygen than babies sleeping in cribs, with some sleeping positions cutting off oxygen to hypoxic levels < 90% (normal blood oxygen levels are 95-100%).[83] Babies can also develop plagiocephaly, or flat head syndrome, by spending too much time on their backs in car seats and swings.

❏ **Expect a "car seat challenge" for preterm infants (born before 37 weeks)** to check for cardiopulmonary stability before being discharged from the hospital. Physiological studies indicate that preterm infants experience episodes of apnea (stopping breathing), bradycardia (slow heart rate), and desaturation (low oxygen levels) while seated in their car seat. Parents may want to limit travel during this fragile period.

❏ **For updated safety information and car seat installation videos** (for all types of car seats), **visit** http://www.safercar .gov/parents/Car-Seat-Safety.htm.

the base and snap directly into strollers, although some may require a special adapter. With a convertible, the seat stays in the car and you must wake baby to transfer him to a stroller.

❏ **Buy a 30-pound model.** I recommend a 30-pound infant carrier, especially if baby's parents or caregivers are petite.

▶ *Why not a 35-pound model?* A 35-pound seat may seem like the best value at first. However, big seats are back breakers, and I can't tell you how many moms I know with back and neck problems. An average baby doubles his birth weight in five months.

▶ *What about ultra-light seats with a 22-pound weight limit?* These are outgrown too quickly. An average boy can expect to reach 22 pounds in eight months, while a girl will hit the seat weight maximum in 12 months. A larger baby could outgrow the 29" seat height or 22-pound weight limit within four to six months.

❑ **Buy your car seat online.** Price compare car seats on different web sites, wait for sales, and stack promo codes. Do not buy your car seat at a store with a baby registry! For example, a Google shopping search for the Britax Marathon in Onyx shows that the same model car seat varies in price from $189.99 at online stores to $299.99 at Buy, Buy, Baby. Warning: This store likes to add a cup holder, an extended warranty, and a couple of letters, such as "XE", to popular car seats, adding $100+ to the price tag.

❑ **Buy an extra infant base (not another seat), if baby will ride in two cars frequently.**

❑ **Register your car seat with the manufacturer** so that you will hopefully receive notice of any recalls.

Infant Car Seats

Brand recommendations:

All attributes are condensed for quick reading

Best Infant Car Seat Overall

❑ **Chicco KeyFit 30 Infant Car Seat and Base** (pronounced KEE-koh)

▸ *Price: $190, extra base $85*

▸ *Pros:* easy to install, high sales after topping *Consumer Reports* safety list, Italian styling and vibrant colors, a best fit pick for newborns, has a removable insert for small newborns, EPS energy-absorbing foam for impact protection, spring-loaded leveling foot to help get proper base angle, bubble level-indicators on each side of the base to show accurate angle in vehicle seat, one-pull LATCH tightening strap for a tight and secure vehicle fit

▸ *Cons:* achieving secure installation without the base is difficult, belt lock-off can slip in some vehicles, short canopy

▸ Note: Check out the KeyFit Zip for a convenient zip-off canopy, zip-on visor, and matching zip-around boot to keep baby warm and stylish.

Other Solid Choices - Infant Seats

❑ **Graco Snugride Click Connect 30 Car Seat** (*Most affordable*)

> ▶ *Price: $100-130, extra base $55*
> ▶ *Pros:* the Snugride family has been a best-seller for years due to safety, affordability, ease of use, and lightweight design, the 7.5 pound seat is easy for Mom to carry, lowest harness slot at 5 inches fits newborns well, two position crotch strap at 4.5 and 6 inches, one step secure attachment to Graco Click Connect strollers, easy to install with LATCH system
> ▶ *Cons:* better suited to LATCH systems as it lacks a lock-off to prevent tilt for some belt installations, entry-level seat has a non-adjustable base and rear adjust harness to keep costs down, some parents complain that the sunshade fit is poor
> ▶ Note: A July 2014 recall required Graco (pronounced GRAY-koh) to send free replacement buckles to any customer, due to concerns that the buckles can get stuck, especially with food and drink on them. Also, for more Graco value, skip the Snugride and try the new **Graco 4Ever 4-in-1 Car Seat** (*$330*), which transforms from an infant rear-facing seat to a toddler seat to a high back booster to a backless booster, as the only car seat you'll need from four to 120 pounds.

❑ **Britax B-Safe Infant Car Seat** (pronounced BRIGH-tax)

> ▶ *Price: $144-200, extra base $65*
> ▶ *Pros:* excellent crash ratings, safety features include vehicle intrusion shield and side impact protection, good seat for smaller vehicles, installs well in many vehicles (good for city dwellers who use taxis often), handle can be locked in any position for travel, compatible with B-series strollers, fits smaller babies four to 30 pounds, comes with infant padding for smaller babies

> ▶ *Cons:* seat belt lock-off can be hard to close, lacks a quick-adjust no-rethread harness, seat has no rebound bar or advanced levels of side impact protection

Convertible Car Seats

The question that most parents ask when buying a convertible seat is, "Are the expensive seats worth the money?" And the answer is, "it depends." Less expensive convertible seats pass the same federal crash tests in the U.S. as car seats that cost hundreds of dollars. While some may not have extra side-impact protection or a harness that re-threads (without having to manually pull the strap out of the seat and thread it yourself as your child grows taller), the seat frames are all built to the same crash standards. The major considerations with less expensive convertible seats are limited size and weight capacities. Some of them top out at 40 pounds and 40-42 inches, which forces parents to move too early to a booster seat. For example, a 40 to 65-pound child is safer in a convertible seat with a 65-pound maximum and a five-point harness than in a basic booster seat with an adult seat belt. Bottom line: If I had purchased the workhorse of budget car seats, a Cosco Scenara, for my children (found at Walmart for $39), my tall toddlers would have outgrown the seat before age two and a half. If your children are petite, a budget convertible may be a wise choice.

Brand recommendations:

❏ **Britax Marathon Convertible Car Seat**
   (*Best choice for safety and value*)
   ▶ *Price: $230-290*
   ▶ *Price: $260-330 for Marathon ClickTight*
   ▶ *Pros:* Britax's best-selling seat can be used rear-facing for a child five to 40 pounds and forward-facing with a harness up to 70 pounds and 49 inches in height, simple to install, HUGS (harness ultra-guard system) chest pads to ensure proper positioning, no-rethread harness height adjuster (this means that harness height is changed by pulling on levers, pushing buttons, or turning

knobs rather than removing the seat and re-threading the seat straps as your child gets taller)

▶ *Cons:* does not offer the side impact protection of more expensive Britax seats, may be bulky in smaller vehicles

▶ Note: With three out of four car seats installed incorrectly, the Britax ClickTight Installation System makes car seat installation as simple as buckling a seat belt. Now parents, grandparents, and babysitters can install convertible seats with confidence. ClickTight Technology is available in the Marathon, Boulevard, and Advocate convertible models.

❑ **Britax Boulevard Convertible Car Seat**

(Best for increased side impact and value)

▶ *Price: $250-320*

▶ *Price: $260-330 for Boulevard ClickTight*

▶ *Pros:* similar to the Marathon with a seat adjuster knob, more side impact protection in the headrest, and HUGS (harness ultra-guard system) chest pads with Safe-Cell Technology

▶ *Cons:* expensive, bulky, this large seat may not fit smaller vehicles, hard to remove for multiple vehicles

▶ Note: A side by side comparison on britaxusa.com shows only one feature difference between the Boulevard and the higher-priced Pavilion and Advocate models—a Click and Safe Snug Harness Indicator (or a mechanical device that makes a clicking noise when the harness is snug.) For the new ClickTight model comparisons, the Advocate edges out the Marathon and Boulevard with its SafeCell Impact Protection and Complete Side Impact Protection MAX, if you can handle the price.

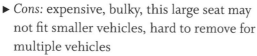

❑ **Britax Roundabout Convertible Car Seat** (*smaller footprint for smaller cars*)

▶ *Price: $144 -190*

▶ *Pros:* less expensive than the Marathon and Boulevard, better Britax option for smaller cars that cannot fit the taller Marathon and Boulevard shells

▶ *Cons:* harness is not as easy to adjust as Marathon, therefore the price savings may not be worth frustration (unless you need it to fit a small car), the maximum Roundabout height is 46 inches and maximum weight is 55 pounds versus 49 inches and up to 65 pounds for the Marathon and Boulevard, which means the Roundabout will not last as long, does not come with ClickTight technology

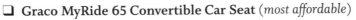

❑ **Graco MyRide 65 Convertible Car Seat** (*most affordable*)

▶ *Price: $140*

▶ *Pros:* most affordable seat for the safety features, high rear and forward-facing weight limits (up to 65 pounds forward-facing and 40 pounds rear-facing), Graco redesigned the MyRide's buckles in 2013

▶ *Cons:* seat is tall, may not fit in smaller cars or in a compact third row when rear-facing

❑ **Clek Foonf Convertible Car Seat** (*best for keeping child rear-facing the longest*)

▶ *Price: $450 fabric ($800 for leather)*

▶ *Pros:* the self-professed "mother of all car seats" starts at 14 pounds and lets your child stay rear-facing until 50 pounds or 43 inches in height; offers luxury fabrics and a modern design; seat has a steel and magnesium frame with honeycombed aluminum fibers for safety, and a recycling

program for the seats; maximum forward-facing weight is 65 pounds and height is 49 inches

▶ *Cons:* starts at $450, specialty fabric patterns, such as toki-doki, are $550 and leather options are $800

▶ Note: Clek has introduced a newborn insert to be used with all Clek model seats starting at 5 pounds. Also, the **Clek Filo Compact Convertible Seat** ($350) includes many of the safety features of the Clek Foonf; although, it is a less expensive, lighter seat that can be used longer with LATCH. The Filo seat weight is 25 pounds (28 pounds with anti-rebound bar).

Booster Car Seats

Brand recommendations:

❏ **Britax Frontier 90 Booster Seat** *(safety pick)*

▶ *Price: $265-320*

▶ *Price: $265-330 Frontier ClickTight*

▶ *Pros:* keeps your child in a five-point harness longer than competing seats up to 90 pounds and 58 inches in height, wider and deeper than other models, easy to install, comes with side impact cushion technology and a quick adjust no-rethread harness

▶ *Cons:* expensive, heavy at 25 pounds, doesn't transfer easily when you start car-pooling

▶ Note: The Frontier 90 ClickTight model comes with Click-Tight installation: squeeze the release in the seat back with two fingers, thread and connect the vehicle seat belt, and click it closed.

Safety Alert!
New LATCH Anchor Rules
• • • • • • • • • • • • • • • • • • •

In 2014, new LATCH anchor rules went into effect, stating that parents should not use the lower anchors of LATCH if **the combined weight of the child *and* car seat is 65 pounds**. Seat belts should be used to secure the seat, and the top tether should be used for forward-facing seats secured with LATCH or a seatbelt.

This means that the weight of the seat really matters. For example, the Clek Foonf is one of the heaviest convertible seats on the market, weighing in at 33 pounds forward-facing and 38 pounds rear-facing. This means that if your child weighs more than 26 pounds rear-facing and 31 pounds forward-facing, then you should *not* use LATCH lower anchors for installation, which is less convenient.

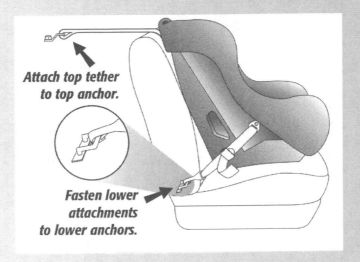

Attach top tether to top anchor.

Fasten lower attachments to lower anchors.

❑ **Graco Nautilus 3-in-1 Car Seat** (*most affordable*)
  ▶ *Price:* $139-190
  ▶ *Pros:* the basic model is half the price of the Frontier, works up to 65 pounds with a five-point harness
  ▶ *Cons:* harness must be re-threaded through seat to adjust height, don't bother with the Nautilus "Elite" model (the fancier fabrics are not worth the price increase)
  ▶ Note: The Graco Highback TurboBooster and other booster seats are significantly less inexpensive ($50 or less) because they do not have a five-point harness. These less costly seats are belt-positioning boosters that use a vehicle's existing seat belt.

■ Stroller

What qualities do you desire most in a stroller? Does it need to be lightweight and compact? Do you want a jogger? What is your budget? Remember that *your* priorities, terrain, and climate may be different from other parents touting their chosen stroller. For example, your sister in Houston may love her stylish, affordable Graco travel system. She nestles her infant carrier into the stroller frame and off she goes. Plastic wheels are fine for smooth terrain; however, navigating cobblestone streets in the snow in Boston will require a lighter stroller with all-terrain wheels and weather protection.

Be sure to test different strollers in a store *before* your purchase. Break them down, pull them out, lift them, and test-drive them with weight in the seat. You may love the look and style of a stroller online and then discover through testing that it is nearly impossible to break down and lift into your car.

Money-Saving Tip
Strollers
• • • • • •

If you are buying a stroller or travel system new, try to get it on sale. It can't hurt to call a store or online customer service number and ask about future discounts. For example, diapers.com runs frequent 20% off brand sales (Britax, Graco, etc.), AlbeeBaby.com has a "Sale" tab, Babyearth.com has a clearance section with closeouts and scratch & dent gear, and Babies R Us holds a Great Trade-In event every February and September, offering 25% off new items for each old item traded in (bring in a friend's old Pack 'n Play, stroller, and car seat to receive 25% off each item). That can add up to big savings with more expensive items.

Different Strokes...and Strollers for Different Folks

- **Fitness Buffs.** Some new parents may be unaware of initial restrictions when buying a jogging stroller. The minimum age recommendation for the BOB Revolution is eight months for jogging or off-road use, though some contend that jogging strollers are best for children over one year of age, due to developing neck muscles.
- **Urbanites or City Dwellers.** Check to see if your compact stroller has a minimum age limit for use, such as three to six months (no newborns). Also, when shopping for lightweights and compacts, consider not only the weight of your stroller but also the rear wheel width. A wide wheelbase may not be able to squeeze through tight entryways, restaurants, and grocery aisles. Look for rear wheels less than 23" to clear narrow 24" doors.
- **Tall Parents.** Most stroller handlebars are manufactured for women of average height, or about 5'6". If you or your partner is taller, you should consider a stroller with an adjustable handlebar that goes to at least 42 inches. Here are some stroller models that are friendlier to tall parents: Mountain Buggy Terrain (46"), BOB Revolution Flex (45.8"), Stokke Xplory (45.5"), Bumbleride Indie (43"), Bugaboo Cameleon3 (44"), Mountain Buggy Urban Jungle (44"), Britax

B-Ready (44"), Baby Jogger City Mini GT (44"), UPPAbaby Vista (42.5"), City Versa (42"), Bugaboo Bee (41.5"), and for umbrella strollers, UPPAbaby G-Lite (44"), G-Luxe (44"), and Maclaren Techno (43"). Other popular stroller handle heights less than 42" are: Baby Jogger City Select (41.8"), B-Agile (fixed: 40"), BOB Revolution SE (fixed: 40.5"), Graco LiteRider (fixed: 39.3"), Graco FastAction Fold (fixed: 39.5"), and most Maclarens (41.5").

- **Petite Parents.** Combi, a Japanese brand, is well-known for low handlebar heights, and many petite moms love easy-to-fold lightweight options, such as the City Mini or UPPAbaby G-Lite.

- **Coffee Connoisseurs.** If you are planning to drink your cup of java and drive baby at the same time, you may want to consider a single handlebar stroller rather than one that requires two hands for pushing.

- **Matchy-Matchy Moms**. Blame the pregnancy hormones; many new moms regret buying a large, matching-fabric travel system (the ones that could mow down small brush). Shortly after birth, this type of system may become too cumbersome for everyday use and a lighter stroller must be purchased. Remember: lighter is always better.

- **Frugal Folks.** Stroller companies, like cars, update models annually, so you may find deep discounts for last year's models. Also, consider buying a stroller used on Craigslist and then re-sell it after use.

- **Accessory Aficionados**. Beware of racking up excessive stroller accessory purchases. Rather than a $35 snack tray, try a $4 Munchkin snack cup. Skip the rain shield unless you live in the city, or need it for regular outdoor use, and remember you do not have to buy brand name accessories. Search for cheaper generic alternatives and read reviews for fit with your stroller. A few stroller accessories that are worth the cost:
  - ► A hard, plastic drink holder (soft, canvas ones let your drink tip)
  - ► Parent console or pouch for keys, cell phones, and tissues
  - ► Toy bar for attaching toys, books, and sippy cups
  - ► Warm bunting for cold weather, if required
  - ► A clear wind and rain shield, if required
  - ► Stroller hooks: Try the **Mommy Hook** for heavier shopping bags and smaller **Think King Mighty Buggy** hooks for your diaper bag

Safety Alert!
Strollers
• • • • • •

Car seats, cribs, and high chairs tend to grab safety spotlights. However, strollers are annually in the top four for most dangerous baby products. In 2012, the Consumer Product Safety Commission reported 12,300 emergency department treated injuries related to strollers. These included babies sliding out of the strollers, sleeping babies sliding down and strangulating in the leg opening, faulty straps, brake failures, small parts causing a choking hazard, and little fingers getting pinched or lacerated as the stroller was folded up.

Strollers – Standard and Mid-Size

Brand recommendations:

Best Overall Standard and Mid-Size

❏ **Baby Jogger City Mini Single Stroller**
   ▸ *Price: $250*
   ▸ *Pros:* lightweight, compact, and nimble award-winning stroller, has a quick, one-handed fold, durable, large sunshade, lightweight for a standard at 16.8 pounds, great value for the price
   ▸ *Cons:* under the seat storage basket is small, wheels are not great on rough surfaces, parent and child trays are sold separately, car seat adapter sold separately

Best Convertible, Grow with your Family Model

❏ **Baby Jogger City Select Stroller**
   ▸ *Price: $500*
   ▸ *Pros:* versatile mix and match stroller designed to grow with your family, as you start with a single seat stroller,

add a bassinet or infant seat adapter, and then a second
seat in 16 different combinations, telescoping handlebar,
hand brake gives more control, quick fold technology

▶ *Cons:* heavy, bulky, expensive for what you get as a single stroller, accessories are all extra (the bassinet, which
parents love as a place for baby to stretch out, is $100, the
second seat is $180, the second-seat mounting brackets are
$20, and the car seat multi-model adapter is $70.)

▶ Note: My top three convertible, grow-with-your-family
strollers are: Baby Jogger City Select (most versatile–look
for free 2nd seat with purchase deals), Britax B-Ready
(good value if used with Britax infant seats), and UPPA-
baby Vista (more value for city families who seldom use
a car since the bassinet is included with the price of the
stroller).

Best Value for Multiples

❑ **Britax B-Ready Stroller**

▶ *Price: $400-500*

▶ *Pros:* smaller, more compact footprint
than City Select, has a built-in receiver
for Britax infant seats (extra value with
Britax infant seats), works with other
major infant car seats (adapters sold
separately), accepts 2 infant car seats in
either forward or rear facing positions,
has 14 different seat configurations,
folds with the second seat in place

▶ *Cons:* main seat for use after 6 months old, 2nd seat costs
$120-150 and makes the stroller weigh 32 pounds, large
when folded, has a lower weight limit in both seats vs. the
City Select and other brands, the compact design is not as
good for tall parents requiring handlebar extension

Best for Stylish, Active Parents

❑ **Bumbleride Indie Stroller**

▶ *Price: $500*

▶ *Pros:* a light jogger at 20 pounds that is more stylish than the BOB Revolution, good mix of form and function, easy to fold and maneuver, durable exterior fabric made from 50% recycled PET, soft interior fabric made from 50% bamboo charcoal, included accessories are: universal car seat adapter bar, bumper bar, and cup holder

▶ *Cons:* skimpy canopy, not as smooth as the BOB, may be too wide for narrow urban aisles

▶ Note: Representing a new "crossover" class of strollers, the **Indie 4** *($599)* offers all terrain functionality for the outdoors combined with a lightweight, compact frame for modern life.

Strollers - Lightweight/Compact

Brand recommendations:

Best Overall Lightweight/Compact

❑ **Britax B-Agile Stroller**

▶ *Price: $250-270*

▶ *Pros:* on par with luxury strollers without the price, easy to maneuver, steers with one hand, folds with one hand, stands folded, lightweight at 16.5 pounds, fits Britax B-Safe seat without an adapter, fits Graco, Chicco, and Peg Perego infant seats with an adapter, best for parents who need a stroller to fit in a smaller car trunk or space in the home, best for smooth surfaces

▶ *Cons:* seat doesn't sit fully upright, under the seat storage is small, fixed handlebar, accessories expensive, accessories must be purchased separately, such as child tray, rain cover, stroller organizer, etc.

Most Compact

❑ **Baby Jogger City Mini Zip Stroller**

▶ *Price: $249*

▶ *Pros:* Zip is Baby Jogger's smallest folding stroller, ultra-compact size for everyday quick trips, travel, and public transit, acts as a full-featured umbrella with a 16 pound weight and 3D fold as it folds in half and then from the sides, front-wheel suspension, rear brake, adjustable leg rest, large canopy, comes with a cup holder, carry bag accessory has backpack straps for easy transport

▶ *Cons:* under the seat basket for storage is small due to 3D fold, lacks a parent and child tray, fixed handlebar, only comes in two colors (black and red)

Fastest Fold with Reversible Seat

❑ **Baby Jogger City Versa Stroller**

▶ *Price: $250-400*

▶ *Pros:* parents love the fast-fold combined with a reversible seat (stroller quickly snaps closed regardless of seat direction), large canopy, adjustable footrest and handlebar, 50 pound weight capacity, and large storage basket for a good price

▶ *Cons:* caregiver must ensure that stroller is locked properly with safety snaps (colored red), parachute material can seem thin for colder climates, and stroller does not turn into a double like the City Select

Lightest

❑ **UPPAbaby G-Lite Stroller**

▶ *Price: $160-180*

▶ *Pros:* one of the lightest full size strollers available at eleven pounds, tall ergonomic handles, convenient carry strap allows you to pick up the G-Lite with one hand, hand level triggers for quick fold (no foot action required), stands when folded, strong and durable, cup holder included

▶ *Cons:* G-Lite does not recline, so the stroller is not suitable for babies younger than 6 months who cannot sit up on their own, lacks parent and child trays, front swivel wheels do not lock, handles not suited well for one-handed driving

▶ Newer features: mesh sling back seat for breathability, complete removable fabric for easy cleaning, slightly larger canopy, under seat basket can hold 15 pounds

Best Inexpensive Umbrellas (for air travel and errands)

❑ **Cosco Umbrella Stroller with Canopy** or the **Babies R Us Umbrella Stroller**

▶ *Price: $18-30*

▶ *Pros:* These inexpensive strollers are great errand runners, if a primary stroller is too bulky for a trip. They can also survive a gate check without parents fretting too much over rough baggage handling.

▶ *Cons:* You get what you pay for, and these are meant to be very basic strollers.

Strollers - Travel System

Brand recommendations:

Best Overall Travel System

❏ **Britax B-Agile Travel System**
- ▸ *Price: $336-420*
- ▸ *Pros:* lightweight, compact 3-piece set includes a B-Safe car seat with side impact protection, base, and stroller that can be used until your child is 55 pounds
- ▸ *Cons:* seat does not sit up all the way, child is still at an angle in the most upright position, storage basket beneath is small, some parents complain about having "sweaty babies" with fabric that doesn't breathe very well (side impact seats often have this issue)
- ▸ Note: The B-Agile received a voluntary recall of strollers in January 2014, due to eight injury reports of lacerations or bruises to the fifth finger upon folding.

Easiest Travel System

❏ **Baby Trend Snap n Go Universal Infant Seat Carrier**
- ▸ *Price: $65-70 (Double $82-100)*
- ▸ *Pros:* easy to use and fold, affordable, cup holder and parent tray included, large basket
- ▸ *Cons:* some seats do not "snap into" this frame (you must secure the seat with straps), only lasts until baby is 6-10 months old, often cheaper to buy an infant seat adapter and a high-quality stroller

- ▸ Note: The **Graco SnugRider Elite** and **Chicco KeyFit Caddy** stroller frames work better with Graco and Chicco brand infant seats. Also, the new 2015 **Cloud Q Infant Car Seat** and stroller frame ($399) from CYBEX will be the first infant car seat to fully recline when used on a stroller or car seat frame, turning the car seat into a flat-lying carrying cot or bassinet (alleviating concerns about pressure on baby's spine and reduced oxygen flow from prolonged time in a typical car seat).

Lightest and Best for Frequent Travel

❑ **Mountain Buggy Nano Stroller**

▸ *Price: $200*

▸ *Pros:* world's lightest compact travel system at 13 pounds, travels as a carry-on item in its own satchel, fuss-free urban stroller with built-in universal car seat adapters (no need for extra accessories) and a full-size seat, accommodates most leading car seat brands

▸ *Cons:* steering may require two hands, expensive if purchased for travel only, cannot recline for use with a newborn (without a car seat), canopy is small

Strollers – Jogging

Brand recommendations:

Best Overall Jogging

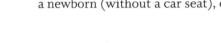

❑ **BOB Revolution SE Stroller**

▸ *Price: $368-460*

▸ *Pros:* always ranks high on top stroller lists due to versatility as a great jogging and everyday stroller, excellent suspension system for a smooth ride, swivel front wheel, 5-point padded harness, reclining seat to 70 degrees, best for parents who can walk or jog right out the front door

▸ *Cons:* heavy at 25 pounds, not ideal for loading in and out of your car, takes up trunk space, requires two-step folding, accessories are sold separately, handlebar is 40 inches tall which may be short for taller runners, tall children may outgrow seat height early

▶ Newer features: The new **BOB Revolution Flex** ($480) has an adjustable handlebar for Mom and Dad (33.5 to 45.8") and new colors.

▶ Note: Many parents wait to buy the BOB Revolution SE for 15–20% off at REI's anniversary sale.

Best Value Jogging Travel System

❏ **Graco FastAction Fold Jogger Click Connect Travel System**

▶ *Price: $250-300*

▶ *Pros:* one-second, one-hand fold has an automatic storage lock and is self-standing, accepts all Graco Click Connect infant car seats with a secure one-step attachment, locking front swivel wheel for transitioning from jogger to daily strolling, includes a Snugride Click Connect 35 pound infant seat and base, fixed handlebar height is taller (42") than the BOB Revolution SE (40") for taller runners

▶ *Cons:* heavier than the BOB at 30 pounds with an inferior suspension system, non-adjustable handlebar

Best for Hard-Core Runners (long training runs)

❏ **BOB Ironman Single Stroller**

▶ *Price: $335-410*

▶ *Pros:* all three wheels are large 16", hand brake good for hilly terrain, reviews are outstanding from serious runners (many had to upgrade from a cheaper jogging stroller)

▶ *Cons:* not an errand-runner, skimpy canopy, water bottle holder sold separately

Most Affordable Jogger

❑ **Jeep Overland Limited Jogging Stroller**

▶ *Price: $165-185*

▶ *Pros:* price is right for an average runner, children fit comfortably, hand brake plus foot brake, affordable jogger for tall runners (one of the few with an adjustable handle to 43 inches)

▶ *Cons:* bulky, fixed front wheel must be lifted to turn, not for long distance runners

Strollers – Luxury

Brand recommendations:

Best Overall Luxury

❑ **Bugaboo Bee Stroller**

▶ *Price: $720*

▶ *Pros:* when in doubt, go compact and light, most adjustable stroller in class, height adjustable handlebar, unfolded width of 21 inches for urban use, outstanding suspension and maneuverability, grows with your family using a seat and wheeled board combination for an older sibling

▶ *Cons:* stroller accessories, including the bassinet, are sold separately, car seat adapter is sold separately, lacks a parent tray and cup holder, storage is okay

▶ Newer features: enhanced frame and wheels for a smoother ride, more seat depth, improved harness, extended sun canopy, larger under seat basket, improved rain cover, new easy-to-carry bassinet (adapters included).

▶ Note: In spring of 2015, Bugaboo is set to release the new **Bugaboo Runner Jogging Stroller Extension** (chassis and seat adapters $425) to be used with the seat of any Bugaboo stroller. The **Bugaboo Runner** will retail for $755 (seat included).

Best for Luxury and Comfort

❑ **UPPAbaby Vista Stroller**

- ▶ *Price: $820-860*
- ▶ *Pros:* the 2015 design builds on the original Vista and becomes a true convertible stroller as your family grows, can comfortably hold two MESA car seats, two bassinets, or two toddler seats, transporting up to three children (by adding PiggyBack Ride-Along board), the redesigned Rumbleseat (the seat that makes Vista a double) can face forward or rear, one-step fold  with or without seat attached, rain shield and mesh bug shield included, one button height adjustment, enhanced suspension, bassinet is included
- ▶ *Cons:* expensive (the Rumbleseat that makes the Vista a double stroller costs $199), heavy (2015 model weighs 27.5 pounds w/ main seat attached), unless you use the MESA car seat you must pay extra for infant seat adapters
- ▶ Newer features: This stroller model has been upgraded significantly for 2015, including updated double options, one step fold, single piece, easy to clean bumper bar, bassinet now features zip out liner and boot cover, aluminum and magnesium frame, and never flat AirGo wheels.

❑ *Runner-Up:* **Bugaboo Cameleon3**

- ▶ *Price: $969-1149*
- ▶ *Pros:* this company's culture is obsessed with quality materials, large 12" wheels tackle any terrain, reversible handlebar lets you put the 12" wheels up front, has a hand-operated brake, foot brake, and adjustable suspension, reversible and reclining seat, one hand release bassinet

> ▶ *Cons:* insanely expensive, the two-piece fold has a bit of a learning curve, stroller does not convert to a true double (though the wheeled board can accommodate an older toddler)
>
> ▶ Newer features: For 2015, Bugaboo paired up with the edgy style of Diesel to create unique fabrics and designs that are rocker and military chic.
>
> ▶ Note: Choosing between the UPPAbaby Vista and Bugaboo Cameleon typically comes down to preferences in style, the way the stroller pushes and rides, and whether parents desire a convertible for a growing family.

Money-Saving Tip
Ditch the Double Stroller

If your children are spaced more than two to three years apart, you may not need a double stroller at all. Supermarkets and warehouse stores often have double carts or special carts for multiple children, and so do popular children's parks and zoos. For the first year, baby can remain in a front carrier for errands, while your toddler or pre-schooler uses the stroller. Also, you may consider using a wheeled board that attaches to your single stroller (an older sibling stands on a rolling board behind the stroller) to streamline your profile and save money.

Strollers - Double

Test all double strollers with older siblings before purchasing.

Brand recommendations:

Easiest Double to Fold

❑ **Baby Jogger City Mini Double Stroller**
  ▶ *Price: $450*

- *Pros:* fold-up requires one action (pull two handles in each seat and it folds in half), maneuverable, fits through a standard door, peekaboo windows, seats lay flat, narrow for a tandem side-by-side design, handy for in-and-out of the car travel, 26 pounds
- *Cons:* storage basket tough to access, too wide for downtown errands and public transportation

Best Convertible Double

❏ **Baby Jogger City Select Stroller with Second Seat**

- *Price: $657-670*
- *Pros:* seating versatility is the main feature with 16 different configurations, having two seats on one frame makes it a narrower and more compact double, great for two kids under age two, sturdy, easy to fold
- *Cons:* any accessories that you want (cup holder, car seat adapter, child snack tray, belly bar, etc.) are sold separately, heavy with two seats at 36 pounds (heaviest child should be closest to the parent driving for easier steering)

Best Double Umbrella/Lightweight

❏ **Maclaren Twin Triumph Stroller**

- *Price: $279*
- *Pros:* double that is actually compact, fully reclines, looks like an umbrella double yet is fairly sturdy, holds up to 110 pounds
- *Cons:* Maclaren brands were recalled in 2009 and 2011 for fingertip injuries (new models have been scrutinized for safety), there is no place to hang a diaper bag, storage space is limited, and canopy is small
- *Note:* Also check out the new **Baby Jogger Vue Double** ($399) with double reversible seats, an umbrella fold, car

seat adapters that can hold one or two car seats, and an adjustable foot rest.

Best Sit or Stand Double (for siblings)

❏ Joovy Caboose Ultralight Stroller

▶ *Price:* $220-270

▶ *Pros:* lighter than other stand-on tandems at 21.8 pounds, offers sit or stand options, can navigate narrow spaces with ease, three-position front seat recline, linked rear brakes, comes with a universal car seat adapter that snaps easily into the tray housings, Joovy parent organizer included

▶ *Cons:* test at the store for toddler's sitting height and comfort before purchasing, must flip up bench to access storage

Best Jogging Double

❏ BOB Revolution SE Duallie Stroller

▶ *Price:* $670

▶ *Pros:* swivel front wheel, always ranks on top stroller lists, independent retracting seats and canopies, padded harness and seat, roomy for kids

▶ *Cons:* really expensive, bulky, heavy (32 pounds), not for urban use beyond jogging, takes up major car trunk space for suburban families

▶ Note: The new **BOB Revolution Flex** Duallie ($690) has an adjustable handlebar for Mom and Dad (33.5 to 45.8") and new colors.

■ Baby Gear: Must-have Items

Bouncer seat

This piece of gear provides an inexpensive, free set of hands for the first six months of baby's life. A bouncer seat also transfers easily room to room. Remember, babies see bright colors, so an archway of cream-colored toys that matches beautifully with your décor may not be very stimulating to baby.

Brand recommendations:

❑ **Fisher-Price Rainforest Friends Deluxe Bouncer**
  ▶ *Price: $44-65*
  ▶ *Pros:* FP Rainforest products are colorful and fun, the green blends with most décor, rainforest sounds are soothing, the waterfall archway is entertaining to baby, chair vibrates
  ▶ *Cons:* design is not modern, has a plastic toy arch

❑ **Fisher-Price My Little Snugabunny**
  ▶ *Price: $52-70*
  ▶ *Pros:* modern design that fits décor, lush material with a newborn insert for stability, compact, has calming vibrations, songs and nature sounds
  ▶ *Cons:* toy mobile is not as exciting as other seats

❑ **Baby Bjorn Bouncer Balance Soft**
  ▶ *Price: $169 -199*
  ▶ *Pros:* simple seat (pronounced bee-YORN) with no lights, music, or vibration, for parents who are willing to pay up for modern design, folds flat for easy travel
  ▶ *Cons:* seat is expensive and so simple that it might be boring, toy bars are sold separately

❏ **4Moms mamaRoo Bouncer**
  ▶ *Price:* $220-240
  ▶ *Pros:* high tech bouncer and swing in one, runs on A/C power
  ▶ *Cons:* can be heavy and bulky, moving track can pinch toddler fingers
  ▶ Note: If you have a 2015 model and beyond, an app lets you control your Mamaroo remotely from your phone.

Activity mat or play gym

This will help develop your baby's sensory skills as he playfully bats at hanging toys. It also doubles as a tummy-time mat.

Brand recommendations:

❏ **Fisher-Price Rainforest Melodies and Lights Deluxe Gym**
  ▶ *Price:* $49-70
  ▶ *Pros:* colorful, plays music and flashes lights under the mat, baby will spend quality time "batting" his/her toys, mat is high quality and machine washable

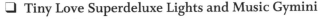

  ▶ *Cons:* rainbow archway or hanging toys must be removed for tummy time, design-conscious parents may dislike the colorful motif (try the **Skip Hop Treetop Friends** mat if this is the case)

❏ **Tiny Love Superdeluxe Lights and Music Gymini**
  ▶ *Price:* $43-60
  ▶ *Pros:* stimulates baby with music and lights, large mirror for tummy time, classical music, mat is machine washable, folds up flat for travel
  ▶ *Cons:* expensive, must remove hanging items for tummy time

Portable crib or playard

You will use a travel crib for several years with multiple children. This product can also double as a newborn bassinet or be used for downstairs naps in multi-level homes. You will also want two playard sheets.

Brand recommendations:

❑ **Graco Pack 'n Play Playard** (with Newborn Napper, if planning to use as a bassinet)

- ▶ *Price: $68-80*
- ▶ *Pros:* essential for travel to grandma's house, can double as a bassinet, easy to put together, also used for napping in upstairs/downstairs homes
- ▶ *Cons:* somewhat bulky item for travel and storage

❑ **Baby Bjorn Travel Crib Light**

- ▶ *Price: $272-300*
- ▶ *Pros:* weighs 11 pounds and folds out in one easy motion vs. the Graco Pack 'n Play, which weighs 30 pounds and must be assembled
- ▶ *Cons:* pricing for this product is expensive and it varies up to $100 on popular web sites. Skip the $40 Baby Bjorn fitted sheet and use a stretchy jersey playard sheet instead.

■ Baby Gear: Other convenient items

Infant swing

Your baby just spent nine months swinging in your belly, so this piece of gear may be just what you need to get everyone through a colicky night. Note: Some babies don't like swings, making them an expensive and bulky bust.

Brand recommendations:

❏ **Fisher-Price Cradle 'N Swing**
  ▶ *Price: $119-165*
  ▶ *Pros:* if your baby needs lots of motion for soothing, this swing has six speeds and two directions of rocking, plus a mobile, plush seating, and neutral tones for a home's décor
  ▶ *Cons:* bulky, takes up living room space

❏ **4Moms Mamaroo Bouncer**
  ▶ *Price: $220-240*
  ▶ *Pros:* high-tech bouncer and swing in one, good swing for a tighter space, five calming baby motions, runs on A/C power, comes in several colors
  ▶ *Cons:* can be heavy and bulky, moving track has history of pinching toddlers' fingers, rocking speed is slow

Activity saucer, ExerSaucer, or Jumperoo

This keeps older babies upright in a safe place, while you cook or surf the web. Buy this gear used if you can, as some babies love them, while others would rather be crawling.

Brand recommendations:

- ❏ **Fisher-Price Rainforest or Precious Planet Jumperoo**

  - ▶ *Price: $84-105*
  - ▶ *Pros:* best activity center for taller babies, colorful, chair swivels, plays music, lights up, great energy burner
  - ▶ *Cons:* takes up floor space, chunky legs can get red and irritated after jumping a short time
  - ▶ *Note:* The new **Fisher-Price Woodland Friends Space-Saver Jumperoo** *($70)* provides a portable, space-saving design that folds flat for on-the-go use or storage and takes up less space, while providing all of the entertainment of a full size Jumperoo. The foldable version comes in Rainforest Friends styling, too.

- ❏ **Evenflo ExerSaucer Triple Fun**
  - ▶ *Price: $100-120*
  - ▶ *Pros:* all-around excellent design, grows with your child as a play mat, ExerSaucer, and activity table all in one
  - ▶ *Cons:* takes up floor space, taller babies can "tip" into saucer toys

- ❏ **Fisher-Price Little Superstar Step n' Play Piano Entertainer**
  - ▶ *Price: $80-110*
  - ▶ *Pros:* for music lovers, as it includes piano keys for the feet, drum sounds activated by the hands, plus lights and songs; grows with baby, using an infant insert seat to gliding seat to rails for a standing baby

  - ▶ *Cons:* bulky, noisy, tough to store

Baby carrier or front carrier

A front carrier allows you to wear baby, or carry baby with you wherever you go. I found this to be a must-have item with my second child, in order to have free hands with an older sibling.

Brand recommendations:

- ❑ **ErgoBaby Original Baby Carrier**
  - ▶ *Price: $115*
  - ▶ *Pros:* allows baby to be carried in front of your chest, behind your back, or slung up on either hip; a consistent top pick for carriers because baby is in a more comfortable seated position vs. legs dangling in front; provides more back support for Mom and Dad than the Baby Bjorn; comes in a winter edition
  - ▶ *Cons:* baby must turn his head to see out, as the straps can block baby's view; tough to use with newborns without the $25-40 insert

- ❑ **ErgoBaby Four Position 360 Baby Carrier**
  - ▶ *Price: $160*
  - ▶ *Pros:* allows baby to face forward; leg pouches are specifically designed to keep baby in a frog position, preventing hip dysplasia
  - ▶ *Cons:* smaller babies may struggle to see out front over the canvas safety flap

- ❑ **Beco Baby Gemini Baby Carrier**
  - ▶ *Price: $130*
  - ▶ *Pros:* modern, stylish, and functional; accommodates new-borns to toddlers; baby can ride front-facing
  - ▶ *Cons:* some parents complain about cost and tricky safety buckles

Baby wrap, sling, or soft carrier

A soft wrap or sling, typically associated with attachment parenting techniques or baby wearing, can be very useful for newborns. However, this product has a finite life. Once baby wants to see out, you may need a front carrier.

Brand recommendations:

❑ **Moby Wrap Baby Carrier**
  ▶ *Price: $45-48*
  ▶ *Pros:* best for newborns, easy to establish hands-free nursing with a younger baby, no straps, no buckles, versatile, easy to wash
  ▶ *Cons:* the amount of fabric can be overwhelming at first, you must watch YouTube videos for instructions, gets hot for Mom and baby in warm weather

❑ **Baby K'Tan Baby Carrier**
  ▶ *Price: $50*
  ▶ *Pros:* simpler than Moby, no buckles, made of 100% cotton, free of chemicals, has multiple positions for babies weighing eight to 35 pounds
  ▶ *Cons:* doesn't fit a toddler, can hurt shoulders if not adjusted properly, can get hot in summer

❑ *Affordable:* **Infantino Sash Mei Tai Carrier**
  ▶ *Price: $25-35*
  ▶ *Pros:* based on a centuries-old style of baby wearing called Mei Tai, easiest to nurse hands-free because the shoulder straps adjust quickly, parents also like the privacy cover for nursing and naps
  ▶ *Cons:* some complain that it doesn't fit a toddler, can hurt shoulders if not adjusted properly, straps are very long and they can get dirty, some reviewers are frustrated by all the tying

Doorway jumper or bouncer

This spring-loaded seat is designed to hang in a doorway, allowing baby to bounce independently while you accomplish household tasks. This is a great hand-me-down item; however, I would not buy it new.

Brand recommendations:

❑ **Graco Bumper Jumper**
  ▶ *Price: $54-60*
  ▶ *Pros:* more portable than a Jumperoo or ExerSaucer, a doorway jumper keeps crawlers contained while Mom is cooking, showering, or getting dressed, has a washable seat pad, non-twist straps, and a no-mark clamp; it is also a great energy burner before bed or naptime
  ▶ *Cons:* another piece of bulky baby gear
  ▶ Note: You must remove any detachable toys and strips of fabric that attach them from hand-me-down Graco jumpers due to a recall in 2009.

❑ **Evenflo SmartSteps Jump and Go**
  ▶ *Price: $36-82*
  ▶ *Pros:* more colorful, stylish bouncer than the competitors, great to take room to room, adjustable height, fully enclosed springs, machine-washable
  ▶ *Cons:* doesn't fit on doors greater than seven feet high or older doors with crown molding

A stroller snug sack or winter bunting

This stroller cover looks like a tiny sleeping bag for baby. It is a must-have if you live in a cold climate, or if you plan to stroll with baby in the cold for any lengthy period of time.

Brand recommendations:

❑ **JJ Cole Urban Bundleme, Infant**
- ▶ *Price: $36-43*
- ▶ *Pros:* This product, which is intended to be used in place of a winter coat or suit, is great for stroller use (not between baby and her car seat straps). I prefer the Urban Bundleme with a smoother interior to the Original Bundleme with the thicker, sheep-like texture because it has a wind- and water-resistant outer shell.
- ▶ *Cons:* Using this product may void the warranty on your car seat, as it interferes with harness tightness and spacing. Parent reviewers say that it doesn't work with Baby Jogger (City Mini, City Elite) or BOB strollers.

❑ **Jolly Jumper Arctic Sneak-A-Peek Infant Car Seat Cover Black**
- ▶ *Price: $27*
- ▶ *Pros:* This fleece-lined, water-repellent "shower cap" cover does not go between baby and the car seat straps. It also comes with an attached swaddle blanket and a peek-a-boo flap with dual zippers that keeps baby from overheating.

- ▶ *Cons:* Reviewers note that it will not cover larger infant seats with a 35-pound maximum.

■ Diapering Supplies

Disposable diapers

Diapers are typically the #1 or #2 biggest expense in your baby budget. The key to choosing the right diaper for your baby is balancing per diaper cost with fit and minimal leaks. Newborns will typically go through 10 to 12 diapers per day, while older babies use six to eight per day. How many

Eco Tip
Eco-Diapers, Not Miracle Diapers

• •

It's true. Disposable diapers take hundreds of years to decompose in landfills. However, before you walk out of Whole Foods with your brown eco-diapers thinking that you are saving the planet, consider this statement from the Seventh Generation web site: "All disposable diapers, including Seventh Generation's, rely on man-made materials to deliver the high-level performance that parents expect of modern diapers. These materials are mostly petroleum-derived and are not renewable, which adversely impacts the environmental footprint associated with these products."

Companies newer to the eco-diaper scene, such as The Honest Company and gDiapers, may have eco-style; however, they also contain Super Absorbent Polymer (SAP), just like Pampers and Huggies. Most SAP used today is petroleum derived. So while I do commend eco-companies for trying to be more environmentally responsible, parents should be aware that eco-diapers charge a hefty premium, yet they do not solve the biggest environmental problem with diapers. Making a diaper chlorine- and fragrance-free is a great step toward protecting baby from trace amounts of dioxin and phthalates, but that diaper will still be sitting in a landfill centuries from now. Even if eco-diapers and eco-inserts blend their SAP with wheat/starch, fluffed wood pulp, and other materials, they are still SAP diapers.

diapers will you need in the first year? An average eight to 10 diapers per day x 365 days per year = 2920 to 3650 diapers a year. If each diaper takes approximately two minutes to change, changing nine diapers per day for one year equals 109.5 hours, or 4.5 days of diaper changing!

Brand recommendations:

Best Disposables for Newborns

❑ **Pampers Swaddlers** *$0.28 each, depending on size ($1022 per year, using 10 diapers per day).* These are softer than Huggies, with a long runway of soft material up the back vs. an elastic band and a pocket to "catch" runny messes.

▶ *Pros:*
- Swaddlers are what many hospitals use (in the green and yellow pack)
- Three sizes fit babies up to 18 pounds
- Extra padding in back (great for inactive "back is best" babies)
- Has a fold-down section for navel area in newborn size
- Sign up on the company web site for digital coupons, or for coupons to be sent to your home

▶ *Cons:*
- More expensive than store-brand or private label diapers
- Not available in larger sizes
- Some parents do not like the powdery smell of Pampers
- Signing up for coupons comes with the price of sharing your personal information

❑ **Huggies Little Snugglers** *$0.28 each ($1022 per year).* These can be helpful for bigger eaters, leakers, and poop-up-the-backers. However, test different brands for fit. You may love one brand for your first child and then figure out that another brand is better for the next.

▶ *Pros:*
- Little Snugglers are designed to "catch" runny messes with a pocket
- Elastic strap in back tries to keep in the "runny mess"
- Huggies are more available in big-name warehouse stores
- Sign up on the company web site for digital coupons, or for coupons to be sent to your home

▶ *Cons:*
- More expensive than store-brand diapers
- May not mold as well around the legs as softer Pampers
- The elastic band in back may irritate sensitive skin
- Signing up for coupons comes with the price of sharing your personal information

Best Disposables for Older Babies

❑ *Conventional brands:* **Pampers Cruisers** *$0.25-0.27 each ($913-986 per year)*, **Pampers Baby Dry** *$0.23-0.26 each ($840-949 per year)*, or **Huggies Snug and Dry** *$0.22-0.28 each ($803-1022 per year)*. Best brand depends on fit with your baby.

❑ *Budget Choice:* **Kirkland Signature Supreme** *$0.15-0.19 each ($548-694 per year)* diapers from Costco or any private label that fits your baby, such as **Parent's Choice** *$0.12-0.14 each ($438-511 per year)*

❑ *Hybrid Choice (part reusable, part disposable):* **gDiapers with gPants** *$18-22 gPants/Cover + $4.75/cloth insert + $0.39/disposable insert ($1423 per year for inserts)*. gPants are colorful, reusable diaper covers that you use with gDiapers disposable inserts.

Best Overnight or 12-Hour Disposables

❑ **Huggies Overnites** *$0.32-0.45 each ($117-164 per year)*. Want to decrease your chances of waking in the middle of the night with a leak? Bring on the Overnites, which are well worth their cost.

❑ **Pampers Baby Dry** *$0.23-0.26 each ($84-95 per year)*. These diapers are really thin, yet 10-12 hours later your baby's diaper remains packed, but not leaky. The tabs on these diapers are also very flexible, expanding and contracting as baby sleeps.

Best Eco-Friendlier Disposables

❑ **Bambo Nature Diapers** *$0.45-0.51 each ($1643-1862 per year)*. This brand receives praise for excellent construction and performance from an eco-diaper, in addition to stricter adherence to eco-friendly practices.
  ▶ *Pros:*
  - The company claims they are 80% compostable
  - They have less SAP; it is replaced with wheat starch and acrylic polymers
  - Least amount of SAP among popular eco-diapers
  - No phthalates, heavy metals, chlorine, or AZO-pigments
  - Excellent overnight absorbency
  ▶ *Cons:*
  - They are twice the cost of regular diapers.

- The back of the diaper is not stretchable.
- These diapers use sodium polyacrylate (SAP) for absorption

❑ **Earth's Best TenderCare Chlorine Free Diapers** *$0.31-0.45 each ($1132-1643 per year)*. This is the Best Value eco-brand of choice for pediatrician-owned BabyGearLab, and it is available in most mainstream stores. Earth's Best are also a more affordable eco-brand across all sizes.
  ▶ *Pros:*
  - They are latex, dye, and perfume free.
  - Some parents prefer to support companies trying to be sustainable.
  - One of the more affordable eco-brands
  - These receive some of the best reviews for not leaking among eco-brands.
  ▶ *Cons:*
  - There are reports of rashes among multiple review sources.
  - These diapers contain corn and wheat, which can be allergens for some babies.
  - These diapers use sodium polyacrylate (SAP) for absorption.

Eco-Friendlier Disposables (Needs Improvement)

❑ **Seventh Generation Free and Clear Diapers** *$0.31-0.42 each ($1132-1533 per year)*. This well-known, widely available green brand has a track record from parent reviewers and diaper testers that is less than stellar, due to complaints of leaks, low absorption, and a reformulation of the brand.
  ▶ *Pros:*
  - The wood pulp used in these diapers is harvested from sustainably managed forests.
  - No fragrances, latex, petroleum-based lotions, or chlorine processing
  - Excellent brand recognition and availability
  - Reasonably priced for an eco-diaper

► *Cons:*

- These diapers are dyed a brownish-tan color to make consumers think they are all natural or biodegradable in appearance. Seventh Generation states on its website, "We use brown pigments to help distinguish Seventh Generation Chlorine Free Diapers from others in the marketplace that are bleached with chlorine-containing substances." Note: The actual color of diapers is translucent like a milk jug.
- Parent reviews are scathing to mixed for absorption and leaks.
- These diapers use sodium polyacrylate (SAP) for absorption.

Money-Saving Tip
Diaper Pricing Unveiled
• • • • • • • • • • • • • • •

Private label size 3 diapers are roughly $0.12-0.22 per diaper, Pampers and Huggies premiums are $0.22-0.28 per diaper, Seventh Generation/Earth's Best are around $0.30+ per diaper, and Honest Company/Nature BabyCare/gDiapers are $0.40+ per diaper. I chose to compare size 3 prices because newborn diapers have much tighter price competition and distribution among brands. For example, pricing for a newborn diaper from The Honest Company is going to be right in the middle of the pack between mainstream and eco-brands. This company is smartly and aggressively offering free trial kits, stylish bundles (with stars, plaids, and little rocker skulls), and lower prices for newborn diapers to hook new parents. However, as baby grows out of newborn sizes (typically in a few weeks), the prices quickly ramp up. By sizes 3 to 6, the Honest Company is leading the most expensive brands, charging $.40-.88 per diaper, depending on the size and type of diaper. Honest offerings at Target stores aren't any cheaper: $.47/diaper for size 3, $.51/diaper for size 5, and $.74 for a 4T/5T training pant. I commend Honest Company for being a legitimately eco-friendly business, but c'mon! Who wants to pay almost $5 per day (over $1800 per year) for cutesy diapers worn beneath baby's clothes and blankets, when you could snag them at Costco for less than $2 per day ($694 per year)? Those prices add up.

Cloth diapers

You may also be considering cloth diapers as an eco-friendly, chemical-free alternative to disposables, or landfill diapers. To help you think through this decision, let's analyze some of the pros and cons of cloth diapers.

▶ *Pros*:
- Better for the environment
- Healthier for baby: there are no chemicals against baby's skin, such as dioxin (a by-product of the bleaching process with chlorine), tributyltin (a toxin linked to hormonal problems in humans and animals), and sodium polyacrylate or SAP (this supposedly non-toxic gel found in nearly all diapers was removed from tampons, due to a link to Toxic Shock Syndrome).[84]
- No more pins: cloth diapers now come in cute colors with Velcro straps or snaps.
- Cloth diapers are more affordable and more convenient than ever.
- If you do not enjoy washing diapers, you can have a service do it for you, although it nullifies the cost and energy savings of cloth.
- A diaper sprayer that attaches to your toilet plumbing can make cleaning the mess off cloth diapers doable.

▶ *Cons*:
- Cloth diapers with stool must be rinsed in the toilet. Disposable users should actually do this too, although few do.
- Parents must be okay with regular laundry duty.
- Parents must be okay with poop on their hands and in the washing machine.
- Many day cares do not allow cloth diapers.
- Travel is more difficult because you must carry soiled diapers with you.
- Runny stool can be messy with cloth, if fit is an issue.

Types of cloth diapers

❑ *Best for frugal parents/most economical:* **Prefolds + diaper covers**

These diapers must be changed as soon as baby gets wet. You may place a stay dry liner, usually made of fleece, on top of the prefold to keep baby drier between changes.

❑ *Best for parents reluctant to try cloth/best for day care/easiest to use:* **All-in-One Diapers**

All-in-one cloth diapers are perhaps your best argument for a day care center to accept cloth diapers—no stuffing required. AIO diapers have absorbent material already sewn into the waterproof cover, and they can essentially be treated like a disposable diaper (with the one difference that the diaper is tossed in a wet bag to wash later rather than disposed of in the trash). The downside to this convenience is cost, although they do come in one-size varieties with adjustable snaps.

❑ *Most popular/most convenient:* **Pocket Diapers**

Pocket diapers, or stuffing diapers, are the most popular type of cloth diapers today because no extra cover is required, and they are more affordable than all-in-one diapers. A pocket diaper has an opening (located along the edge that touches baby's back) that allows an absorbent pre-cut insert or foldable diaper to be placed in a pocket between the diaper's waterproof outer shell and an inner layer that touches baby's skin. A pocket diaper may be a one-size diaper or one that comes in different sizes (newborn, S/M/L); it also comes with Velcro or snap closures. For nighttime, you can add super absorbent hemp inserts for extra protection.

Compromise: using cloth and eco-diapers

If you find yourself stuck in the middle of the cloth debate (caring about the environment and health of your baby, but not ready to commit to 100% cloth), there is a compromise solution. Do a mix of both: use cloth diapers at home and eco-friendly alternatives, such as hybrid diapers or

eco-diapers, for travel and day care. Note: Hybrid diapers are biodegradable, flushable inserts that fit into an outer diaper cover, such as gDiapers and Kushies. Inserts with stool on them get flushed down the toilet,
while wet ones can be flushed or added to a compost pile. However,
reviews from parents say the inserts clog the toilet.

Cost: cloth vs. disposables

It can be difficult to assess the true cost of cloth vs. disposable diapering since many variable factors go into these calculations, such as cost
of supplies, laundry service, electricity, water, etc. For example, if you're
a style-conscious parent buying limited print all-in-one cloths, such as
bumGenius' Albert or Audrey diapers (inspired by Albert Einstein and
Audrey Hepburn), you're not going to save $2,000 on cloth diapering, as
favorite eco-websites claim. Therefore, in a cost-benefit analysis for one
child, the cloth vs. disposable debate may be "a wash" on dollar cost, with
the long-term environmental savings going to cloth. Pass a full set of cloth
diapers and inserts on to a younger sibling, and the scale tips to cloth.
Bottom line: Disposable diapers are easy to toss and they're convenient.
That's why 90-95% of U.S. parents use them. However, with the option
of all-in-one diapers, flushable inserts, and eco-diapers for travel and day
care, cloth diapers can work for busy, environmentally conscious parents.

Brand recommendations:

Best Cloth Diapers

*The best advice for cloth diapers is to never buy too many of one kind up front.
Try a sample of different brands because they all fit differently.*

❑ **bumGenius One Size Cloth Diaper** (*$15-25/diaper*) (Pocket, All-
in-One, and Hybrid versions)
   ▶ *Pros*:
      • Fits from birth to potty training
      • Adjustable enough to be used with siblings in diapers
      • Snap-down front to adjust size (most parents prefer the
        longevity of snaps to Velcro)
      • Diapers are bundled with two inserts: a newborn insert
        and a one-size insert for older babies up to 35 pounds

▶ *Cons:*
- Fasteners wear out over time
- May not work for heavier babies
- You may need separate newborn diapers for babies under seven pounds

❑ **Rumparooz G2 One Size Pocket Diaper** *($16-26/diaper)*
▶ *Pros:*
- One diaper for four sizes
- Fits birth to potty training (6-35 lb)
- Winner of numerous awards for cloth diapers
- Dual inner gussets (inner row of elastic for leaks)

▶ *Cons:*
- Double gusset can be bulky
- Elasticity can wear out over time
- More expensive up front

Best Hybrid Cloth Diapers

❑ **gDiapers** (reusable gPants cover with option to use prefolds, cotton inserts, or disposable inserts)
▶ *Price: $18-22 gPants/Cover + $4.75/cloth insert + $0.39/disposable insert ($1423 per year for inserts)*
▶ *Pros:*
- Style and versatility
- Easy for multiple caregivers to use because they fasten like disposables
- Product is widely available online and in mainstream stores, such as Walmart, Target, and BRU

▶ *Cons:*
- Marketed for convenience, but the shell, pouch and inserts should be washed separately
- You can't put the liner in the dryer so the diaper must be disassembled
- Diapers do not come with inserts (must buy separately)
- Diapers must be purchased for each size (try **Flip** hybrid cloth diaper covers and inserts for a one-size option)
- Disposable inserts are expensive

Supplies for Cloth Diapering

❑ **Cloth diapers:** A newborn needs 12+ cloth diapers for changes every one to three hours, while a solid cloth collection (for parents who are slower with the laundry) may have 20-25 diapers. Baby shower gifts can be helpful to any budget; however, you may want to wait until baby is here before you invest big bucks on a single cloth brand. Try several different brands and assess which are most convenient for you to wash and fit best on your baby.

❑ **Wipes:** Reusable cotton wipes can either be immersed in a wipes solution and placed in a wipes warmer or dispenser, or sprayed with a spray bottle of solution at your changing station. **GroVia** *($0.91 each)* and **bumGenius** *($0.99 each)* make popular cloth wipes. **OsoCozy Flannel** *($0.73 each)* baby wipes are also a top pick.

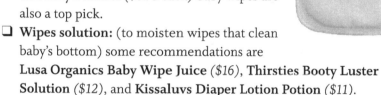

❑ **Wipes solution:** (to moisten wipes that clean baby's bottom) some recommendations are **Lusa Organics Baby Wipe Juice** *($16)*, **Thirsties Booty Luster Solution** *($12)*, and **Kissaluvs Diaper Lotion Potion** *($11)*.

❑ **Diaper pail with a waterproof liner or large zip bag:** You will need something to keep your dirty cloth diapers in until you can wash them. **Mother-Ease Diaper Pail** *($50)* is an eco-friendly pail made of recycled plastic that is fairly well-reviewed, despite the price tag. It uses a natural odor control system with carbon filters and airflow. **Kissaluvs' Antibacterial Pail Liner** *($20)* is a washable substitute for trash bags, as it is made from a high quality PUL (polyurethane laminate) fabric with a special anti-microbial effect. **Kushies** *($12-14)* and **Planet Wise** *($16-19)* are favorite large hanging zip bags.

❑ **Wet bag/travel bag:** This waterproof bag stores dirty diapers and soiled clothes until washing. **Munchkin Damp Goods Bag** *($15)*, **Itzy Ritzy Travel Happens** *($13-18)*, and **Planet Wise Wet Bags** *($16-19)* are a few among many brands of reusable bags.

❑ **Cloth diaper sprayer:** This handy sprayer, similar to a dish sprayer on a sink, attaches to toilet plumbing with adjustable spray

172 • Baby Registry

for cleaning off messes from cloth diapers. **Bumkins** *($45-50)* and **bumGenius** *($57)* sprayers receive good reviews.

❏ **Extra inserts:** Hemp is the most absorbent material for nighttime and heavy wetting.

❏ **A drying rack or clothesline:** Maximize value from your cloth diapers by air-drying them. Let the sun bleach out stains while drying diapers on a line outside.

■ Supplies for All Diapering

Wipes

Try out different brands and note the ingredients on the package. All disposable baby wipes, including natural and biodegradable ones, have some type of synthetic preservative in them to prevent bacteria growth. To save money, buy wipes in bulk and transfer them to empty travel-sized pouches for the diaper bag.

Brand recommendations:

❏ *Best Overall:* Costco's **Kirkland Signature Baby Wipes** *($20 per 900 count or $0.02 each)* are a budget-friendly favorite made from 100% renewable resources. They are biodegradable, hypoaller-genic, and alcohol free, although they do have trace preservatives that eco-parents question.

❏ *Best Mainstream Eco-Wipe:* **Seventh Generation Wipes** *($13-15 per 384 count or $0.03 to $0.04 each)* are chlorine and alcohol free, although they are made from a blend of wood pulp and synthetic materials polypropylene and polyethylene (rayon and polyester).

❏ *Best Biodegradable:** **Honest Company** *($5 per 72 count or $0.07 each)* and **Nature Babycare** *($25 per 700 count or $0.04 each)* are hypoallergenic, alcohol and chlorine-free, and biodegradable*, using the gentlest cleansers and preservatives among disposable wipes.

Eco Tip
Biodegradable Diaper Wipes
• • • • • • • • • • • • • • • • • • • •

You will almost always see an asterisk* next to biodegradable labeling for diaper wipes. In fact, Seventh Generation contends that no wipe can authentically claim to be biodegradable because biodegradable wipes do not biodegrade if they are disposed of in a landfill, which is why the brand chooses to focus on chlorine-free wipes products. Biodegradable diapers and wipes can break down in roughly 12 months using a compost tumbler or open air composting method.

Diaper rash cream

With my sensitive-skinned children, I tried many different organic and natural creams. However, it didn't take long to convert to good, old-fashioned Desitin for major diaper rashes, since rubbing beeswax, castor oil, and olive oil on my baby's bottom just didn't do the trick. If your child's bum isn't particularly sensitive, try a favorite eco-brand.

Brand recommendations:

❑ **Desitin** is tried and true, winning over "organic-only" parents because it actually works. For severe rashes, try **Desitin Maximum Strength** (*$6.50*) in the purple tube.

❑ *Organic brands:* **Burt's Bees Baby Bee** (*$8*) **Diaper Ointment, Nature's Baby Organics Organic Diaper Ointment** (*$8*), and **Earth Mama Angel Baby Bottom Balm** (*$13*) all smell better than Desitin.

Diaper pail and liners

Diaper pails have a printer and ink cartridge business model, with the refill bags making all the money. Therefore, you must decide which option you dislike more: 1) paying for expensive, airtight refill bags, or 2) pungent poo smells in your nursery. For more sensitive noses, buy a sealed pail with patented refill bags. For less sensitive noses or eco-buffs who prefer not to wrap their landfill diapers in extra plastic, try a small trashcan with a reusable liner. Expect to empty this bag often.

Brand recommendations:

- ❏ **Playtex Diaper Genie** *($28-38)* controls odor but requires expensive refill bags *($7 for 270-count)*.
- ❏ **Baby Trend Diaper Champ** *($35)* uses regular kitchen bags, but may not control odor as well.
- ❏ **Mother-Ease Diaper Pail** *($50)* is an eco-friendly pail made of recycled plastic. It uses a natural odor system with carbon filters and airflow.
- ❏ **Kissaluvs' Antibacterial Pail Liner** *($20)* is a washable substitute for trash bags, and it is made from a high quality PUL (polyurethane laminate) fabric with a special anti-microbial effect.

Wipes dispenser (may be a wipes-warming dispenser or a no-heat dispenser)

Once you purchase diaper wipes at the store, you have multiple options for dispensing: a) use the bag provided with the plastic pop-top as your dispenser; b) take the wipes out of the bag and place them into a warming box with a moist pillow inside (the warming container plugs into the wall with an AC cord); or c) take the 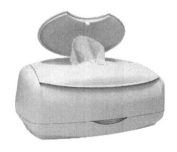 wipes out of the bag and place them into a dispenser that does not heat. I initially thought that wipes warmers were ridiculous baby products. However, I became a believer with two winter newborns. If I were a baby, I would want warm wipes on my bottom for $20, too.

Brand recommendations:

- ❏ *Best Heated Wipes Warmer:* **Prince Lionheart Wipes Warmer** *($18-25)*
- ❏ *Best No-heat Dispenser:* **OXO Tot PerfectPull Wipes Dispenser** *($20)* is a solid dispenser without the warming mechanism.

Diapering organization station

If you have a changing table, you may want to purchase a caddy that hangs on the rail. However, if you have a pad on a dresser, organize baby's creams and lotions with non-baby caddies or baskets.

Brand recommendations:

- ❏ **Prince Lionheart Diaper Depot** *($10-16)* is great to hang from a changing table.
- ❏ **IKEA Skubb** canvas drawer organizers *($8)*, or a non-baby caddy or basket will work on a dresser.

Diaper bag

You are going to be carrying diapers, wipes, snacks, toys, changes of clothes, and many other things in your diaper bag for years. Consider a bag that allows your torso to bear the brunt of the weight (not your neck and shoulders) and leaves your hands free, such as a cross-shoulder style, messenger bag, or backpack. Consider a unisex-style bag for use with Mom, Dad, and caregivers of both genders. If you desire two diaper bags, make sure that one of them is a small backpack. You will get value out of your diaper bag(s) well beyond most items in your baby registry.

Brand recommendations:

- ❏ *Functional, durable:* **Skip-Hop**
- ❏ *Stylish, head-turning fabrics:* **Petunia Pickle Bottom, JuJuBe**
- ❏ *Urban, sleek design:* **Kate Spade**
- ❏ *Versatile, looks like a large purse:* **Timi and Leslie, Storksak, Nest**

- ❏ *Sophisticated:* **OiOi, Marc by Marc Jacobs**
- ❏ *Affordable, yet stylish and practical:* **JJ Cole Collections, Graco**
- ❏ *Colorful, soft:* **Vera Bradley**
- ❏ *Unique, Stylish, and Monogrammed:* **Thirty-One** (via consultant)
- ❏ *Bag for multiples:* **Skip Hop Duo Double, Timi and Leslie Dual, JuJuBe Be Prepared**
- ❏ *Man bag for a practical dad:* **Diaper Dude**
- ❏ *Man bag for a metro dad:* **OiOi, Jack Spade**
- ❏ *Man bag for a cool rocker or alternative dad:* **DadGear**
- ❏ *Unisex:* **Skip Hop, SoYoung**

If the sheer number of diaper bag choices overwhelms you, start here for a few specific bags that are well-reviewed online:

Diaper bag model recommendations: **Skip Hop Duo** *($45-65)* in any color, **Skip Hop Versa** *($70)* in black, **Petunia Pickle Bottom Boxy Backpack** *($189)*, **JuJuBe Be Prepared** *($180)* in black/silver, **Timi and Leslie Charlie** or **Hannah** *($130-170)*, **Kate Spade Stevie** *($210-400)*, **SoYoung Charlie** bag *($175)*, **OiOi** leather satchel *($325)* or **OiOi Ikate** tote *($110-160)*, **JJ Cole Satchel** *($70)* in green pattern, and **Storksak Olivia** *($198)*.

Backpack model recommendations: **Fisher-Price FastFinder** *($45)*, **Skip Hop Via** *($70)*, **Columbia Trekster** *($50)*, **Petunia Pickle Bottom Boxy Backpack** *($189)*.

■ Feeding: Supplies for Breastfeeding

Nursing or feeding pillow

This C-shaped pillow is designed to support baby while nursing, bottle-feeding, or learning to sit up. It frequently tops parenting lists as a "most used" baby product.

Brand recommendations:

❑ **Boppy® Feeding and Infant Support Pillow**
- ▶ *Price:* $30-40
- ▶ *Pros:* Consistently ranked a #1 baby item, this pillow is a top registry item for moms nation-wide. The original Boppy® has a versatile design used for nursing, bottle feeding, propping, tummy time and learning to sit.

- ▶ *Cons:* These pillows flatten with time, so a hand-me-down original Boppy® pillow may be a product that was used so much that you have to hunch over to nurse.

❑ **Boppy® Two-Sided Nursing Pillow**
- ▶ *Price:* $45
- ▶ *Pros:* Developed with a lactation con-sultant, this pillow is specifically for nursing with features such as a remov-able belt, wide-arm design, and revers-ible surfaces (one side firm for feeding and one side soft for cuddling).

- ▶ *Cons:* Some mothers complain about the two-sided design. Though wider out front, it doesn't wrap around the body as the original Boppy® pillow does. It also does not have a removable slipcover, so the entire pillow must be machine washed and dried.

❑ **My Brest Friend Nursing Pillow**
- ▶ *Price:* $35-45
- ▶ *Pros:* Some parents prefer this product to other pillows, due to its wrap-around design with back support and higher positioning. It also has interchangeable covers.
- ▶ *Cons:* The wraparound design can be awkward for some seating arrangements.

Breast pump

This can be a simple hand pump, or an electric, double-pumping model. Both work-outside-the-home and stay-at-home moms need a way to express milk—to provide milk while Mom is away and to prevent clogged milk ducts. If you are unsure about how long you might breastfeed, consider renting a hospital pump for the first month. Also, you may be wondering why hospital pumps are able to be shared, while pumps purchased from a baby store have warnings that say, "Single user only." The FDA and La Leche League International point out that milk particles do not reach the inner motors on hospital-grade, closed system pumps, which is why they can be reused with multiple users. Most commercially produced breast pumps have an open system, which cannot provide protection from infectious diseases from other users. Viruses, such as cytomegalovirus (CMV) and HIV (AIDS) can be transmitted through breast milk, which is why the FDA and LLLI continue to support a single-use policy for commercial breast pumps.

Brand recommendation:

I recommend the **Medela Pump in Style Advanced Breast Pump** (*$250-350*), due to its history of positive reviews and years of my own personal use. However, if I became pregnant today, I might also consider a **Hygeia EnJoye LBI Breast Pump** (*$320-350*), a closed-system pump designed for multiple users with personal accessory sets.

Pumping accessories

Small bottles, caps, funnels, tubing, storage bags, and a small cooler are needed for pumping. If you can commit to pumping for at least a few months, I would recommend a hands free pumping bra, an elastic strap that holds the catching bottles to your body. Otherwise, you have to hold the bottles every time you pump. You can cut holes in an old sports bra for the same purpose.

Eco Tip
Reusable Breast Pumps
• • • • • • • • • • • • • • • •

Hygeia's "No Pumps in Dumps" motto makes sense to me, as the single use, open system design of breast pumps today is wasteful and outdated. Some moms may only pump for a few short weeks or months with a pump and accessories that cost $300-500, so why not recycle?

Brand recommendation:

Medela has the market cornered for breast pumps and accessories, and **Lansinoh** storage bags are a favorite. However, if you purchase another brand pump, such as **Hygeia** or **Philips AVENT**, you will use that brand's matching tubing and catching accessories.

Lanolin/nipple cream

Lanolin is a yellow, waxy substance secreted from the sebaceous glands of wool-bearing animals, and it is used to soothe and protect sore, cracked nipples. Lanolin is listed in the Skin Deep database as a low hazard. If you plan to nurse, you need this cream.

Brand recommendations:

Lansinoh HPA Lanolin *($9-12)* in the purple tube is a favorite because it is thick and soothing, not runny like Medela cream. For vegans or others desiring lanolin-free brands, choose **Motherlove Nipple Cream** *($9-10)* or **Earth Mama Angel Baby Natural Nipple Butter** *($9-13)*.

Soothing gel pads

These pads provide instant pain and cooling relief for sore nipples after your first feedings. Most are made with a vegetable glycerin, and they are reusable.

Brand recommendations:

Lansinoh Soothies Gel Breast Pads *($11)* provide a cool reprieve to sore nipples upon contact. Aah! Bring on the relief.

Nipple shields

These thin, silicone shields may be worn over Mom's sore nipples during the first weeks of feedings, especially if your nipples are so cracked or sore that you cannot feed without them. Some lactation purists will discourage use, saying that baby may get less milk if the shield is used incorrectly. However, these shields (sometimes labeled for inverted nipples) were a lifesaver for me with my firstborn. Be sure to note the different sizes of shields.

Brand recommendation:

Medela Contact Nipple Shields *($9-11)* choose your size

Nursing tanks

You'll want two to four, depending on how long you nurse. A good nursing tank can make any outfit a nursing outfit.

Brand recommendations:

I recommend **Glamourmom, Gilligan and O'Malley** at Target or **Gap** brand nursing tanks; the **Undercover Nursing Mom Tank** acts as a long undershirt that attaches to most nursing bras.

Nursing bras, day and night

Do not skimp on this purchase. You will wear and clip and unclip these things every single day, several times per day. You'll want two to four day bras, depending on how long you nurse. Wait until your milk supply stabilizes around six weeks before you make a big investment in bras, and avoid too-tight bras, which can cause clogged ducts. You will need a soft nighttime nursing bra to hold nursing pads and prevent leaks on your mattress, as well.

Brand recommendations:

Day bra: I recommend the **Bravado Body Silk Seamless** *($44)* bra for comfort and a smooth style, due to removable thin inserts, or the **La Leche League Padded Contour** *($33-34)* bra for underwire support. A smooth silhouette is a big deal while nursing. If a bra's material is too thin, inserting circular nursing pads with a thin T-shirt can make you look like a Fembot with robo-boobs from an old Austin Powers movie. Not good.

Nighttime bra: The **Medela Sleep Bra** *($17-20)* is inexpensive and comfortable. If you are in between sizes, get a size larger. Don't bother with eco-marketed nursing bras. Your breast pads will be covering baby's eating surface in any bra, and toxic chemicals are required to make bamboo into a wearable fiber.

Nursing pads

These small, round "must-have" absorbent pads go inside of a nursing bra to prevent leaks. Some women like disposable nursing pads; however, I think they itch like crazy with dried milk on them. I recommend washable ones.

Eco Tip
Don't Be Bamboozled by Bamboo Rayon

The Federal Trade Commission has filed several lawsuits in recent years claiming that textiles made of bamboo are essentially rayon. Rayon is a manmade fiber created from plant cellulose and processed with a chemical that releases hazardous air pollutants. Any plant or tree, including bamboo, can be used as a source for the fiber, but the chemically-processed textile is still rayon. Patagonia won't use bamboo fiber for this reason, making the "green" marketing of bamboo nursing pads and bras to new and expecting moms sketchy at best.

Brand recommendations:

For washables, try **Medela** *($8/4-pack)* or **Philips AVENT** pads *($7/6-pack)*. For disposables, try **Lansinoh** pads *($8-11/60-count)*.

Nursing cover

A nursing cover is a convenient around-the-neck cover that looks like a loose apron for nursing discretely in public. A rigid yet slightly contoured neckline allows ventilation for baby and a line of sight for Mom.

Brand recommendation:

My favorite is the **Bebe au lait Nursing Cover** *($31-36)*, which comes in many different colors and styles.

Nursing friendly shirts

Button-downs, V-necks, and layers with a nursing tank all work well as nursing shirts. However, you may want one or two special nursing shirts that you can count on for maximum flexibility and coverage, especially as baby gets older and starts tugging at your nursing cover.

Brand recommendations:

For any occasion when you might be nursing frequently in public, such as during a long flight with baby or while traveling, try a **Momzelle** or **Expressiva** nursing shirt.

■ Feeding: Supplies for bottle-feeding (breast milk and formula)

Bottles

You'll want six to eight bottles, depending on frequency of use. Be prepared to try various types of bottles and nipples to see what your baby prefers, and don't turn down a free bottle as part of any pregnancy grab bag. Overall, you want to select a bottle that is easy to hold and easy to clean, and make sure that your bottles fit in your bottle warmer. Be aware that nipples come in different sizes representing different volumes of flow: Preemies/Newborns = size 1, age 1mo+ = size 2, age 3mos+ = size

Safety Alert!
Hand-Me-Down Bottles and Sippy Cups (pre-2012)
• •

If you are using older, used bottles, make sure they are BPA-free. The FDA banned the use of BPA in baby bottles and children's cups in 2012. Bisphenol A (BPA) is a synthetic, carbon-based compound used to make plastics and epoxy resins. BPA exhibits hormone-like traits, which have been identified as a hazard to fetuses, infants, and young children in high doses.

3, age 6mos+ = size 4 fast flow. Assess how hard baby must work to get milk to determine when to upgrade to a higher flow nipple.

Brand recommendations:

❑ *Best Overall:* **Tommee Tippee Closer to Nature Bottle**
   ▶ *Price: $8*
   ▶ *Pros:* These affordable, wide-mouth bottles with soft nipples get solid reviews for ease of use and functionality, especially for babies going back and forth from breast to bottle.
   ▶ *Cons:* Because they are so wide, they often need an extra tip to get the last bit of milk out. Some parents complain that the nipple collapses too much.

❑ *Best for Gas/Colic:* **Dr. Brown's Natural Flow**
   ▶ *Price: $9-11*
   ▶ *Pros:* A vent system keeps air from getting into the milk, reducing gas, spit-up messes, and colic. Bottles come in plastic and glass.
   ▶ *Cons:* The little tube inside the bottle is used for gas reduction and requires a separate pipe cleaner to clean.

❑ *Best for Breastfeeding Babies:* **Comotomo Natural Feel Baby Bottle**
   ▶ *Price: $14-18*
   ▶ *Pros:* Comotomo bottles were made to mimic the breast, with a soft silicone nipple. You can also squeeze the bottle for a "let-down" effect, and parents love the eye-catching, modern design with a no-leak, venting system.
   ▶ *Cons:* The curved bottles tip over easily, and the measurements are hard to read.

❑ *Best for Travel and Day Care:* **Playtex Drop-In Nurser BPA free**
  ▸ *Price: $10/3-Pack*
  ▸ *Pros:* These bottles come with a disposable plastic liner that you fill with formula or milk and then toss, making clean-up a breeze. Drop-ins can be helpful for moms and dads on the go.
  ▸ *Cons:* The disposable, drop-in liners create additional waste and can be costly over time.

❑ *Best Glass Bottle:* **Lifefactory Glass Baby Bottle with Silicone Sleeve**
  ▸ *Price: $15*
  ▸ *Pros:* Due to concerns over leaching chemicals in plastic baby bottles, this glass bottle comes with a colorful, 100% non-toxic silicone sleeve to protect from breakage. The sleeve and bottle can be boiled or put in the dishwasher together.
  ▸ *Cons:* These are slightly heavier and more expensive than your average plastic bottle, and there is no separate venting system.

❑ *Best Stainless Steel:* **Pura Kiki Stainless Infant Bottle**
  ▸ *Price: $16*
  ▸ *Pros:* This award-winning 100% plastic-free bottle has a lid that is compatible with several popular wide mouth nipples. The Pura Kiki also grows with your child and converts to a sippy cup.
  ▸ *Cons:* This bottle is expensive, and it has another hidden cost: a silicon sleeve that is helpful for grip and temperature control for little hands, yet must be purchased separately for $7-9. The sleeve is also difficult to remove.

Bottle brushes

You will need a big brush for bottles and little brushes for bottle parts.

Brand recommendations:

❑ *Big brush:* **Dr. Brown's** *($2.50-5)* and
Munchkin *($5)* have good brushes
with a suction cup on the end, while
OXO Tot *($10-12)* has colorful brushes
with a nipple cleaner and stand
included.

❑ *Little brushes:* **OXO Tot Straw and Sippy Cup Top Cleaning Set**
($5) are several little brushes for cleaning valves and parts held
together on a ring like keys.

Bottle-drying rack

Provides a handy place to air-dry pump and bottle parts after hand washing or pulling them out wet from the dishwasher.

Brand recommendations:

❑ *Inexpensive:* **Munchkin Sprout drying
rack** *($9-12)*

❑ *Best functional design:* **Skip Hop Splash**
($15-20), price includes a brush

❑ *Best aesthetic design:* **Boon Lawn Countertop Drying Rack** *($15)*, though the
tree and flower attachments must be
purchased separately

❑ *Compact/Small kitchen:* **OXO Tot Rack** *($18-20)*

Burp cloths

You'll want many of these (thick, simple, and soft) to throw in the wash
for spit-up and to protect your newborn's face from wool sweaters, clothing appliques, and jacket zippers. Don't waste your money on too many

fancy ones. If you are cloth diapering, use prefolds as newborn burp cloths, then transition them to extra layers for diapering as baby gets older. Baby will use more burp cloths in the first few months as her digestive system is developing and less after she learns to sit up.

Brand recommendations:

❑ *Inexpensive:* **Gerber Terry Burp Cloths** *($7/3-Pack)* are great for everyday use.
❑ *Best cloth diaper/prefolds/burp cloths:* **OsoCozy Flat Unbleached Gauze Prefolds** *($12/6-Pack)* or **Bumkins Prefolds** *($14/6-Pack)*
❑ *Best going out burp cloth:* **aden + anais Organic Burpy Bib** *($14/6-Pack)* made from 100% organic cotton

Infant Formula

Choosing the right formula for baby can be overwhelming. Formula makers *intentionally* produce many different versions of their formulas, such as hypoallergenic, sensitive, for fussiness and gas, for colic, with prebiotics and probiotics, etc. so that you never quite have an accurate price point for your formula.

Formula comes in three forms:

- **Ready-made.** This form is convenient, although it's also 20% more expensive than powdered formula.
- **Liquid concentrate.** This form requires mixing equal parts formula and water. It is more expensive than powdered formula, because it makes less of a mess, and it is less expensive than ready-made because it requires mixing.
- **Powdered formula.** This is the most economical and environmentally friendly option. Powdered formula has a one-month shelf life after opening and must be mixed exactly as the manufacturer recommends. Moms with older children may warn you about BPA and formula cans; however, in July 2013, the FDA banned the use of BPA-based epoxy resins in the use of formula packaging.

Money-Saving Tips
Infant Formula
• • • • • • • • • •

- **Do not stock up too early on formula.** Formulas have a "use by" date, and you never know which brand your baby may, or may not, tolerate in the first few months.

- **Strongly consider generic and store brand formulas.** *All formulas sold in the U.S. must meet basic nutrient requirements,* including store brands from Walmart, CVS, Target, Sam's Club, Babies R Us, Costco, BJ's, and Walgreens. Differences in formulas lie in the fillers. Store brand formulas, such as Walmart's Parent's Choice, can be up to 50% cheaper than leading name brands, such as Enfamil and Similac, saving parents $600-700 per year.

- **Buy formula at warehouse stores and through mass merchandisers.** A leading consumer magazine revealed that prices for one ounce of a popular name brand formula varied by almost 25%, with the lowest prices found at Costco and Walmart and the highest prices at retail drugstores like Walgreens and CVS. Babies R Us, Target, and supermarkets were in between.

- **Collect formula coupons and carry them in your wallet.**

- **Save money on formula with an online subscribe and save program, such as Amazon Mom.**

Types of formula

Most infant formulas contain cow's milk whey and casein as a protein source, a blend of vegetable oils as the fat source, lactose or sugar from milk as a carbohydrate source, a vitamin and mineral mixture, and other filler ingredients, depending on the manufacturer.

- **Cow's milk based.** Most formula is made from cow's milk, although the milk protein is significantly altered for digestion. Most babies do well with this type of formula, which strives to mix the right amounts of protein, carbohydrates, and fat. Your baby will not be able to digest regular cow's milk until he is one year old.

- **Lactose-free**. This formula may be used if baby cannot digest the sugar naturally found in milk, which is rare.
- **Soy-based**. If you are a vegan, or your baby cannot digest cow's milk, you may try soy-based formula. About half of babies with milk allergies also have soy allergies.
- **With added probiotics or prebiotics.** A probiotic supplement is a food product that has enough tiny, active organisms to alter baby's microflora, while prebiotics are non-digestible ingredients that stimulate growth of indigenous probiotic bacteria. Breast milk has lots of prebiotics. You may consider formulas with these additives if your baby was born via C-section, or if baby has a high risk for asthma or eczema based on your family history.[85]
- **Extensively hydrolyzed.** In this formula, protein is broken down even further for digestion and may be used for babies with multiple allergies or preemies having difficulties absorbing nutrients.
- **Other specialty formulas**. These formulas are for babies requiring specialized nutrition, due to premature birth, diseases, or digestive disorders. Talk to your doctor before buying expensive "specialized" formulas.

Organic formula

I strongly recommend using organic formula, if you can afford it. The question of whether to feed baby organic formula versus regular formula isn't about nutrients; it's about the chemicals and processes used to alter the ingredients.

Pros: Formula is derived from cow's milk. The USDA organic label for livestock verifies that producers met animal health and welfare standards, did not use antibiotics or growth hormones, fed the cows 100% organic feed, and provided animals with access to the outdoors. Also, the formula sweeteners and fatty oils are not Genetically Modified Organisms (GMOs).

Cons: The extra price tag for organic formula can add up ($5-10 more per 23 oz. can). Use coupons and buy in bulk to offset higher costs.

Organic formula ingredients

Read organic formula labels. Not all brands are the same. Similac Organic, the market-leader in organic formula, sweetens its more expensive organic formula with cane sugar, or sucrose, which is significantly sweeter than lactose sugar (sugar extracted from milk). Babies need added sugars to help digest the protein in cow's milk. However, pediatricians warn that sucrose can harm tooth enamel faster than other sugars, and might lead to baby refusing less sweet formulas and foods in the future. Sucrose is banned in infant formula in the EU and Canada, except when ordered by a doctor. Similac Organic also contains other synthetic nutrients, such as lycopene and lutein, touted for health benefits in the U.S. Those two substances are banned in EU formulas, too.

Similac is not the only brand looking to lure customers with sweeter, cheaper ingredients. PBM Nutritionals (owned by private label health conglomerate Perrigo), makers of Earth's Best, 365/Whole Foods, Bright Beginnings, Parent's Choice, and Vermont Organics brand formulas are also transitioning to less or no lactose sugar, which mimics mother's milk best. To cut costs, PBM is replacing lactose with cheaper, plant-based sweeteners, such as "organic glucose syrup solids" (another name for "corn syrup solids") and "maltodextrins" (starch molecules derived from cheaper potatoes, rice, and corn). In 2007, Earth's Best formula contained *only* organic lactose, but by 2011, it contained both organic lactose and organic glucose syrup solids. Today organic lactose still remains in Earth's Best and Vermont's Organics formula but has disappeared altogether in Parent's Choice, Bright Beginnings, and Whole Foods' 365 organic formula brands.

Bottom line: Ingredients in organic formulas must meet USDA standards for no hormones, no antibiotics, and no GMOs, but that doesn't mean that organic formula makers aren't trying to sneak in cheaper ingredients.

Sensitive formula

Talk to your doctor before switching to an expensive sensitive formula. Feeding sensitivities may be helped by something as simple as burping baby more often, switching bottle nipples, or holding baby upright for

30 minutes after feedings. Some parents switch formulas and then tout miraculous changes in their baby. However, keep in mind that colic often improves between four and six months, regardless of formula type. Also, more expensive, sensitive formulas are typically sweeter than basic formulas, and these companies are well aware that babies have more sweet taste buds than adults and are predisposed to having a "sweet tooth." This may explain why the first two ingredients of Similac Sensitive, labeled the #1 formula for sensitive tummies, are corn syrup and sugar (sucrose). No wonder baby likes his sensitive formula! For a further look at the ingredients of leading infant formula brands, see Appendix B: Infant Formula Ingredients.

DHA-ARA in infant formula: a sticky topic

So how do oils extracted from fermented micro algae and lab-produced soil fungus mimic human fatty acids in breast milk? I have no idea. However, several studies support small but positive effects on visual and neural development with added DHA-ARA to infant formulas, and that is enough for health care providers and lawmakers to pay attention.[86]

However, the DHA-ARA debate is not clear-cut. Other studies show no benefit at all, and policy makers and non-profits who advocate for moderate and low-income families are questioning whether companies wanting to add DHA-ARA, prebiotics, probiotics, lutein, and other additives are just trying to drive up costs. The USDA's Women, Infants, and

Children (WIC) program buys over half the infant formula sold in the U.S. with a set budget amount each year. Formula with DHA-ARA costs 15% more. Wouldn't we rather provide more infant formula to more families? What are the clinical benefits of these additives? This is the debate.

Organic certification experts are also scratching their heads about infant formula additives since DHA-ARA oils are extracted using a synthetic technique. Dried, lab-made algae is blended with hexane in a continuous extraction process, which is typically an immediate disqualification for the USDA organic label (yet DHA-ARA is in organic formulas). After this process, synthetic preservatives, such as ascorbyl palmitate and beta-carotene, must be added to keep the algal oils from turning rancid.

The AAP has stayed conspicuously silent on DHA-ARA in infant formula, and the FDA approved its use because the additives are believed to be safe. Why not add DHA-ARA if it helps? The verdict is still out for determining whether the long term eye and brain benefits are worth the extra cost. If your baby has gastrointestinal upset, avoid DHA-ARA additives.

Brand recommendations (for all formulas):

❑ *Conventional formula:* If buying organic formula is not an option, leading consumer organizations and other pediatric groups recommend private label **store brand formulas for cost savings,** and I think their argument makes sense. If differences only lie in filler ingredients, established name brand formulas, such as **Similac** and **Enfamil**, have no incentive to use high quality fillers. Look for infant formulas with the first two ingredients: nonfat milk and lactose.

❑ *Organic formula:* I recommend either **Earth's Best Organic Formula** *($23 per 23.2 oz.)* or **Vermont Organics** *($23-25 per 23.2 oz.)* because they use organic lactose as the formula sweetener. For GMO purists who do not desire synthetic DHA-ARA, try **Nature's One Baby's Only Dairy Organic** *($19 per 12.7 oz.)*. Labeled as a toddler formula to promote breastfeeding, Baby's Only advertises superiority to other organic brands, using no organic corn syrup or glucose syrup, no organic palm oils, and no hexane-produced DHA (an organic-compliant process extracts DHA-ARA from eggs).

There are lingering questions about arsenic levels in Baby's Only, but the company has been using a process since 2012 to remove all heavy metals, including arsenic, and since then cans have been tested safe with undetectable levels. Soy infant formula should always be organic (no GMO or hexane ingredients), if possible.

■ Breastfeeding and Bottle-feeding: Other convenient items

Dishwasher basket

This basket allows you to put small bottle parts in the dishwasher rather than hand-washing them. Some newer dishwashers already have a small rack on the top level for this purpose.

Brand recommendations:

❏ **OXO Tot** *($8)* or **Munchkin** *($3-5)* for bottles, bottle parts, pacifiers, pumping parts, etc.

Bottle warmer

A microwave not only causes uneven heating for mixed formula, but it also changes the chemical composition of breast milk. You can use a bowl full of warm water to heat bottles of breast milk or formula; however, a bottle warmer is much more convenient. Many parents would consider this a must-have item.

Brand recommendation:

❏ *Affordable:* **Dr. Brown's Bottle Warmer** *($29-45)* warms formula and breast milk at home with a narrow, space-saving design.
❏ *Safest heat:* **Kiinde Kozii** *($70)* is simple, safe, and easy to program. It receives high marks for a slower, safer, healthier heat than its competitors.

- *Best for travel:* **Tommee Tippee Travel Bottle** *($18-20)* is essentially a thermos, making fresh formula bottles without having to access warm water.
- *Best splurge:* **Baby Brezza Formula Pro** *($149)* looks like a sleek cappuccino machine on your kitchen counter as it makes a per- fectly warm bottle of formula with one click of a button.

Microwave sterilization bags

These bags are convenient to steam-clean breastfeeding pump accesso- ries and bottle parts, especially during the newborn feeding phase.

Brand recommendations:

- **Munchkin** *($6/6-pack)* bags are less expensive than **Medela** *($7/6- pack)* or **Dr. Brown's** *($6/5-pack)* bags with similar reviews.

Bottle sterilizer (microwave or electric)

You can sterilize bottles either in a steaming dome that goes in the microwave, or with an electric ster- ilizer that sits on your countertop, killing 99.9% of harmful germs. This product could be especially useful for cleaning bottles for multiples. For just one child, you could skip this product altogether, using microwave bags, the dishwasher, and/or boiling water for sterilization.

- *Microwave Dome:* **Philips AVENT Micro- wave Steam Sterilizer** *($26-32)*
- *Countertop Electric:* **Philips AVENT 3-in-1 Electric Steam Steril- izer** *($80)* cleans in a six-minute cycle with automatic shut-off.

Formula dispenser

This provides a convenient way to take pre-measured powder samples with you while on the go.

Brand recommendations:

❑ **Munchkin** *($7)* or **Phillip's AVENT** *($9)*

■ Feeding Supplies

Highchair

Baby needs a secure place to eat. Wait for sales since you do not need a highchair right away, and test in the store. Make sure that your high chair is stable and sturdy, fits your space, and is easy to clean. A convertible chair that comes with a separate booster seat and an adjustable base can be convenient to use through several ages and with multiple children. Certification by the Juvenile Products Manufacturers Association (JPMA) may provide a layer of assurance for your high chair's safety.

Brand recommendations:

❑ *Best Overall:* **Graco Blossom 4-in-1 Seating System** *($190)* this chair wins the overall award because it comes with a high chair and separate booster chair for an older and younger sibling. The Blossom has four useful configurations: 1) a full infant high chair, 2) a high chair that can be removed from the base and strapped to a regular chair, like a Fisher-Price Space Saver, 3) a seat with a height-adjustable base to push baby up to the family table with the tray removed, and 4) a separate toddler booster seat, for travel  or an older sibling. The 4-in-1 also comes with a large tray and plastic cover for the tray, and a seat insert for smaller babies. The downside is price, although Graco has frequent sales and typically accepts coupons at major baby stores unlike many luxury brands.

❑ *Best Space Saver:* **Fisher-Price SpaceSaver High Chair** *($50-60)* can be strapped to dining chairs, minimizing its space required while still providing a large, wide tray and padded seat. The SpaceSaver is also quite affordable; however, it must be secured to a sturdy chair for safety.

❑ *Best Modern Design:* **Boon Flair Pedestal High Chair** *($280)* is easy to clean, glides on wheels, and has a pneumatic lift so it can be adjusted to any table height. This chair also fits modern décor, and you can change colors with a $30 removable seat and tray. However, the overall package can be pricey. Note: The **Stokke Tripp Trapp Chair** *($249)* fits the modern design bill, too, and beckons to the yuppie crowd (pronounced STOH-keh). However, I don't get it. Sure it's a sleek space-saver, but it's also hard and uncomfortable, and Amazon is filled with reviews of shoddy straps and tipping over.

Bibs

Waterproof, quick-drying bibs are best with a pocket to catch crumbs and liquid spills. You'll want two to four, depending on how much you travel.

Brand recommendations:

❑ **Tommee Tippee Closer to Nature Milk Feeding Bib** is a terry cloth soft bib for younger babies.
  ▶ *Price: $8/2-pack*
  ▶ *Pros*: this bib has a thick neck ring to keep milk and spit up out of baby's neck folds
  ▶ *Cons*: circumference may be too small around the neck for bigger babies

❑ **Bumkins Waterproof SuperBib**
  ▶ *Price:* $12-17/3 pack
  ▶ *Pros:* highly rated bibs, great designs, a must-have product, folds easily for travel
  ▶ *Cons:* easy for baby to rip off the Velcro around the neck

❑ **Baby Bjorn Soft Bib**
  ▶ *Price:* $16-19/2-pack
  ▶ *Pros:* baby cannot rip this bib off, has a deep pocket to catch spills and crumbs
  ▶ *Cons:* plastic can be rigid and uncomfortable around the neck for some babies

Sippy cups

You'll want three to five. Buy ones with two handles for beginners. Label them with dishwasher safe labels, such as **Mabel's Labels**, for day care. You will lose more sippy cups than you can imagine, so eco-friendly stainless steel cups may be out of your budget.

Brand recommendations:

❑ *Best overall:* **Playtex First Sipster** (*$7-8/2-pack*) cups with two handles are the very best cups for minimizing leaks and accommodating first time drinkers. The handles also provide nice hooks for strollers and shopping carts. **Nuk Gerber Graduates** (*$15/4-pack*) are a close second place. The hard plastic inserts are easier to assemble than Playtex's softer valve.
❑ *Best design:* **ZoLi Baby Straw Sippy Cups** (*$12*) come in cool colors and have a unique, bendable straw that goes to the bottom of each cup.
❑ *Inexpensive:* **The First Years Take and Toss** (*$3-4/6-pack*) cups are cheaper cups for travel that you won't mind losing.

Baby spoons

You'll want five or six soft, small gummy spoons for the first feedings.

Brand recommendations:

- ❑ *Best Overall:* **Gerber Soft Bite Infant** *($7-9/6-pack)*
- ❑ *Best Value:* **Munchkin Soft-Tip Infant** *($6/6-pack)* spoons can work for first feedings, and they are perhaps better for older babies because they have a deeper contour for holding more food than Gerber spoons.
- ❑ *Eco-friendly:* **Green Toys Green Eats** *($6/8-pack)* serving spoons are made from recycled plastic.
- ❑ *Best for older babies/toddlers:* Register now for **Nuk Gerber** *($4-7/4-pack)* graduates utensils with stainless steel tips and easy to grip handles. These are great inexpensive baby registry gifts that you will use years later.

Teethers

A baby teething toy should be colorful and easy for tiny fingers to hold. Look for teethers made with 100% natural rubber and food paint, which means no lead paints. Ensure that the product is free of phthalates and BPA.

Brand recommendations:

- ❑ **Vulli Sophie the Giraffe Teether** *($20-25):* This pricey little giraffe, made from 100% natural rubber, does get mocked by parents as a status teether, but the skeptics and the haters can't argue with her sales numbers. Truthfully, Sophie does have a certain *je ne sais quoi* about her—her vintage blushed cheeks, her soft supple legs, and her thin spotted neck are the perfect size for tiny fingers to grasp. Created in France in 1961, Sophie is almost a rite of passage for French babies, perhaps adding to her allure (though she costs half the price in France—silly Americans).

❏ **Manhattan Toy Winkel** *($13-14)*: This toy with soft, mesmerizing loops looks like a classic 3D model of an atom with orbiting electrons. Toy Winkel is BPA-free and great for hooking to your stroller or car seat for chewable entertainment.

❏ **ZoLi Gummy Stick Baby Gum Massagers** *($10)*: These small teething sticks look like mini toothbrushes. Note: Here's a look into your future. Small children + toothbrushes = obsession.

❏ **Dr. Bloom's Chewable Jewels** *($18)*:
Fashionable for Mom and safe for baby, chewable jewels were invented by a dentist and provide a more discrete way for baby to chew. Because they are small and less conspicuous than teething toys, chewable jewels have also become popular with autistic and special needs children. Dr. Bloom's jewels are made of medical grade silicone and are phthalate-free, lead-free, and BPA-, PVC-, and latex-free.

Pacifiers

You may have to try several different brands and nipple shapes at first, and again, never turn down a free trial pacifier. Use silicone pacifiers, as baby may develop an allergy or sensitivity to latex. Consider giving baby a pacifier at bedtime or naptime, when SIDS risk is greatest. However, after age two, pacifiers can cause protruding front teeth and an improper bite. The AAP recommends waiting until your breast-fed baby is one month old before introducing a pacifier to avoid nipple confusion, although some doulas and lactation consultants disagree. Some babies may not adopt pacifiers at all, especially if they are breastfed.

Brand recommendations:

❏ **Philips AVENT Soothie** *($3-7/2-pack)*:
Soothies are made of hospital grade silicone that can be sterilized. They are latex-free and do not have an angled nipple like

other pacifiers (similar to the breast). Some lactation consultants say they are the best pacifiers for breastfeeding babies.

❑ **Playtex Binky Pacifier** *($6/2-pack)*: Many parents prefer this more fitted design to the Soothie. The Binky is lightweight and well reviewed for preemies and smaller babies.

❑ **Philips AVENT Free Flow Pacifier** *($6/2-pack)*: These pacifiers have become very popular because they are inexpensive and come either in translucent designs or colors. The orthodontic nipple is also made of a taste- and odor-free silicone.

❑ **Natursutten BPA Free Natural Rubber Pacifier** *($17/2-pack)*: This natural, organic pacifier is manufactured in Italy and made straight from the natural rubber of the Hevea brasiliensis tree. The natural rubber is softer than silicone, so it will not leave marks on baby's face. Natursutten conforms to the highest safety standards in the EU, but be aware that these imported pacifiers are pricey, and they may be rejected.

■ Feeding: Other convenient items

Splat mat

This waterproof mat goes under your baby's highchair and protects rugs and flooring from spills and squished food.

Brand recommendations:

❑ *Simple:* **Jeep** *($8-11)* and **Prince Lionheart** *($14-15)* make simple, inexpensive mats.

❑ *Best design:* **Sugarbooger** *($15)* makes floor mats in more sophisticated designs, such as Vintage Alphabet (resembling old writing paper), Numbers (farm animals to help teach number recognition), and Cupcake (a little girl wearing a beret with a French poodle and the Eiffel Tower).

Roll-up or fold-up travel placemat

If you travel or eat out often, this is a must-have item.

Brand recommendations:

- ❏ *Inexpensive:* The **Summer Infant Kiddopota-mus Tinydiner** *($14)* placemat rolls up with a small-cupped edge for catching crumbs.
- ❏ *Eco-friendlier:* **ZoLi Baby Matties Silicone Travel Mats** *($25)* are eco-friendlier mats free of BPA, Phthalate, PVC, VOCs, and lead.
- ❏ *Disposable:* **Neat Solutions Neat-Ware Table Toppers** *($17)* are disposable travel mats that come in 60-count bags.

Baby food maker

You can use your blender or other kitchen appliances; however, some parents prefer an all-in-one baby steamer, cooker, and blender.

Brand recommendations:

- ❏ *Inexpensive:* If you just want a food processor, the **Baby Bullet** by Magic Bullet *($60-80)* gets the job done.
- ❏ *Classic:* The **Beaba Babycook Baby Food Maker** *($100-120)* is a French-made blender, steamer, and re-heater all in one. Look for a used one on Craigslist, if possible, since they have been popular for several years but are only needed for a short time.

- ❏ *Best value:* The **Cuisinart Baby Food Maker and Bottle Warmer** *($115-170)* steams and purees food in the same bowl with a built-in bottle warmer. Voila! Two products you need in one.

Baby food ice trays

Pour homemade baby food into trays and freeze. Empty the frozen cubes into freezer tight bags or containers.

Brand recommendations:

- ❑ *Infant/First Feedings:* **Fresh Baby So Easy Baby Food and Breast Milk Trays** *($9-14)*
- ❑ *Older baby/larger servings:* **OXO Tot Baby Blocks Freezer Storage Containers** *($10)*

Electric swivel sweeper, or cordless vacuum

You will be sweeping up cheerios, green peas, and food bits for years to come, especially with multiple children.

Brand recommendations:

- ❑ *Best inexpensive:* **Swivel Sweeper G2 Rechargeable Sweeper** *($30-40)* is an inexpensive option for cleaning up crumbs and food on the floor.
- ❑ *Best splurge:* **Dyson DC35 Digital Slim Multi floor cordless vacuum** *($265-329)* or **Dyson DC58 Handheld Vacuum** *($280)*. These products are awesome! They have amazing suction for cordless vacuums, and you squeeze a trigger like a gun to operate them, which encourages my husband to vacuum.

■ Bathing Supplies

Bathtub

If you buy a tub, look for a small, inexpensive one that fits in your kitchen sink. If you live in a small space, do not spend $45-70 on a collapsible tub. Simply buy a thick pad or fold up a clean towel and wash baby in the sink or

tub. You will be holding him with your hands anyway, and infant tubs are used for a very short time.

Brand recommendation:

❑ **The First Years Infant to Toddler Tub with Sling** *($16-22)* fits in your kitchen sink and comes with a sling for newborns.

Bath sponge cushion

For $8-15 you can bypass an infant tub. Simply use a large bath sponge to support baby in the sink, tub, or on a countertop to prevent slipping. Use towels around the sponge, if desired, and just throw them in the wash.

Brand recommendations:

❑ **Summer Infant Comfy Bath Sponge** *($7-8):* This sponge comes in gender-neutral yellow.
❑ **Leachco Safer Bather Infant Bath Pad** *($13-25):* This sponge comes in several print designs.

Inflatable safety tub

This small tub fills in the gap between an infant tub and the big tub. It can also be used for travel, or for playroom fun.

Brand recommendation:

❑ **Munchkin Inflatable Safety Duck Tub** *($15-17):* Baby can sit up assisted in this cute, little duck tub that quacks when you squeeze the beak. It also serves as a great play toy when dry.

Hooded bath towels

You will want two to three of these towels, though expect to receive more as shower and baby gifts. I am also not a big fan of personalizing everything for baby, so that items can be reused for siblings, friends, or as donation items.

Brand recommendations:

❏ **aden + anais** *($20)* makes a great muslin hooded towel.
❏ **Jumping Beans** *($21)* hooded bath towels come in cute designs and can be used years later.

Washcloths

You'll want 10 to 12. Why so many? You will use them for bathing and for washing dirty faces and hands after eating for years to come. Get soft cloths without decorative appliques.

Brand recommendations:

❏ **Kushies Washcloth Set** *($7/6-pack)*
❏ **Gerber Washcloth Set** *($5/6-pack)*

Bath toys

Go ahead and register for bath toys. Newborn items will come and go; however, bath toys live on for years. Make sure that you scoop out toys after each bath to dry and minimize mildew. Look for bath toys that are BPA, PVC, and phthalate-free. Note: The "rubber" in most rubber ducks is actually polyvinyl chloride or PVC, a product that has minted money in the chemical industry for decades siding homes, making plastic credit cards, etc. Phthalates are a class of chemicals used to soften or "plasticize" otherwise hard PVC.

Brand recommendations:

❏ **Munchkin Shampoo Rinser** *($5)*. This bendable rinsing container with a handle is indispensable for washing your child's hair.

- **Skip Hop Bath Spout Cover** (*$13*). This protects little heads from bumps on the tub's metal spout, especially for baths with multiples or siblings. However, it doesn't fit some spouts in older homes.
- **Munchkin 'White Hot' Duck Bath Toy** (*$4*) tells you when the bath water is too hot for baby since adults don't quite have a sense for how cool that water should be for baby's tender skin. Not chemical-free. The caterpillar spiller is the only Munchkin toy that passes the chemical-free test.

- **Boon Water Bugs** (*$8*). These three little bugs and a net encourage hand-eye coordination. They are BPA, PVC, and phthalate-free.
- **Boon Odd Ducks** (*$6-8*). You can pay $7 for a BPA, PVC, and phthalate-free duck, or $.50 for a phthalate-PVC-containing duck. Since bath time is essentially splash and chew time for babies, I'm going to support cutting the toy budget elsewhere. Go green with your bath toys.
- **Green Toys Ferry Boat with Mini Cars Bathtub Toy** (*$19-25*) is a bestseller for toddlers, and the small cars are great for baby to hold. The Green Toys ferry boat, submarine, tugboat, and sea plane are all BPA, PVC, and phthalate-free.

ECo Tip
Rubber Ducks
• • • • • • • • • •

Phthalates make rubber ducks soft and squeaky, so be mindful when your pediatrician's office hands you a new, straight-from-the-discount-store duck after each visit. Environmentalists Rick Smith and Bruce Lourie have written a book about this very subject *Slow Death by Rubber Duck: The Secret Danger of Everyday Things.*

❑ **Green Sprouts Stacking Cups** *($9)* are great for pouring and stacking. BPA, PVC, and phthalate-free.

A bath toy container or basket

I have tried several types, and I like the scoop and store containers best for drying and storing bath toys.

Brand recommendations:

❑ *Best design:* **Boon Frog Pod Bath Toy Scoop** *($30)* BPA, PVC, and phthalate-free.
❑ *Inexpensive:* **Munchkin Scoop Drain and Store Bath Toy Organizer** *($14-20)* is half the cost of the Boon scoop, yet it works just as well. Baby shouldn't chew on it if it's hung on the hook.

■ Nursery

Crib

Like car seats, all cribs, regardless of price, must meet federal safety requirements. Therefore, more expensive does not mean safer. Proper assembly of your crib is very important so follow the instructions. Never place a crib near a window with blinds, curtain cords, or baby monitor cords, as they pose a strangling hazard. To prevent suffocation, bare is best in the crib. Do not put pillows, toys, or thick quilts in baby's sleeping environment. Crib bumper pads are also banned by the AAP. There are currently no federal standards for round cribs, bassinets, cradles, or co-sleeping cribs.

Brand recommendations:

Best in Class

❑ *Best Value:* **Graco Lauren Classic** *($180):* If you are budget-conscious,

Safety Alert!
Used Cribs
• • • • • • • •

I do not recommend buying a used crib or using a drop-side crib made before 2011. The U.S. Product Safety Commission (CPSC) banned drop-side cribs in 2011 after they were blamed for the deaths of at least 32 infants and toddlers. Millions of older crib models also have been recalled for faulty rail design, spindle width, formaldehyde, and the use of lead paint. If you are using a used drop-side crib, be sure that a product recall kit or reinforcing brace has been installed.

safety-minded, and seeking style, then the Lauren is a great choice. It has three mattress heights and is easy to assemble.

❏ *Best Inexpensive:* **IKEA Gulliver** *($99):* If you like simple, sturdy, and affordable then the Gulliver is the value crib for you. Shorter parents like that the Gulliver only adjusts to two heights so they do not have to bend as far to reach baby. The downside is that your toddler may climb out of the Gulliver faster.

❏ *Best Buy (mid-level):* **Europa Baby Palisades Lifetime** *($282-300)* receives praise year after year for a blend of high quality materials, safety, and ease of use.

❏ *Boutique Design:* **Baby Cache Heritage Lifetime Convertible** *($550):* If you want your nursery to look luxurious without paying upscale boutique prices, try this crib. Parent reviews praise the ease of assembly and durability of the wood.

❏ *Eco-friendly (luxury):* **Oeuf Classic Crib** *($970):* If safety and modern design are a worthwhile investment to you, then you will love this solid birch crib with non-toxic lacquer. Oeuf (pronounced uhff) is named after the French word for egg with the same double-O sound as took or book.

- ❏ *Eco-friendly (expensive):* The **Oeuf Sparrow Crib** *($760)* is also about as ecologically-friendly as a crib can get. Note: The Sparrow was recalled in July 2014 for a slat and top rail repair.
- ❏ *Eco-friendly (less expensive):* **Babyletto Modo 3-in-1 Convertible Crib** *($329):* This sleek, modern crib is made from sustainable New Zealand pine and non-toxic finishes.

Crib mattress

Crib mattresses are typically made with either innersprings or dense foam, while modern eco-mattresses feature natural materials or blended synthetic and natural materials. An innerspring mattress is heavier than foam and will usually hold its shape better. For innersprings, select a firm mattress with 135 or more coils and a gauge of 15.5 or lower. A soft mattress can conform to the shape of baby's head or face, increasing the risk of suffocation, or even sudden infant death syndrome (SIDS). A too-small mattress can leave space for baby's head to get trapped. Test mattress for fit: if you can squeeze more than two fingers between the mattress and the crib, then your mattress is too small. Test the firmness of a crib mattress by putting one hand in the center of the mattress. Assess how much pressure is required to touch your hand placed on the other side of the mattress. If you are considering a used mattress, clean thoroughly. Mold can grow in improperly stored mattresses, and bacteria can fester on the surface from bio-liquids that were not cleaned properly.

Brand recommendations:

Best Value

- ❏ **Colgate Classica I** *($150):* extra firm foam crib mattress, light-weight, triple layer waterproof vinyl cover is well-reviewed for stopping leaks, #1 crib mattress of a leading consumer magazine, #1 crib mattress for a leading bargain book
- ❏ **Sealy Baby Posturepedic Crib Mattress** *($140):* has 220 Posture-tech coils for support, heavy gauge steel border rods, multi-layer covering for durability

Eco Tip
Organic Crib Mattresses
• • • • • • • • • • • • • • • • •

Are non-toxic, organic crib mattresses worth the money? I say yes. Prioritize your budget. Cut out non-essential clothes and baby gear to buy a non-toxic mattress. Baby will sleep on this product 14 to 16 hours per day during the first year. That's 5110-5840 hours in one year lying on this mattress, not including the toddler years! Conventional crib mattresses are typically made with dense polyurethane foam, treated with flame retardants, covered in PVC (or vinyl), potentially treated with more flame retardants, and then splashed with stain guard for good measure. Please note, concerns with conventional mattresses are not about chemicals physically touching baby; they are focused on the gases baby breathes while lying on the mattress. If you are unable to purchase an organic crib mattress, air out the mattress outside to off-gas chemicals, until there is no longer a chemical "new mattress" smell.

Nevertheless, not all eco-mattresses are the same. There is little enforcement of what these labels mean, so be sure to check mattress labels carefully. A mattress with 5% organic cotton can be called an organic mattress, and anything that is labeled as "waterproof" is not truly natural or organic (some parents compromise on this feature by using a removable waterproof mattress cover or pad). Also, if you live in a building that advocates bed bug encasements, you may not want to spend the extra dollars on a breathable organic mattress since a bed-bug covering would negate this feature. Bottom line: If your budget is tight, buy a cheaper crib and spend more on a non-toxic mattress.

Eco-Friendly (selections meet fire standards naturally)

❑ *Best for the budget-minded:* **Naturepedic No Compromise Organic Cotton Classic Mattress** *($260)*: three versions vary in pricing with Classic Lightweight *($260)*, Classic *($260)*, and Classic Seamless 2-Stage *($299)*; waterproof mattress has high coil orthopedic innerspring; non-toxic fire protection; winner of numerous awards for baby products

❏ **Natura Classic II Mattress** *($360-375):* contains ingredients that you can pronounce, featuring two inches of Talalay latex at the core and two inches of coconut coir. Parent reviewers note that a $50 mattress pad is required because the terry cloth cover does not stop leaks from seeping into the mattress.

❏ **Pebble Pure by Nook Sleep Systems** *($395):* takes no shortcuts with questionable chemicals; designed to promote airflow and temperature regulation with 100% non-toxic and natural materials like moisture-wicking eucalyptus, microbe and mold-preventing zinc, temperature-regulating organic cotton, and flame-retardant organic wool

❏ **Pebble Lite by Nook Sleep Systems** *($295):* a more affordable Nook mattress with similar high quality materials as the Pebble Pure; however, the mattress is not labeled organic.

Waterproof crib mattress cover or pad

You'll want two of these mattress covers to protect the mattress from diaper leaks and fluids.

❏ *Inexpensive:* **Carter's Keep Me Dry Waterproof Pad** *($13)* has great reviews, if you are okay with vinyl used for leak protection.

❏ *Eco-friendlier:* **American Baby Company Organic Waterproof Natural Quilted Fitted Crib Mattress Pad** *($32-43)* contains Face: 100% Cotton, Middle: 100% Polyester, and Back: 100% Waterproof Polyester. **Lifekind** also makes certified organic-flannel mattress pads *($140-175).*

Crib sheets

You'll want three to five sheets, and these will be used for years. Do not underestimate how many crib sheets can get soiled in a night, especially if baby has a stomach virus. Also, organic cotton sheets and linens are not absolutely essential, especially if your budget is tight. However, they are increasing in popularity, due to high insecticide and pesticide use with cotton.[68]

Brand recommendations:

❑ *Best value:* **Carter's Crib Sheets** *($13-14):* These are cute, 100% cotton, and affordable.

❑ *Eco-friendlier:* **aden + anais Crib Sheets** *($20-30):* These crib sheets come in classic 100% cotton muslin, organic cotton, or bamboo muslin.

Changing table

This piece is often part of a baby furniture set. Tall or long babies can outgrow a compact changing table in a year, so you may choose to place baby's changing pad on a dresser top. Always have a hand on baby when changing his diaper.

Brand recommendation:

❑ This will probably be the same brand of changing table or dresser as your crib, or a hand-me-down

Changing table pad or cushion

This piece is a thick, contoured pad for regular diaper changes at home. Baby does not lie on a changing pad for hours like a mattress, and many children are in day care for a good portion of their diapering. Therefore, I think organic cotton changing pads are not worth the money. Most will have some type of waterproof coating on the surface anyhow.

Brand recommendations:

❑ *Best overall/inexpensive:* **Summer Infant Contoured Changing Pad** *($16-29):* This inexpensive pad has a PVC/vinyl-free top layer, and it is double layered for durability.

❏ *Eco-friendlier:* The **NaturePedic Organic Cotton Contoured Changing Pad** *($99)* is for hard-core eco-parents, and it is five times more expensive than the Summer Infant pad. Also, its organic cotton cover has a 100% polyethylene stain-resistant coating. Polyethylene is a common plastic that is used in bags, films, bottles, and other containers.

Changing table cover

This is similar to a fitted sheet for a mattress that is used to cover a diaper changing pad. You'll want two to three, since they get soiled often. The softer, the better.

Brand recommendations:

❏ *Best value:* **Carter's Super Soft Dot Changing Pad** *($16):* These pad covers have five-star reviews everywhere. They are really soft, affordable, and durable (mine have lasted for years).

❏ *Eco-friendlier:* **aden + anais Changing Pad Cover** *($20-30):* These pad covers come in classic 100% cotton muslin, organic cotton, or bamboo muslin. Check out the "For the Birds Medallion," "For the Birds Owls," and "Up, Up, and Away" elephant and star balloon styles.

Baby hangers for clothes

Regular hangers are too big for baby's clothes.

Brand recommendations:

❏ *Best value:* **Babies R Us Hangers** *($3/10-pack)* come in white, light green, light pink, and light blue.

❏ *Space-saving:* **Closet Complete Baby Size Ultra-Thin No Slip Velvet Hangers** *($16/25-pack)* in ivory are thin, gender-neutral hangers that maximize closet space.

Rockers and gliders

I completely underestimated this purchase with my first baby and convinced my husband to buy a cheap, fixed-back nursing chair from the clearance section at Babies R Us. With our second child, we opted for a padded rocker-glider and recliner that would fit into the living room later. If you are still doubting this chair, as I did, let's do the math. A new mom and dad plus caretakers will nurse or feed and rock baby for an average of four hours per day. That is 1,460 total hours for the first year in this chair. Now apply that over multiple years with multiple children as a prime nursing, rocking, and book reading chair. If your baby will be spending most of the day away from home, then you don't need a fancy chair. Other rocker-glider tips: Rocker-gliders with multi-position reclining for the back are best, and you want to make sure that the arms of the chair are well-padded for feedings. Price-compare online and test chairs in the store, if possible. Some chairs fit taller or more petite people better. Also, white or pastel fabrics may look great in the nursery; however, they get dirty easily, especially the ottomans.

Brand recommendations:

❑ *Inexpensive:* **Stork Craft Bowback Glider and Ottoman** (*$130-180*)
❑ *Best quality:* **Dutailier** (*$379-450*) Splurge on this item for nursing, feeding, reading, and rocking your child. This brand (pronounced doo-tal-YAY) sells leather or faux leather chairs that wipe clean.

Nursery paint

The Best Zero-VOC Paints

Volatile Organic Compounds (VOCs) include a variety of chemicals that are emitted as gases from certain solids and liquids. They are found in thousands of products—paints, glues, adhesives, and permanent markers—and they are linked to numerous health problems, such as cancer, nervous system damage, headaches, and irritation of the ears, nose, and throat. Some readers may decide that zero-VOC paints are just too expensive for baby's nursery ($50/gallon vs. $25-35/gallon) and might choose to compromise with a low-VOC paint. Also, ladies, I don't know what it is about men and paint, but you may have to do some sales work to get your significant other to use an eco-brand.

- ❏ *Best Overall:* **Benjamin Moore Natura** Paints (tint with Gen-X zero-VOC colorants)
- ❏ *Best Bright Colors:* **Mythic Paint** Bright Colors
- ❏ *Least Odor/Natural Paint:* **BioShield Clay**
- ❏ *Best for Painting Furniture:* **Milk Paint SafePaint** (made from milk protein, starts as a powder to mix with water, leaves a textured feel to furniture)

Rugs and carpet for baby

I once read on a message board, "I just want a rug that doesn't try to kill me in my sleep." This is due to the off-gassing of fire retardants and stain-resistant chemicals, and many expecting parents have similar concerns about rugs and flooring for their child. While no baby wants to crawl on a crunchy eco-mat that feels and smells like hay, there are environmentally friendlier rug attributes to look for: 1) natural fibers, such as organic cotton, wool, silk, bamboo, hemp, and jute; 2) non-toxic backing, sewn and not glued (wool, jute, or natural latex); and 3) certifications and assurances that the rug was not treated with stain guard, flame retardants, or insecticides, which can emit VOCs.

Safety Alert!
VOC Paint
• • • • • • •

The EPA warns that VOC concentrations can be up to ten times higher indoors, with paint as a major VOC contributor. VOCs emit gases long after paint is dry, and babies are much more susceptible to these gases. Low-VOC paint should have less than 50 grams/liter and zero-VOC paint less than five grams/liter. Check to make sure that your tint is not adding to the VOC content, and paint baby's nursery months in advance, if possible, to off-gas fumes.

- ❏ *Best Affordable Rugs:* **IKEA** natural fiber rugs
- ❏ *Best Style Rugs:* **Pottery Barn Kids** or **Land of Nod**
- ❏ *Best Rugs for Eco-purists:* **Bio-Floor** wool rugs
- ❏ *Best Wall-to-Wall Eco-Friendly Carpet:* **Nature's Carpet** or **Flor**

Floor mat or covering

Many parents desire a softer crawl and play space for their baby on hard floors. I recommend *using untreated rugs* for this purpose, budget permitting, if you are concerned about petroleum-derived foam mats and flooring.

■ Sleeping Supplies

Swaddling blankets, also called receiving blankets

You'll want at least three to four of these for wrapping your newborn in a tight burrito or swaddle. Muslin blankets are popular today (muslin is a loosely woven cotton fabric that is breathable like medicine gauze), and blankets with Velcro flaps are convenient for parents who aren't into fussy wrapping. Many parents prefer blankets with a little bit of stretch to make a tight swaddle.

Safety Alert!
Interlocking Foam Flooring
. . . .

In Belgium and France, EVA foam puzzle-type mats have been banned due to the toxic substance formamide. In addition to chewing and noshing on the corners of these foam pieces, babies and toddlers like to pull apart the squares, which can be a tripping hazard.

Brand recommendations:

❏ **aden + anais Classic Muslin Swaddle Blankets** *($32/2-pack):* This company (pronounced AY-den and uh-NAY) has taken over the swaddle world. aden + anais was founded in 2006 by an Aussie mom who moved to the U.S. and could not find muslin wraps similar to what Australian moms used to swaddle their babies. Today, these blankets are everywhere. Prince George singlehandedly increased sales of the Jungle Jam pack of four swaddles 600% in one week, following his royal exit from St. Mary's Hospital in July 2013.

❏ **Halo SleepSack Swaddle Microfleece** *($17-25):* These zip-up blankets have swaddling flaps that use Velcro to stay together. Sales for these swaddles go way up in winter, although baby will outgrow them quickly.

❏ **Under the Nile 100% Organic Egyptian Cotton blankets** *($32/2-pack):* These blankets use organic material with a little bit of stretch for a tight swaddle (the stretch makes them worth the cost). Parents who find aden + anais blankets too large appreciate the "right size" of fabric with Under the Nile.

❏ **Miracle Blanket** *($32):* Babies either love or hate this Houdini-like, super-tight swaddle. The Miracle Blanket is over six feet long, and it can seem complicated at first. However, if your baby is fussy and breaks out of swaddles easily, you might want to try a hand-me-down blanket.

❏ **Summer Infant Kiddopotamus Swaddle Me Organic Cotton** *($21-25):* In winter, this blanket can be secured with Velcro straps over a tightly swaddled thin blanket for additional warmth, or it can be used alone.

Wearable blankets or sleep sacks

You'll want two or three for each size in gender-neutral colors. These sleep sacks, used after baby outgrows a swaddle, zip over baby's pajamas to keep her warm at night. They are usually made of cotton for summer and fleece for winter, and they reduce crib climbing ability for older babies and toddlers.

Brand recommendations:

- ❑ **Halo SleepSack** *($17-28)*: My children slept in these zip-up blankets for years in increasing sizes with no loose covers in the crib.
- ❑ **aden + anais Sleeping Bags** *($32)*: Made of 100% cotton muslin, these blankets come in Classic, Cozy, and Cozy Plus versions with three levels of thickness. Sleeping bags are also offered in bamboo fiber muslin and organic cotton muslin.

Nightlight

You will need a nightlight more powerful than a tiny hall light for late-night diaper changes and feedings.

Brand recommendations:

- ❑ **Cloud b Twilight Constellation Nightlight** *($34)*: This product will bring joy to your child for many years, as a turtle or ladybug projects stars and a crescent moon onto your child's ceiling.
- ❑ **IKEA children's lighting**: If you live near an IKEA, or like to browse IKEA products on Amazon (warning: some products have big price markups online), check out their fun, inexpensive lighting options.

▮ Sleeping: Other convenient items

Sound machine, MP3 player, or iPod with docking station

I prefer an iPod/mp3 docking station to a baby-specific sound machine. You can download white noise, womb sounds, heartbeats, and lullabies to your iPod and drown out older children playing, dishes clanging, TVs, and street noise. If you do buy a sound machine, make sure that it has an MP3 player port.

Brand recommendations:
- ❏ Any non-baby iPod/MP3 speaker dock with a light
- ❏ **Graco Sweet Slumber Sound Machine** *($42)*: This travel-friendly nightlight/speaker has 12 soothing sounds from white noise to nature sounds to lullabies. It also has a port to insert your own MP3 player.

Blinds, shades, and/or a blackout curtain

These items will hopefully keep baby from rising with the sun. Assess your blackout budget by how long you think you will be living in your home, especially if you have non-standard windows.

Brand recommendations:
- ❏ *Inexpensive:* **Eclipse Kids Blackout Curtains** *($22-25)* or **Redi Shade Blackout Pleated Shade** *($30-35)*
- ❏ *Best higher quality:* **Pottery Barn Kids** blackout curtains *($59-99)*

Mobile for the crib

Think lights, music, and motion for your crib mobile, if the goal is for the mobile to help you sleep in more. Otherwise, a simple handmade mobile may mesmerize baby and spark up your décor without all the noise.

Pros: Some mobile models turn on and off remotely, buying valuable extra minutes in bed for Mom and Dad.

Cons: A crib mobile only lasts five to six months for safety or until baby can pull it down from the crib rail.

Brand recommendations:

❏ **Tiny Love Classic Mobile** *($44-48):* This mobile has vibrant colors, lights and melodies, with a remote control. For extra value, try the well-reviewed **Tiny Love Take Along Mobile** *($21-25),* which attaches to regular cribs, travel cribs, and car seat handles.

❏ **Fisher-Price Rainforest Peek-a-Boo Leaves Musical Mobile** *($48-52):* This remote-controlled mobile plays soft, classical music while cute rainforest animals spin around giant green leaves.

❏ *Handmade "quiet" mobiles on Etsy:* **Everydays Beautiful** *($33)* see the elephant, fish, and butterfly mobiles or **BabyJivesCo** *($60-100)* for the cloud or star cloud mobiles.

Bassinet, cradle, or co-sleeper

This allows your newborn to sleep right next to your bed in the early weeks of life. I cannot recommend buying a separate, arms reach-type co-sleeper or bassinet because a travel crib has nearly an identical raised platform or bassinet for newborns. The travel crib can then sleep a toddler on the bottom level for several years.

Brand recommendations:

❏ **Graco Pack 'n Play Playard with Newborn Napper** *($180-200):* This playard and travel crib grows with your child: a newborn sleeps in the cocoon-like napping station, an infant < 25 pounds sleeps on a wrapover bassinet that secures to the frame, and a toddler sleeps on the bottom platform.

❏ **Halo BassiNest Swivel Sleeper** *($230):* If I had a bigger budget for a bassinet, I would buy this model. A dual-swivel design allows the BassiNest to rotate 360 degrees from two pivot points: to pull the co-sleeper into the bed

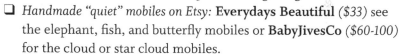

toward Mom and then to angle the sleeper for nursing, or getting into and out of the bed. This product, which swept the 2013 JPMA Innovation Awards as the Judge's Pick Winner, also has a night-light, soothing nature and womb sounds, vibration, and a timer to remind nursing moms when to put baby back into his sleep space.

▌Health and First Aid Supplies

Bulb syringe or nasal aspirator

Skip the expensive health and first aid kits and use the bulb syringe from the hospital to suction mucus and fluid from baby's nose and mouth.

❏ **Nosefrida "The Snotsucker" Nasal Aspirator** *($15-19)*: If you left your bulb at the hospital, the Nosefrida nasal aspirator gets rave reviews. This Swedish design features a tube that is placed against the nostril. Parents then use their own suction to draw out mucus, while filters prevent mucus and bacterial transfer.

Saline drops

This is a must-have product, as you will use saline drops and a suction bulb to clear baby's first stuffy nose (there will be many). Use drops before feeding or nursing, if baby has a cold.

Brand recommendation:

❏ **Little Remedies Little Noses** *($4 for 1 fluid oz.)*: This over-priced bottle of salt-water is used to help break up mucus in the nose.

Money-Saving Tip
Health and First Aid Supplies
• • • • • • • • • • • • • • • • • • •

Do not buy general health and first aid supplies at a baby store, unless you want to pay 20-50% more. Mass merchandisers and warehouse stores will almost always be cheaper. For example, an Exergen temporal scanner for monitoring baby's temperature is $38 at Babies R Us and $28 at Target or Walmart, while a Vicks FilterFree Humidifier is $75 at Babies R Us and $40 at Walmart (with the same model number).

Digital temporal scanner and back-up rectal thermometer

These are must-have items for your medicine cabinet to monitor baby's fever. The temporal scanner is a go-to fever checker, while the rectal thermometer can provide back-up and a more reliable reading for small infants. Note: taking a rectal reading is less intimidating than it sounds. Simply place baby on the changing table as if changing a diaper, put a dab of Aquaphor or Vaseline on the tip, and insert gently.

Brand recommendations:

❑ *Temporal scanner*: The **Exergen Temporal Thermometer** *($27-50)* is a consumer scanner similar to those used in pediatricians' offices.

❑ *Rectal:* **Vick's Baby Rectal Thermometer** *($10-18)* has a flexible tip and short probe for safety.

Infant acetaminophen

Babies should not be given any type of medicine under age three months. Ask your doctor about appropriate dosages, and use only the dosing dropper that comes in the package with your medicine.

Brand recommendation:

❑ **Infant Tylenol** *($9-10 for 2 oz.)* or **store brand** acetaminophen since the FDA strictly requires generic medications to have the same active ingredients as patented medications. Be sure to select infant-labeled medicine and not children's medicine.

Note: In a recent study analyzing Nielsen data from more than 77 million shopping trips, researchers found that pharmacists, physicians, and nurses were significantly more likely to buy store-brand drugs and other health products. Pharmacists devoted 90% of their purchases for headache remedies to private labels, versus 71% for the average consumer.[87]

Infant ibuprofen

Do not give ibuprofen, such as Advil or Motrin, to a child less than six months old. Ask your doctor about dosages, and use only the dropper that comes in the package with your medicine.

Brand recommendation:

❑ **Infant Advil** *($6-7 for half oz.)* or **store brand** ibuprofen

Gas relief medicine

Anti-gas simethicone drops can bring relief to some babies. Simethicone is generally believed to be safe because it is not absorbed by the body. Rather, it is an anti-foaming agent that decreases the surface tension of gas bubbles, allowing them to pass more easily.

Brand recommendations:

❑ **Little Remedies For Tummys Gas Relief** *($7-11 for 1 fluid oz.)*

Cough and cold relief

The AAP recommends that babies and young children should not be given OTC cough and cold medicine because it is not proven to be effective and can be harmful. Steam from a warm shower, saline drops, and a suction bulb are typically recommended instead. A humidifier in baby's room may also help.

Cotton balls

Use the biggest 100% cotton balls you can find to clean your newborn's face, neck folds, and diaper area between baths during the first weeks and months.

- ❏ *Inexpensive:* any brand that is 100% cotton (not bleached polyester fibers)
- ❏ *Eco-friendlier:* **Swisspers Organic Triple Size Cotton Balls** *($3)*

Baby Q-tips

Use safety swabs with a bulb on the tip to clean the outer ear area. Never insert Q-tips into the ear canal.

Brand recommendations:
- ❏ **Johnson and Johnson Safety Swabs** *($3)* in the purple box.

Hair brush

This is helpful for taming unruly hair and flaking off cradle cap.

Brand recommendations:
- ❏ *Inexpensive:* **Safety 1st Easy Grip Brush and Comb** *($4-7)*
- ❏ *Eco-friendlier:* **Green Sprouts Wooden Brush and Comb Set** *($7-8)*

Nail clippers

Buy two pairs, in case you misplace them. Even if baby cries, use your best distraction techniques to get those nails clipped. Plastic magnifiers with clippers are silly because they get bent and scratched.

Brand recommendations:

- ❏ **Summer Infant Dr. Mom Nail Clippers** *($4)* with an oval-shaped handle are good clippers.
- ❏ **Safety 1st Sleepy Baby Nail Clippers with Built-In Light** *($6)* also receive great reviews.

Baby nail files

I don't see the point in buying a $25 electric baby nail filer when I can file babies nails with a $0.10 emery board. Nevertheless, nail filing is no simple task with a squirmy, fussy baby. If you are struggling to hold baby while filing, have someone else help after a bath when nails are softest or during a feeding when baby is distracted.

Baby shampoo and body wash

Baby's skin is 20-30% thinner and more porous than adult skin, allowing product ingredients to be more readily absorbed. Children also drink bath water and eat soap bubbles, so the fewer chemicals, the better.

Brand recommendations:

- ❏ *Best Value:* **Burt's Bees Shampoo and Wash Fragrance Free** *($7-9/12 oz.):* I heart Burt's Bees. I fell in love with Burt's Lip Balm in the mid-1990s, and I bathe my children in their products every day.
- ❏ *Runners-Up:* **California Baby Shampoo and Body Wash** *($21-25/19 oz.),* **Nature Babycare Eco Shampoo** *($8-9/8.5 oz.)*

Eco Tip
Baby Shampoo and Skin Products
• •

Avoid these substances in baby skincare products: Parabens & phthalates, DMDM Hydantoin, Fragrance, Triclosan, Sodium Laureth/Lauryl Sulfate, Formaldehyde/quaternium-15, FD&C Color Pigments, PEG (Polyethylene Glycol) & Propylene Glycol, Talc, DEA (Diethanolamine), MEA (Monoethanolamine), and TEA (Triethanolamine).

Baby lotion

Look for no dyes, fragrances, and perfumes. Baby care products with an ingredient labeled "fragrance" may contain phthalates. A 2008 study published in *Pediatrics* found that 81% of the 163 infants tested had phthalates in their urine above limits of detection, and infant exposures to lotion, shampoo, and powders were significantly associated with higher urinary concentrations, especially in the younger infants. [88, 89]

Brand recommendations:

❑ *Best overall:* **Burt's Bees Fragrance Free Lotion** *($9-10)*
❑ *Inexpensive:* **Aveeno Baby Daily Moisture Lotion Fragrance Free** *($9-12)*
❑ *Certified Organic/Non-toxic/Vegan*: **Earth Mama Angel Baby Lotion** *($14-16)*

Baby sunscreen

Babies and children have sensitive skin that is easily irritated by the chemicals in adult sunscreens, so try to avoid chemical sunscreens with anything that ends in –benzone. Look for sunscreens that protect against both UVA and UVB rays, also called broad-spectrum protection. Know that if you see an SPF above 50, it is likely a chemical-based sunscreen. Also, check your baby's sunscreen in the EWG Skin Deep database. Some

Did You Know?
Sunscreen
· · · · · · · ·

In 2013, the FDA ruled that companies can no longer use the term sunblock. Sunscreens, which are classified as drugs, are to be differentiated into "chemical" and "physical barrier" categories. Mineral-based formulas (also called physical sunscreens) that use zinc oxide and titanium dioxide are preferred to chemical formulas, since they are not absorbed into the skin. Zinc oxide is preferred to titanium dioxide, due to its broad-spectrum coverage, although many "natural" sunscreens contain both. Micronized zinc or titanium is recommended vs. nano zinc or titanium, which may contain small enough particles to cross into the skin.

brands will game the system by creating one or two formulas with a "1" or "2" low hazard rating and then market the whole line as "EWG rated and approved." In summary, just say yes to: zinc oxide and titanium dioxide as active ingredients, SPF 15 to 50, hats and shade in the mid-day sun, and reapplication often. Just say no to: oxybenzone and the benzones, retinyl palmitate, aerosol spray, SPF above 50, and sunscreens with added insect repellant.[90]

Brand recommendations:

❑ *Best Overall:* **ThinkBaby Sunscreen SPF 50+** *($16 for 3 oz.)*: first sunscreen to pass the Whole Foods Premium Care line requirements, rated "1" or low hazard on EWGs Skin Deep web site, not thick or greasy, mineral-based formula goes on easily

❑ *Best Classic Physical Barrier (zinc-oxide only):* **Badger All Natural Sunscreen** *($12-13 for 2.9 fluid oz.)*, a longtime organic favorite, is formulated with non-nano, uncoated zinc oxide, which is considered the safest, most effective sunscreen element.

■ Cleaning Supplies

Household cleaners

If mixing your own cleaning products is just not your thing, buy eco-friendly brands.

Brand and product recommendations

(using factors of cost, green ratings, and online reviews):

❑ *Best Dishwashing Soap:* **Seventh Generation Free and Clear Dish Liquid** *($3)*

❑ *Best Dishwasher Detergent:* **Seventh Generation Automatic Dishwasher Detergent** *($5-7)*

❑ *Best All-Purpose Cleaner:* **Seventh Generation Disinfecting Multi-Surface Cleaner** *($4)*

❑ *Best Toilet Bowl Cleaner:* **Method Toilet Bowl Cleaner, Spearmint** *($4)*

❑ *Best Scrubbing Powder:* **Mrs. Meyer's Clean Day Surface Scrub** *($5)*

❑ *Best for Food Prep Surfaces:* **Begley's Multi Surface Cleaner** *($7)* (pH neutral for eating and food prep surfaces, made in the USA)

❑ *Best Countertop Spray:* **Mrs. Meyer's Countertop Spray Lemon Verbena** *($3.50)*

❑ *Best Glass and Window Cleaner:* **Ecover Glass and Surface Cleaner** *($5)*

❑ *Other favorites:* **Mrs. Meyer's Clean Day All Purpose Cleaner Lemon Verbena** *($8)*, **Seventh Generation Glass and Surface Cleaner** *($5)*

Baby friendly laundry detergent

Choose brands with no dyes, fragrances, or perfumes. Do not buy laundry detergent pods or tablets. In 2012 and 2013, U.S. poison control centers received over 17,000 calls (about one per hour) about children mistaking laundry pods for candy or toys.

Brand recommendations:

❑ *Best Value:* **Kirkland Free and Clear Laundry Detergent** from Costco *($16 for 110 loads or $0.14/load)*

❑ *Best National Brand:* **Method** *($19 for 85 loads or $0.22/load)* has a lower cost per load than many eco-brands with a higher green rating for ingredients.

❑ *Best for Cloth Diapers*: **Rockin' Green Cloth Diaper and Laundry Detergent Remix** *($17 for 45 loads or $0.38/load)* with a lower pH than leading brands.

Baby clothes stain remover

You will become a professional clothes scrubber by the time your child goes to kindergarten.

Brand recommendation:

❑ **OxiClean Baby Stain Soaker** *($9 for 3 lb.)*: This product receives the only "A" in EWG's database for laundry stain remover.

Steam mop

Steam mops clean and sanitize your floors without the use of harsh chemicals.

Brand recommendations:

❑ *Best Overall:* **Oreck Steam-It Multi-Purpose Steam Wand** *($136-150)*
❑ *Inexpensive:* **BISSELL Powerfresh Steam Mop** *($79-100)*

■ Safety Supplies

Baby monitor – audio and video

If you live in a city, an apartment building, or a house full of electronics, buy a digital DECT (Digitally Enhanced Cordless Telecommunications) monitor to eliminate chances of interference and unintended eavesdropping. DECT models work in the 1.9 GHz frequency range, instead of operating within 900 MHz or 2.4 GHz, the same bands as many cordless

phones and wireless networks. Note: video monitors work on either the
900 MHz or 2.4 GHz band, so you may experience overlap with a neighbor. Analog audio monitors are inexpensive; however, they send signals
directly to the monitor without being encrypted. Two receivers, or parent units, are convenient. Look for ones with rechargeable batteries, or
else take stock in a battery company. Do not put the monitor, or cord,
within baby's reach of the crib, due to risk of strangulation.

Brand recommendations:

Best Digital Audio

❏ *Best Overall:* **Philips AVENT DECT
Monitor SCD570** *($80-100)* is the
runaway winner due to excellent
range and long battery life.
❏ *Best Inexpensive:* **Graco Secure Cov-
erage Digital Baby Monitor Single
Parent Unit** *($36-45)*
❏ *Best Inexpensive (for 2-story homes):*
Graco Secure Coverage Digital Baby Monitor Two Parent Unit
($54-65)

Best Analog Audio

❏ **Sony Babycall 900 MHz Nursery Monitor** *($50):* If you are not
concerned with interference, then save some money with this analog monitor. It comes with two rechargeable parent units and has
excellent battery life. The downside is there is no battery backup
to the base/receiver unit, so if the base is not plugged in correctly
or the power goes out, the traveling units do not beep.

Best Video

❏ *Best Performance:* **Motorola 36 3.5" Color Video Monitor** *($240-250)*
  ▶ *Pros:* This monitor has wireless technology, infrared
    night vision, zoom functionality, and a room temperature
    monitor.
  ▶ *Cons:* Even with the hefty price tag, there is still some
    Wi-Fi interference, and the battery life is limited.

❑ *Best Inexpensive:* **Infant Optics DXR-5 2.4 GHz Digital Video Monitor** *($95-170)*
- *Pros:* This budget-friendly monitor provides a surprisingly clear picture and has an audio standby mode (when baby makes a noise, the video comes back on).
- *Cons:* You can't turn off the video if there is constant noise, such as a white noise player, and there are no extras like room temp, zoom, or the ability to talk to baby through the device.

❑ *Best App:* **Cloud Baby Monitor** *($3.99 App Store or $6.99 Mac App Store)* Just download this app to two iOS devices (iPhone, iPad, Ipod touch, or Mac), and you have live audio and video streaming of your baby.

Breathing monitor

The AAP states that doctors are not to prescribe breathing monitors, even for premature infants. Breathing movement monitors, such as Graco-owned **Angelcare**, or **BabySense**, do not prevent SIDS, and the companies themselves steer clear of this claim. However, some parents assert that peace of mind is worth the cost of this product. Note: In late November 2013, the U.S. Consumer Product Safety Commission and Angelcare Monitors Inc. voluntarily recalled 600,000 Angelcare movement and sound monitors with sensor pads, due to a strangulation hazard presented by cords between the mattress sensor and monitor.

Safety gates

Safety gates are typically used between the ages of six months and two years old. They can be multi-purpose barriers: protecting children from falling down or climbing up stairs, keeping a child out of a non-child-proofed room, or separating a child from a pet. Also, measure twice and buy once; make sure that safety gates purchased are larger than the opening. Finally, if you visit grandparents often, you may want to purchase some inexpensive or pre-owned gates for protecting their home.

Safety Alert!
Safety Gates
• • • • • • • • •

Use a hardware-mounted gate for the top of the stairs, regardless of how much you want to avoid drilling holes in your wall. Pressure mounted gates are not strong enough to prevent your child from falling. A hardware-mounted gate bolts to framing inside the walls of your home; although, one side of the gate may have to bolt to a wooden railing or banister, depending on your top-of-stairs configuration. You can use pressure-mounted gates for the bottom of stairs, inside doors, or to block off non-childproofed rooms.

Brand recommendations:

Top of stairs hardware-mounted

Best Value

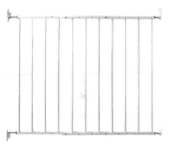

❑ **KidCo Safeway** *($43):* Parents love this gate because it is tough and made of coated steel. Many also report that the gate is a good value, although the downside is that you have to remember to close it.

Best for Households with Multiple Children

❑ **Dreambaby Swing Closed Security Gate** *($50):* This gate, which comes in an extra tall model, has a mechanism that closes the gate automatically behind you, so parents never have to worry about an open gate, especially one left open by an older sibling. We upgraded to this model with our second child, although elderly family members and guests struggled with the tricky pull-up-and-out latch.

Bottom of stairs and pressure-mounted doorway

Best Overall

❑ **Regalo Easy Step Gate** *($32-37)*: This gate is the runaway top seller on Amazon and other baby web sites because of its versatility and affordability. The Easy Step is easy to install. In our family, we have used it both as a hardware-mounted, top-of-stairs gate (with just one child) and a pressure-mounted, bottom-of-the-stairs gate in four different homes (with four different banister configurations).

Sleekest Design

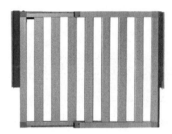

❑ **Munchkin Loft** *($60-140)*: This gate has a cool, modern design with dark wood and brushed metal slats. The hardware-mounted Loft can also fit irregular openings between 26.5 and 40 inches wide.

Safety devices

Safety devices for baby proofing include: electrical outlet covers or sliding safety plates, cabinet locks, anti-tipping straps, cord shortening or wind-up devices, toilet seat locks, doorknob handles, stove guards, furniture edge guards, smoke alarms, and carbon monoxide detectors. This list is probably more comprehensive than you will need for every location in the house. However, if you are not the primary caretaker for your child in your home, then I would invest in some critical childproofing items. You will also have a better sense of your child's personality and level of curiosity prior to childproofing, which affects the number of items that you may or may not need to purchase.

Brand recommendations:

❑ *Best Cabinet Locks:* **Safety 1st Magnetic Locking System Complete** *($23-30)*
❑ *Best Cabinet Locks (no drilling):* **Kiscords Child Baby Safety Cabinet Lock Latch** *($5)*

- ❏ *Best Electrical Outlet Covers:* **Kidco Standard Outlet Cover** (*$25/6-pack*): replaces the entire plate
- ❏ *Best Stove Knob Covers:* **Safety 1st Stove Knob Covers** (*$8-10*)
- ❏ *Best Oven Lock:* **Safety 1st Oven Front Lock** (*$5-6*)
- ❏ *Best Furniture Edge Guard:* **Prince Lionheart Table Edge Guard with 4 Corners** (*$19-25*)
- ❏ *Best Table Corner Protectors:* **Prince Lionheart Cushiony Corner Guards** (*$8*)
- ❏ *Best Toilet Seat Lock:* **Mommy's Helper Toilet Seat Lid-Lok** (*$5-8*)
- ❏ *Best Blinds/Cord Wraps:* **Dreambaby Blind Cord Wraps, Clear** (*$6*)
- ❏ *Best Electronics/DVD Guard:* **Parent Units DVD Guard** (*$13*)

Water filtration system

These eco-friendlier costs are adding up, I know. Nevertheless, I would prioritize installing a water filtration system in your home over many baby products, especially if your annual water quality report is poor. Check local drinking water online at www.water.epa.gov/drink/local/ or through your provider's consumer confidence report (CCR). Caution: A CCR may tell you about your water but does not include what is coming out of your pipes. Lead and other substances can leach from pipes, joints, and fixtures in older homes. Contact your local health authority for a free or low cost water testing kit and send your sample to an EPA approved lab at www.epa.gov/safewater/labs. **First Alert** also sells a Drinking Water Test Kit on Amazon for $15. If you know what contaminants are in your water, you can match a filter to the problem substances. Recommended filtration systems:

- ❏ *Maximum filtration:* **Kinetico K5** (*$1800*). Rated best overall by a leading consumer magazine, customizable filters for your local contaminants, very expensive
- ❏ *Larger tank with wide range of chemicals removed:* **Culligan Aqua-Cleer** (*$1000*). Pricey yet excellent for lead and organic compounds

❑ *Best value:* **Kenmore Elite 38556** or **38000-series** *($170-260)*. Relatively low-priced upfront and for annual upkeep with solid filtration tests

❑ *Best Under-the-Sink:* **Multi-Pure MP750SB** *($430)*. Best flow rate among under-the-sink filters, or **Aqua-Pure** *($300)*: less expensive up front but higher annual filter costs, so-so flow

❑ *Faucet-mounted:* **Culligan FM-15A** or **FM-25** *($20-25)*. Best filtration and flow rate, or **Pur FM-3700B**: excellent filtration, okay flow rate

❑ *Carafe:* **Clear2O** *($23)*. Superior carafe in leading consumer magazine, removes lead and organic compounds, or runner-up **ZeroWater 10-cup Pitcher** *($38)*: great for lead, doesn't claim to remove organic compounds.

■ Baby Clothing

Baby clothes are easy, inexpensive baby gifts, so expect to receive more clothes than you need. Consider registering for basic clothing in larger sizes than newborn, such as ages six months and beyond. A baby three months and younger will spend most of his time swaddled in a blanket or sleeping. So skip the newborn sweaters, dresses, jeans, and hoodies and focus on onesies and sleep suits that are soft and comfy, depending on the season. To keep a newborn warm at night, pajamas with feet work great as a first layer, wrapped with a swaddle blanket or seasonally-appropriate sleep sack.

❑ **Pajamas or sleep-and-plays**

You'll want five to seven for every three-month size band. For ages 0-6 months, choose outfits that zip down the front for maximum convenience, if multiple snaps frustrate you.

❑ **One-piece short sleeve bodysuit, or onesie**

You'll want five to seven. One-piece bodysuits, or onesies, are great undershirts for winter or stand-alone outfits in the summer. White onesies pass down well for both genders.

❑ **Shirts**

You'll want five to seven. Many parents prefer bodysuit-style shirts that snap at the crotch because cropped shirts get pushed up over baby's belly while picking up or holding baby.

❑ **Leggings or pull-on pants**

You'll want five to seven. Look for stretchy waistbands that fit easily over baby's belly and diaper.

❑ **Outer layers and winter gear**

You'll want four to seven layering pieces. Fleece jackets and one-piece buntings are best for infants in cold weather because they collapse beneath car seat and stroller straps, unlike heavy coats. Thick puffer coats should not be worn in car seats—in a crash, a puffer coat can compress, making elongated straps too loose and ejecting a child from the seat. Little socks may stay on baby's hands in the winter better than gloves.

Clothing brand recommendations:

Affordable clothing

❑ *Best Bargains:* **Old Navy:** This may not be the highest quality clothing. However, it may be all that you need given how quickly young children grow out of clothes. *Runner-Up:* **Target**

❑ *Best Bodysuits and Pajamas:* **Carter's:** This brand is the top choice for inexpensive short-sleeve and long-sleeve bodysuits and non-organic cotton and microfleece pajamas.

❑ *Best Trendy Basics:* **H & M:** I am always surprised at how many cute clothes I find here. Most of the pants have elasticized waistbands and ties to secure the waist. *Runner-Up:* **Baby Gap**

❑ *Best Comfy, Conservative Style:* **Gymboree:** You will only find cute and cuddly kid-themes on these soft clothes with no licensed characters or mature adult looks.

Mid-to-higher priced clothing

❑ *Best Classic and Preppy:* **Mini Boden:** This brand is famous for its crisp British style. Parents especially love the unique applique T-shirts and extra-colorful swimwear.

❑ *Best Globally Inspired Clothing:* **Tea Collection:** Inspire your little one to dress like a global citizen in a kimono-style dress or a New Year Dragon romper. **Naartgie kids** is also a good option for comfortable cotton clothing designed in a Cape Town studio. The name "Naartjie" (pronounced nar chee) is an Afrikaans word for "a small, sweet citrus fruit" found in South Africa.

❑ *Best for Mini-Adult Clothing:* **J. Crew Crewcuts:** If you envision your baby boy in madras shorts and seersucker pants or your baby girl in cashmere sweaters and embroidered shirts, try this store.

❑ *Best Boutique Clothing:* For unique clothing without boutique prices, try flash-sale sites, such as **Zulily, Fab,** and **Gilt.**

❑ *Best Eco-friendlier brand:* **Hanna Andersson:** This brand's focus is on 100% cotton clothing and much of it is organic or Oeko-Tex certified, meaning that it has been checked for over 100 chemicals and substances. Signature items are: organic cotton sleepers and long john pajamas, play dresses and matching leggings, boy tees with appliques, and colorful tights.

Organic cotton baby clothing:

❑ **Under the Nile Organics** or **Baby Soy:** organic basics at reasonable prices, found together at babyearth.com

❑ **Hanna Andersson:** beloved Swedish inspired brand with every style of sleeper or romper in pure organic cotton

❑ **Bibi and Mimi:** offers fun prints on onesies, such as "Insomniac," "Milk Junkie," and "Chicks Dig Me."

❑ **Kee-Ka:** wearable greetings with an artistic icon, such as a whimsical pear with "Perfect pair" for a twin gift set, or "Sweet pea" with a pea pod icon

❑ **Kate Quinn Organics:** vibrantly colored baby clothing that hardly looks organic and bland

Hats

You'll want at least two of these, a broad-brimmed sun hat for the summer and a warm hat that covers the ears in the winter, preferably with a Velcro strap under the chin to keep it on for older, active babies.

Brand recommendations:

- ❏ *Newborn:* **Gerber** Cap, **BabySoy Janey Baby Hat**, and/or **Under the Nile Solid Skull Hat**
- ❏ *Best for Summer:* **iPlay Babywear Brim Hat** *($11)*, **Under the Nile Poplin Sunhat** *($15-18)*, or **Flap Happy Flap Hat** *($10-16)* with ties and neck flap
- ❏ *Best for Winter:* **Zutano Cozie Fleece Hat** *($10-15)* with ears or **JJ Cole Original Bundleme Hat** *($8-10)*

Socks and booties

You'll want five to seven, though you will probably have more. Skip all hard-soled shoes, which are bad for baby's feet. Instead, buy cute socks for newborns and soft, flexible shoes for crawlers/standers.

Brand recommendations:

- ❏ *Best Overall:* **Trumpette** *($21-24/6-pair)*: This brand has adorable "Skater" socks for boys that look like tiny, checked Vans, or try their signature "Mary Janes" for girls—socks that make baby look like she is wearing little black shoes.
- ❏ *Inexpensive:* **Target** Circo *($1.50)* and **Old Navy** *($1.50)* white socks that fold down work great for both genders.
- ❏ *Best Value:* **Gymboree** *($2-4 each)* socks with bows for girls and **Baby Gap** Triple-roll socks *($11/4-pair)* for boys are fashionable and durable favorites.
- ❏ *Best Fashion Socks:* **Jefferies** *($9-12/3-pair)* are good for classic argyle crew styles and no-itch ruffle socks.
- ❏ *Eco-friendlier:* **Hanna Andersson's Best Ever First Socks** *($4-8)* and **BabySoy** Soy Soft Signature Solid socks *($4)* are eco-friendlier choices for baby's feet.

Shoes

Your baby will not need shoes until he or she starts walking. A good baby shoe is one that bends easily when you try to bend it in half, although more flexible shoes are pricier. First time walkers need good shoes. So if faced with the dilemma of buying one pair of $35-40 Stride-Rite shoes, or three pairs of sparkly Target shoes, buy the high quality shoes. Take your baby to a brick-and-mortar store at least once to test fit, width, and thickness, or try a **Squatchi** measuring tool, invented by a mom entrepreneur, to take the guesswork out of online shoe ordering.

Brand recommendations:

- ❏ *Best Overall:* **Stride Rite:** These are my favorite brand of shoes for young children because they are both high quality and affordable with sales and coupons. Admittedly, I am not a fan of their shoe collaborations with Disney, Marvel, Star Wars, and Sesame Street (who wants to pay extra to promote mature movies and TV characters on their baby's feet?), but otherwise, Stride Rite is great.
- ❏ *Best Indoor Shoes:* **Robeez** (pronounced RAH-beez after the founder's son, Robbie): This brand of suede-bottomed, soft shoes and fleece-lined boots are perfect for crawlers, standers, and babies who refuse to keep on socks in the winter.
- ❏ *Best Splurge:* **Pediped** (pronounced PEE-dee-pehd like pediatrician): This brand has been awarded the American Podiatric Medical Association Seal of Acceptance for creating shoes that promote healthy foot development. Look for more affordable Pedipeds on flash sale websites, such as Zulily, Gilt, or HauteLook, or buy discontinued styles at Pediped.com.

▌ Books, Toys, and Other Fun Gifts

- ❏ **Books**: build baby's library with these top picks (select a few)
  - ▶ *The Very Hungry Caterpillar* by Eric Carle
  - ▶ *Goodnight Moon* by Margaret Wise Brown

- ▶ *Guess How Much I Love You* by Sam McBratney
- ▶ *Moo, Baa, La La La* by Sandra Boynton
- ▶ *The Barnyard Dance* by Sandra Boynton
- ▶ *My Very First Mother Goose* edited by Iona Opie
- ▶ *I am a Bunny* by Ole Risom
- ▶ *Hand, Hand, Fingers, Thumb* by Al Perkins
- ▶ *Brown Bear, Brown Bear, What Do You See?* by Bill Martin, Jr.
- ▶ *The Rainbow Fish* by Marcus Pfister
- ▶ *Goodnight Gorilla* by Peggy Rathmann
- ▶ *C Is for Coco: A Little Chick's First Book of Letters* by Sloan Tannen
- ▶ *More, More, More Said the Baby* by Vera B. Williams

- ▶ *The Runaway Bunny* by Margaret Wise
- ▶ *Pat the Bunny* by Dorothy Kunhardt Davis
- ▶ *Fuzzy Bee and Friends* cloth book by Priddy Books
- ▶ *Five Little Monkeys Jumping on the Bed* by Eileen Christelow
- ▶ *Dear Zoo* by Rod Campbell
- ❑ **Baby Toys** (select a few)
  - ▶ Vulli Sophie the Giraffe teether *($20-25)*
  - ▶ Green Toys Twist Teether Toy, colors vary *($9-10)*

  - ▶ Green Toys Stacker or Nesting Cups *($12-16)*
  - ▶ Under the Nile Organic Veggies *($23-30 for the crate, $6-8 each)*. The carrot and banana are favorites.
  - ▶ Baby Einstein Take Along Tunes music player *($8-10)*
  - ▶ Sassy Spin Shine Rattle Developmental Toy *($4-6)*

  - ▶ Sassy Crib and Floor Mirror *($10-20)*
  - ▶ Manhattan Toy Whoozit *($10-15)*
  - ▶ Manhattan Toy Winkel *($13-14)*

- Tomy Lamaze Freddie the Firefly ($10-16)
- IQ Baby Knock Knock Blocks ($27-35)
- Munchkin Mozart Magic Cube ($18-25)
- Fisher-Price Brilliant Basics First Blocks ($10)
- The Land of Nod Nesting Xylophone Blocks ($30)
- Plan Toys Assorted Fruits and Vegetables ($20-25)
- Skip Hop Giraffe Safari Nest and Play Blocks ($20): three boxes, two wooden balls.
- Bright Starts Lots of Links ($5): for attaching toys to baby's car seat handle and stroller without the strangulation hazard of a cord

Unique and fun baby gift ideas

These are some fun items that you might subtly suggest to family or friends, or simply purchase for yourself.

- ❏ **Little Sapling Toys** makes small, solid wood teethers in the shape of all 50 states for ($12). California is the best seller.
- ❏ **Babiators** ($20) these UVA-blocking, BPA-free shades protect baby's eyes *Top Gun*-style. "Goose, it's time to buzz the tower."
- ❏ Pair your Babiators with a Top Gun Aviator Onesie ($20) from **Ovelo Designs** on Etsy.
- ❏ **DadGear** makes a hilarious Diaper Vest ($79) for dads who can't be bothered with a diaper bag. Special pockets are made just for wipes, diapers, bottles, a cell phone, and a thin changing pad.
- ❏ **Babylegs** ($9-12) are cute, colorful baby leg warmers that make diaper changes a snap.
- ❏ **BooginHead** makes several innovative products for modern parents: **Pacigrip** ($7), a stylish strap that clips a pacifier to baby, **SippiGrip** ($8), which straps sippy cups to strollers and high chairs,

SplatMat *($22)*, which protects floors from messy spilled foods, or **Squeez 'Ems** *($10/2-pack)*, reusable homemade baby food pouches.

❑ **Melondipity** makes boutique baby hats that are newborn photo-worthy *($16-25)*.

❑ **Baby Bunch**: With this product, Martha Stewart teaches you how to pick a "bunch" of 100% organic cotton baby clothes rolled tightly into a beautiful flower bouquet.

❑ For photography buffs, try a "Love at First Sight" sonogram picture frame from **Pearhead** *($17-20)*.

❑ A **Belly Bandit** *($50-72)* helps mom get back into her pre-baby form by flattening out the tummy and supporting the back. It keeps C-section incisions in place, too.

❑ **Rockabye Baby CDs** *($12-17)* are lullaby renditions of familiar tunes, covering artists such as the Beatles, Coldplay, Michael Jackson, Jay-Z, Guns N Roses, Madonna, U2, and more.

❑ A **Monthly Onesie Set** allows a new parent to photograph baby each month wearing a numbered onesie. Search Etsy for your preferred design, or buy a set of stickers for $10-20 at the **Lucy Darling** or **MyLullabug** shops on Amazon.

❑ A thoughtful parenting book, such as *Minimalist Parenting: Enjoy Modern Family Life More by Doing Less* by Christine Koh and Asha Dornfest *($15-20)*, makes a wonderful baby gift.

❑ **Citrus Lane** is a subscription service *($25/month, with free shipping)* that delivers a "Best of" gift box each month with age appropriate products, gifts, and free samples. Price is reduced for 6+ months.

❑ Go handmade and support a small business on **Etsy**. A few favorites: Top pick **ThreeLoves** (fabulously styled bibs, burps, pacifier clips, and onesies), **Happy Family** (geeky onesies such as "Chillin' in my Crib", sibling and birthday shirts), **Karenisa** (cute crochet baby hats), **HaddonCo** (baby bowtie onesies, baby suspenders, preppy goods), **KeepsakeToys** (personalized wooden toys, such as baby's own wooden iPhone, shape sorter, or bowling set), and **Finny and Zook** (unique personalized wall art).

❑ If you came to the U.S. from another country, and you long for native children's clothing, books, and toys, try these websites:

Boston-based **RedPatang.com** (offers Indian language learning materials and books, comic books, clothing, and toys for children), **ChinaSprout.com** (offers high quality Chinese educational and cultural products, including clothing, books, toys, and other fun items, such as bakery-made mooncakes shipped from the U.S.), **SpanglishBaby.com** (offers books and materials for raising a bilingual child), **Dosborreguitas.com** (offers unique clothing celebrating Latino culture), and finally **Rakuten Global Market** (Japan's #1 e-commerce site offers baby and children's products from around the world. Double-check shipping costs, depending on the country selected.)

▌ Just for Mom: Maternity Products

Natural personal care

Since cosmetic and personal care companies are in charge of policing themselves when it comes to chemical safety, I thought I would point out some favorite green brands for Mom. Of course, you don't have to toss out all of your existing toiletries and makeup. However, when you run out of a product, you may want to try a more natural alternative.

Did You Know?

Stretch Mark Creams and Lotions

What? There's no such thing as a miracle stretch mark cream? Many maternity lotions and products make promises they simply cannot keep. For example, whether you get stretch marks or not is attributed to your genetic predisposition, weight gain, and rate of weight gain, and not to the brand of belly butter you slather on at night (although moisturizing your skin daily should help with the itch).

Brand recommendations:

- ❑ *Belly Lotion (for stretch marks):* **Burt's Bees Mama Bee Belly Butter** (*$10-15*) or **Bio-Oil** (*$15-20*)
- ❑ *Belly Lotion for the Ingredient Purist:* **Belli Say No to Stretchmarks Set** (*$83 for the stretchmark cream and oil, $48 cream, $34 oil*) for extra-sensitive pregnancy skin
- ❑ *Body Lotion:* **Weleda Regenerating Body Lotion** (*$14-17*)
- ❑ *Body Oil:* **Weleda Pregnancy Body Oil** (*$20-25*) or **Burt's Bees Mama Bee Nourishing Body Oil** (*$8-9*)
- ❑ *Blemish Skin Care (no salicylic acid):* **Belli Anti-Blemish Facial Wash** (*$22-27*) or **Burt's Bees Herbal Blemish Stick** (*$6-8*)
- ❑ *Sulfate Free Shampoo Inexpensive:* **Organix** or **Loreal Everstrong**
- ❑ *Sulfate Free Shampoo Splurge:* **Pureology Nano Works**
- ❑ *Sulfate Free Shampoo Curly:* **Kinky Curly Come Clean**
- ❑ *Body Scrub:* **De-luxe BAIN Foaming Body Scrub** (*$19*)
- ❑ *Foot Scrub:* **Burt's Bees Mama Bee Leg and Foot Crème** (*$11*)
- ❑ *Best Natural Toothpaste:* **Tom's of Maine** with fluoride
- ❑ *Best Natural Deodorant (Inexpensive):* **Alba Botanica**

Did You Know?
Sulfate-free shampoos
• • • • • • • • • • • • • •

Salons offering color and smoothing treatments have been recommending sulfate-free shampoos for years to help women preserve their expensive treatments. However, sulphate-free products can now be found in drugstore aisles. Sodium lauryl sulphate (SLS) is a detergent used for cleaning and making stuff lather. SLS is used in a wide variety of industrial products, such as floor cleaners and engine degreasers, and it is also found in soaps, shampoos, and toothpaste. SLS is not typically found in baby products, although its milder cousin, sodium laureth sulphate (SLES), may be used. Many websites claim that SLS is a carcinogen, but major cancer groups agree there is not enough evidence to support this claim. What is clear about SLS is that it can be an irritant in higher concentrations, especially if left on the skin or used regularly. Individuals with eczema or sensitive skin should use sulfate-free soaps and shampoos.

❑ *Best Natural Deodorant (Most Effective):* **Weleda Deodorant** or **Lavanila Laboratories Lavanila Healthy Deodorant**. Note: The aluminum in deodorant has long been a suspect linked to breast cancer, especially considering the area of application. However, beware that many natural deodorants do not work for certain individuals.

Natural cosmetics and beauty products (green beauty award winners)

❑ *Best Inexpensive Brand:* **Physician's Formula Organic Wear**
❑ *Best Splurge Brand:* **RMS Beauty** (top products: Living Luminizer, Lip2Cheek, and cream shadows)
❑ *Makeup Removing Towelettes:* **Burt's Bees Facial Cleansing Towelettes**, grapefruit ($9-12)
❑ *Mineral Makeup:* **Bare Escentuals bareMinerals** *($10-25)* or **Mineral Fusion** *($18-25)*. Mineral-based makeup generally sits on top of skin.
❑ *Foundation:* **Vapour Organic Beauty Luminous Foundation** *($42)* or **Dr. Hauschka's Translucent Makeup** *($36-61)*
❑ *Concealer:* **Ecco Bella FlowerColor Coverup** *($17-22)* or **Dr. Hauschka's Pure Care Cover Stick** *($22)*
❑ *Mascara:* **Josie Maran GoGo Natural Volume** *($40)* or **Organic Wear 100% Natural Lash** *($14)*
❑ *Lipstick:* **Josie Maran Argan Color Stick** *($15)* or **Honeybee Gardens** *($8-11)*
❑ *Lip-gloss:* **Jane Iredale PureGloss** *($20)* or **Burt's Bees Super Shiny Natural Lip Gloss** *($9)*
❑ *Lip balm:* **Eos** *($4)*, **Burt's Bees** *($3)*, **Alima Pure tinted** *($7)*
❑ *Lip balm, Vegan:* **Crazy Rumors** with no beeswax *($6)*
❑ *Nail Polish:* **Zoya** *($8)* or **Dr.'s Remedy Enriched Nail Care** *($17)*
❑ *Nail Polish Remover:* **Scotch Naturals** *($15)*
❑ *Hair Color:* **Lush Hair Hennas** *($48)* or **Surya Henna Cream** henna-based hair dyes *($17)*

Maternity clothes

❑ *Favorite maternity brands and stores:* **A Pea in the Pod, Top Shop, Motherhood, Kohl's Oh Baby by Motherhood, Target, Gap, Ann Taylor Loft,** and **Old Navy.**

Practical Tips from Real Parents
Just for Mom
(personal care, clothes, shoes, etc.)

• •

- If you are diligent with applying your belly lotion, you will loathe the smell of cocoa butter by the end of pregnancy.

- I have friends who swear by their stretch mark cream. They say, "I put it on every night and never had stretch marks….blah, blah, blah." I did the same thing, and I have dark red marks all over my belly years later.

- If you have a darker complexion, be prepared for melasma. I had blotches of dark coloration all over my face and arms. Always use sunscreen but definitely don't use a skin bleacher.

- The worst side effect of pregnancy, by far, was my melasma. I am an Indian-American woman, and I already had a few dark patches on my face, but pregnancy made them much worse.

- You have no idea how much your body will change week to week, so be cautious when buying maternity clothes. I ended up wasting lots of money.

- Every pregnant woman needs a simple black maternity dress for work and special occasions. Dress it up with a sparkly neck-lace or dress it down with a cardigan.

- Wear comfortable shoes and put your feet up several times a day. Toward the end of my pregnancy, I had to wear black flip-flops to work because my feet were so swollen.

- Get your husband to rub your feet with a peppermint oil foot rub at night.

- Try a postpartum girdle after you give birth. I think they really help to shrink your stomach.

❑ *Higher end, trendy collections:* **StellaMaternity.com, PinkBlush Maternity.com, Asos.com, OlianMaternity.com, Seraphine .com, IsabellaOliver.com,** and **JapaneseWeekend.com.**

Maternity intimates

❑ *Cotton Maternity Underwear:* **Gap Maternity**
❑ *Maternity Thong Underwear:* **Hanky Panky** Signature Lace Low Rise Thong
❑ *Maternity Lingerie:* **You! Lingerie** or **Hotmilk**
❑ *Maternity Underwear with belly support:* **Belevation**

Comfort support pillow

Some women choose to place an extra standard pillow between their legs, or under their hips, for support while sleeping. Others will tell you that they couldn't have survived pregnancy without their Snoogle.

❑ *Body pillow:* **Leachco Snoogle Total Body Pillow** *($55-58)*

Other useful maternity products

❑ *Bra Extenders:* **Maidenform** *($8)* or **Motherhood Bra Back Extender** *($2)*
❑ *Pants Extenders:* **Belly Belt Kit** *($20),* **Ingrid & Isabel Bellaband** *($26),* **BeBand** *($17),* or a hair tie or rubber band looped around your pants button
❑ *Belly Button Covers:* **Popper Stoppers by Miss Oops** *($13),* or a simple **Band-Aid** when wearing tight shirts or work shirts
❑ *Postpartum belly support:* **Bellefit** *($109-145)* high end medical-grade compression, **Belly Bandit** *($50-72),* a popular belt that you may be able to borrow, or **Leonisa** shape wear (prices vary depending on the product) lifts your butt and shrinks your belly

Baby Registry: A Waste of Money

I couldn't tell you how many silly baby registry items my husband and I thought we had to have that turned out to be a total waste of money. The survey for this book turned up similar comments from other parents who wished they had been more prudent with their dollars. Many also wanted to pass on that the infant phase is a very short time in a child's life, though it can be difficult to look beyond that stage while pregnant. Here is our collective list of baby registry duds.

- ❏ **Healthcare and grooming kits.** These kits get larger and larger each year, yet they are filled with completely useless items. Will baby need a plastic medicine spoon? A toothbrush? A wide-toothed comb for fine baby hair? Or a tiny plastic bottle for medicine? No. Once baby arrives, you should only use the medicine dropper that comes with baby's medicine. Also, the kit suction

Safety Alert!
Crib Bumper Pads

In 2011, the American Academy of Pediatrics (AAP) recommended that crib bumper pads should never be used in cribs, due to the deaths of 27 children between 1985 and 2005. Bumper pads can trap an infant's head in the space between the pad and mattress causing suffocation, or the tie can cause strangulation.

bulbs are too hard for newborn noses (use the bulb from the hospital), and the kit thermometers are junk. Buy a hairbrush, nail clippers, and thermometer separately, and skip the kit altogether.

❏ **Expensive crib bedding sets.** The AAP has banned crib bumper pads, blankets, quilts, and pillows from cribs for years. So why in the world are companies still selling 4- to 13-piece crib sets comprised of these items? Because parents buy them. The companies don't care that you can't actually use them. Instead, buy separate crib sheets and accessorize baby's nursery with colorful paint, window treatments, and wall decals.

❏ **Bassinet.** Unless you are using a family heirloom, save your money and don't register for a bassinet. For baby's first weeks, consider a firm portable crib or Pack 'n Play, a product that you already need for travel.

❏ **Moses basket.** This item pops up on useless baby product surveys across the globe. Babies get heavy fast—too heavy to carry any great distance in a Moses basket without a river flowing beneath.

❏ **Baby shoes.** Who can resist that teeny-tiny pair of Nikes? Though seriously, even LeBron's kids didn't need high tops at three months old. In fact, your baby will likely kick them off as soon as you put them on. Save your money and buy high quality socks for ages 0-6 months.

❏ **Baby bathrobe.** Cut out the middleman. Baby will likely go straight from her towel into pajamas.

❏ **Ear thermometer**. Ear thermometers are not effective for infants, and they are definitely not worth the $60 price tag.

❏ **Infant winter coats and snowsuits.** Hand-me-downs and consignment sales are great sources for infant winter gear and bunting, especially for urban families who walk everywhere. However, baby does not need a waterproof snowsuit, as those will not work with car seats and stroller straps. Return bulky, infant-sized coats and exchange them for fuzzy one-piece suits (with legs for the car seat), or use a fleece jacket and pants while covering baby with a blanket.

❏ **Disposable breast pads**. Why add more trash to our landfills with a product that makes your boobs itch mightily with the slightest bit of dried milk on them? Enough said.

❏ **Too many clothes.** It is hard to resist buying outfits for your first baby. However, newborns sleep 14-16 hours per day. When baby is not sleeping, she will be feeding, playing, and spitting up on her clothes.

❑ **Too many baby blankets.** I would not register for any blankets. It's a fact: older people cannot resist buying soft, fuzzy blankets for a new baby. Maybe it's their Heparin talking, but if you have a large family, expect lots of blankets.

❑ **Too many bottles and pacifiers.** You may appreciate sampling a few bottles and pacifiers to see what your infant prefers before investing in a whole collection of a specific brand. Otherwise, expect your partner to freak out when 15 different bottles and 45 different bottle parts are falling out of the kitchen cabinets.

❑ **Too many mom-to-be labeled items.** Special pregnancy pillows, lotions, belly oils, stretch mark creams, foot scrub, lollipops, nursing tea, and more. Just add the words "maternity" or "pregnant," much like "wedding," and the prices go up for everything.

For those on a tighter budget, here are some other larger items that can be chopped from a registry:

❑ **Changing table.** Longer babies may outgrow a changing table in 12 months. Opt for using the top of a dresser with a changing pad instead.

❑ **Diaper Genie.** Some parents are disappointed with the small size of the diaper genie and the high cost of refill bags. Save money with a covered trashcan that uses regular bags.

❑ **Bottle warmer.** This item can be convenient for warming formula, or pumped breast milk. However, if your baby has a stay-at-home mom who almost exclusively nurses then a bottle warmer may be a waste of money.

❑ **Too many slings and baby carriers.** Try out the Moby Wrap, Ergobaby, Beco Soleil, etc. at a baby store, and decide which one is useful for you. When prioritizing this type of item, choose a front carrier, such as an Ergobaby, over a wrap or sling. Baby will not want to be buried in a warm, fabric pouch for very long, especially in the summer.

❑ **A big, bulky infant swing.** Some babies love them, some babies cry in them, and all parents cheer loudly on the day when their bulky infant swing gets packed up.

PREPARING
FOR BABY

Recovery from Pregnancy and Childbirth

• •

After the exhilaration of childbirth, you can expect a wide range of postpartum outcomes. For some, childbirth is the most physically demanding event ever experienced, and fatigue hits like a freight train. For others, the physical recovery may be quicker than expected; yet the emotional ups and downs catch them by surprise. A woman who has just given birth has had her body chemistry turned upside down and to describe her as "hormonal" is actually quite accurate. During labor and birth, the stress hormone linked to physical exertion (norepinephrine) may spike to 50% above pregnancy levels, while hormones linked to psychological stress (epinephrine/adrenaline and cortisol) increase 500%. Those levels normalize after birth. Talk about an emotional roller coaster![91]

This intense hormonal experience lies beneath other physical issues after childbirth, which may include (are you sitting down?): perineum soreness, tissue tears, C-section incision sensitivity, backaches, hemorrhoids, headaches, nausea, urinary incontinence, constipation, and breast soreness, due to breastfeeding. Gasp! Of course, this list of pleasantries isn't meant to frighten anyone, but rather to sharpen the view ahead and educate partners about the realities of the recovery phase. What can you do to help?

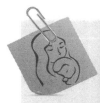

Going Deeper
Postpartum Expectations
• • • • • • • • • • • • • • • • •

It has been said that the formula for happiness is simple: *happiness = reality minus expectations*. If your expectations for everything exist in the stratosphere or are unrealistic, then happiness may be forever out of your reach. I think this formula sometimes comes back to bite new parents. For women, having a child is often characterized as the pinnacle in life, and truthfully, childbirth is one of the most amazing and joy-filled experiences ever. It's a miracle. It's a marvel, and the anticipation leading up to the event naturally takes expectations into the stratosphere. However, then comes the reality of the recovery, such as a body that still looks pregnant, lack of sleep, the routine of caring for a newborn, and the certainty of impending self-sacrifice. I am telling you these things not to rain on your pregnancy parade, but to prepare you for a possible delta between your reality and expectations.

Postpartum recovery

❑ For all of your postpartum needs, don't forget to raid your hospital room for postpartum swag, such as extra mesh panties, pads, perineum-bottles, ice packs, pads to cover your C-section incision, and so forth.

❑ For perineum pain, take a sitz bath several times a day for the first week. Try lining a maxi-pad with Tuck's cooling pads, or make a "padsicle" to place inside your underpants by pouring witch hazel on a maxi-pad and popping it into the freezer. Use your squirt bottle, or peri-bottle, to rinse the perineum area, especially if stinging occurs when urine hits your stitches. If pain persists, try a numbing spray, such as Dermoplast.

❑ For postpartum bleeding (vaginal and C-section births), buy a large supply of maxi-pads, preferably a low-chemical, natural brand. You will have four to eight weeks of vaginal discharge, called lochia (LOH-kee-uh), which is comprised of tissue and blood that lined your uterus during pregnancy. If the bleeding is heavy, try an adult incontinence pad or diaper.

❑ For constipation (your first poops after birth will be unpleasant, regardless of whether you had a C-section or vaginal delivery), drink plenty of water and eat high fiber foods. Go for a bowel-inducing walk, or drink a cup of hot water to get things moving. Ask your doctor for a stool softener, if required.

❑ For hot and cold flashes, expect to change sweaty pajamas at night and to get cold at random times during the day, due to changing fluid and blood-flow levels. By the end of pregnancy, your blood volume increased 30-50% and now your body must normalize.

❑ For post-pregnancy incontinence, or peeing in your pants, especially after laughs, coughs, and sneezes, try daily kegel exercises. You may need to wear panty liners for several months after childbirth.

❑ For latch problems and breast pain, talk to a lactation specialist. If you desire immediate help, try the La Leche Breastfeeding Helpline at 877-4 LA LECHE (1-877-452-5324).

❑ For swollen gums, gingivitis, and periodontal disease, brush and floss regularly. Consider buying a water pick, don't forget to floss, and see your dentist. Pregnancy causes hormonal shifts that reduce the body's response to bacteria and increase the risk of gum disease.

❑ For healthy skin (breastfeeding and other postpartum changes can leave your skin dry and depleted), avoid harsh soaps and hot water, which can strip oil from your skin. Use gentle cleansers. Pat your face dry, allowing some moisture to remain.

❑ For painful sex (after four to six weeks), use a water-based lubricant and take it slowly. Pain in the beginning of sex may last from three months up to a year after delivery and can be caused by childbirth stress (including a C-section), vaginal dryness (caused by dropping levels of estrogen and dehydration), and/or a yeast infection. Pain after deep penetration is not normal. Talk to your doctor if this occurs.

❑ For the first of your low impact exercise sessions, consider wearing a tight, stretchy tank top, or an ACE bandage, around your belly for support. If desired, use a postpartum girdle or abdominal compression binder to help support your shrinking uterus.

❑ For healthy weight loss, target a goal of one pound per week. It may take nine months or longer to return to your pre-pregnancy weight, and even then your weight will be distributed differently.

Typical restrictions for a C-section recovery (talk to your doctor)

These rough guidelines are listed to set expectations for the recovery period following a C-section:

❑ Avoid lifting anything heavier than your baby, until your doctor says it is okay, especially during the first two to three weeks. This restriction, which may last until six weeks, is particularly difficult to honor when you have older children, although lifting prematurely is not worth a hernia.

❑ Avoid climbing stairs, until your doctor says it is okay (typically two to six weeks). If you cannot avoid them, go slowly and use them only a few times a day to avoid straining abdominal muscles.

❑ Avoid driving, until your doctor says it is okay (typically two to three weeks, especially while taking pain medications). Driving is restricted until you can safely twist your body without pain and perform sudden movements like slamming on the brakes.

❑ Avoid household chores that require abdominal bending or stretching, such as lifting laundry or vacuuming, for at least two weeks. Woo hoo!

❑ No sex for six weeks or until your doctor clears it.

Safety Alert!

Narcotics after a C-Section or Vaginal Tear

Finally, I have one last tip, which will be controversial with other moms. **Stop taking any narcotic medications as soon as possible.** I am definitely not suggesting that you suffer in pain, and you will still have ibuprofen. However, try to cut any narcotic pills in half or cut back the dosages after the first few days, at least. In addition to concerns with breastfeeding compatibility, post-surgery narcotics, such as hydrocodone (Vicodin) and oxycodone (Percocet, OxyContin), can be highly addictive. In my research for this book, I have discovered countless op-ed articles, media posts, and blogs from women highlighting prescription drug abuse that began after a C-section surgery. Of course, your obstetrician is going to limit your script and not refill it. However, these pain relievers work on the same brain receptor as heroine and other illicit substances, and they can lead vulnerable, postpartum women down a slippery slope, such as begging friends for leftover pills, feigning pain to get meds, etc. If you have experienced opioid addiction in the past, talk to your doctor. Also, do not leave an unfinished bottle around the house with addictive friends or family members nearby.

Depression and
Postpartum Depression

. . . .

Admittedly, this subject matter can be heavy for an enthusiastic parent-to-be with no context for what may lie ahead. However, when experienced moms and dads are asked for their most sincere advice to pass on to other new parents, there is almost always an outpouring about postpartum depression, general anxiety, and adjustment to life with a baby.

In my observations, certain compounding factors are making today's mothers even more susceptible to anxiety and postpartum depression than previous generations:

- ❏ *Parents are older when they have their first child:* Caring for a helpless human being after years of independence and self-discovery can be a major adjustment for anyone, but especially for Mom.
- ❏ *More "I":* In general, our society has become more individualistic. Life is more about the "I" and less about the "we." We're a selfie generation, yet when we put ourselves at the center and become obsessed with the extent of our own possibilities, any setback can be devastating. Parenting naturally draws focus away from self and self-pursuit, which can lead to a condition of the "I" called depression, meaning that we have failed relative to our own goals.
- ❏ *Less "we":* When our grandparents struggled with life transitions, they generally had their spiritual faith, extended family, a tighter-knit community, and a cohesive nation to provide comfort and support. This social safety net has all but eroded in the last few decades.

❏ *Intersection of career and motherhood:* Today, a record share of new moms are working and are college educated—66% of women with a child under age one have at least some college, compared to 18% in 1960.[92] Women are now 33% more likely than men to earn college degrees by age 27, and women are earning the majority of degrees awarded. While this academic success is terrific for women's resumes, a great deal of stress and anxiety can occur when one is confronted with choices between career and raising children.

What is depression?

Depression is more than feeling sad, blue, or down in the dumps for a few days. Depression is having despondent, empty, and anxious feelings that do not go away and affect your ability to function. Depression affects families, relationships, work performance, and day-to-day activities.* One in 10 Americans have depression at some point in life, but this number is likely to be low since many cases go unreported. The rate of depression for women is twice that of men, regardless of race or ethnicity.[93]

Depression typically results from a combination of factors, rather than a single cause. Stressful life events, such as the death of a loved one, loss of a significant relationship, loss of a job, abuse, neglect, or poverty can trigger depression. Areas of the brain involving mood, memory, and decision-making can be physically and chemically altered, due to a strong physiological response to a stressful event.

What is postpartum depression?

About 80% of postpartum women experience some form of the baby blues, while 15% have postpartum depression (PPD).[94] Change is stressful, and the combination of biological, hormonal, and emotional changes after birth can pack a powerful punch when combined with one another.

❏ *Biological changes:* Postpartum women have endured physical pain from childbirth and considerable changes to their bodies after

---

* For an illustration of how depression looks day-to-day, see the World Health Organization's video called "I Had a Black Dog, His Name was Depression," which can be found on YouTube.

months of pregnancy. Some women are disappointed that certain changes may never return to a pre-pregnancy normal, such as stretch marks, stretched skin, breast uplift, and belly fat. Postpartum women are also sleep-deprived, and the lack of rest affects all other body systems.

❏ *Hormonal changes:* Changing hormone levels can trigger symptoms of postpartum depression, similar to hormone changes that affect a woman's mood before she gets her period. Levels of thyroid hormones may also drop after giving birth, which can exacerbate symptoms of depression (the thyroid is a small gland in the neck that helps regulate how your body uses and stores energy from food).

❏ *Emotional and psychological changes:* As if there isn't enough going on in the change department, postpartum women must shift emotionally from a period of high anticipation with freedom in their schedule to a loss of anticipation and a more restricted schedule. Mom is also no longer the center of attention, and the effects of weight gain (without a baby) can adversely affect self-esteem. Low self-esteem paired with low energy and social isolation can lead to disconnection from others. Disconnection from others leads to depression.

Disconnection, denial, and depression

Many women feel embarrassed and ashamed about feeling depressed after the birth of a child. A new mom with PPD may refuse to tell family or friends how she is feeling, worrying that she will be seen as self-absorbed and ungrateful, or worse–an unfit mother. Someone with PPD may also be concerned that an employer or co-worker might find out about her depression and view her as unstable. Family and friends with children may offer little empathy because they have forgotten about their own difficulties adjusting to life with a newborn.[95]

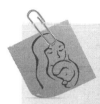

Going Deeper
The Postpartum Paradox

• • • • • • • • • • • • • • • • •

Having a baby is one of life's most joyous *and* stressful events. This paradoxical relationship may also explain why postpartum depression is often undiagnosed and untreated. I had undiagnosed, untreated postpartum depression. I didn't want to hurt my child, and my world never hit rock bottom. However, I had sad, anxious feelings that did not go away in the days and weeks after birth, and they profoundly affected my marriage and my life.

I loved my newborn wholeheartedly, but the changes to my daily schedule overwhelmed me. I was on a round-the-clock breastfeeding tether that was more demanding than I expected, and being in an unfamiliar city left me homebound. Watching my husband pursue his own career and fatherhood with hardly a bump in the road made me resentful. I felt conflicted and crazy. I had longed to be a mom, but my new schedule was exhausting, lonely, and dare I say–boring. So what did I do? I pulled myself up by the boot-straps and poured myself deeper into my new role (I was going to be the best mom ever!), but I was still unhappy. The incongruity between what I thought I was supposed to be and what I actually was triggered a flood of disappointment. I languished in my own mother's guilt: "*You're pathetic, sitting around in your comfy clothes, with your healthy baby, wondering if you'll ever 'have it all.' Most women are already out there doing it all. What are you complaining about?*" I responded by withdrawing from the world.

As far as my doctor knew, I only had "minor baby blues," but I was sputtering on empty. One small spit-up or diaper leak before heading out the door unraveled me, and this is coming from a lady who flew combat missions in Afghanistan and Iraq. The isolation and thankless nature of care taking had gotten the best of me. By the time I found myself suddenly and mysteriously captivated by the life of Abraham Lincoln (whose melancholy both challenged and fueled him), I knew I was depressed.

What are some differences between "baby blues" and postpartum depression?

The baby blues often go away within a few days or weeks. The symptoms are not severe and do not require a doctor's treatment. If you have baby blues, you may...

- ❏ Feel sad, anxious, or overwhelmed with your new life
- ❏ Have rapid mood swings
- ❏ Cry very easily, or have crying fits
- ❏ Lose your appetite, or eat too much, for a few weeks
- ❏ Have trouble sleeping, even when others are encouraging or allowing you to rest

If you have the following symptoms of depression **for more than two weeks** without relief, you may have postpartum depression:

- ❏ Feeling sad, overwhelmed, and hopeless about your life
- ❏ Crying a lot, or not being able to stop crying
- ❏ Having no energy or motivation to accomplish life's tasks
- ❏ Isolating yourself from family and friends
- ❏ Losing interest in activities that you used to enjoy
- ❏ Eating too little or too much
- ❏ Sleeping too little or too much (beyond normal sleep interruption with a newborn)
- ❏ Experiencing headaches, aches and pains, or stomach problems that don't go away

Postpartum depression can include more severe outcomes, such as:

- ❏ Thoughts of hurting the baby
- ❏ Thoughts of hurting yourself
- ❏ Not having any interest in caring for the baby

Untreated depression can lead to risky behaviors that affect both Mom and baby.[96]

❑ Out-of-control responses to stimuli, especially crying and noise
❑ Neglect of an infant
❑ Excessive alcohol use
❑ Drug addiction

The recovery period after birth can be *substantially* better for Mom with support from a partner, family, and friends. Although no one can predict postpartum outcomes, families can anticipate known predictors. Here is a list of markers collated from several studies on postpartum depression. Read each predictor and think about ways that you might ease potential burdens for yourself or your partner. Early identification and preventative measures could alleviate months of suffering for a new mom and the whole family.[97-99]

❑ Previous history of depression
❑ Prenatal depression and anxiety (during pregnancy)
❑ Recent stressful life events (death in the family, moving, etc.)
❑ Lack of relational support from a significant family member or friend
❑ Marital dissatisfaction/dysfunction
❑ Unplanned pregnancy
❑ Childcare stress
❑ Financial strain
❑ Low self-esteem (includes body image dissatisfaction)
❑ Perfectionism (high concern over making mistakes)
❑ Breastfeeding challenges
❑ Difficult infant temperament

Breastfeeding Preparation

. . . .

Breast milk is the ideal nutrition for babies. The American Academy of Pediatrics (AAP), American Medical Association (AMA), World Health Organization (WHO), and Central Intelligence Agency (CIA) all recommend breastfeeding. The last one is a joke, of course, but this topic deserves multiple interjections of humor and compassion. To better understand the sensitivities involved let's take a closer look at some breastfeeding issues for mothers today.

Women are working more hours outside the home than ever before, yet the social pressure to breastfeed has skyrocketed, especially when compared to previous generations. For example, breastfeeding initiation rates are currently 79%, up from 24% in the early 1970s. Today, a tax deduction exists for breast pumps and other supplies (formula supplies do not qualify), and photos of breastfeeding celebrities appear in the same news feeds as major world events—first, a stand-off in the Ukraine, followed by Gisele Bündchen lounging in her bath robe, nursing her baby with a glam squad in attendance. This is all helpful news for babies; but a working mom pumping in a small back office or storage closet, while her boss and co-workers grumble outside, may indicate that certain expectations for breastfeeding are unrealistic. The truth is most new moms acknowledge that breast is best, but exclusively breastfeeding a baby for six months or a year is a whole different story.[100]

Benefits of breastfeeding

Breast milk is made especially for baby. It is easier to digest than the protein in cow's milk, and it helps fight disease. Colostrum (pronounced coh-LOSS-trum), also called "liquid gold," is the thick, yellow breast milk that you make during pregnancy and just after birth. This milk is rich in nutrients and antibodies that protect your baby for life. Colostrum changes into mature milk by three to five days after birth, and this milk has just the right amount of fat, sugar, and protein to help baby grow. Formula cannot match the precise chemical makeup of human breast milk.[101]

Breastfeeding provides instant, healthy food, without bottles to sterilize or warm at night. It is also less expensive than formula feeding and beneficial to Mom. Formula and bottle supplies can cost over $1500 per year, whereas breastfeeding is nearly free (though Mom will probably need a breast pump.) Moreover, breastfed babies are sick less often, which can lower health care costs. Breastfeeding is also linked to a lower risk of disease in women, such as postpartum depression, breast cancer, ovarian cancer, and Type 2 diabetes. Other studies link breastfeeding to higher IQ, lower rates of osteoporosis, and less postpartum bleeding.[102, 103]

Breastfeeding for preemies, multiples, or babies with health issues

Breastfeeding can be particularly difficult with preemies, multiples, or babies with health issues. If your baby is whisked away to the Neonatal Intensive Care Unit (NICU) immediately after birth, try not to worry about the guidelines for breastfeeding within the first hour. Pumped breast milk can be fed through a tube, and nursing isn't the only form of bonding. Bonding starts long before your baby is born. One study found that three-day-old infants could not only recognize the smell of their mother's amniotic fluid, but those smells were soothing prior to experiencing pain, such as a heel prick.[104] Another study reports that newborn babies less than three days old prefer their mothers' voices to those of strangers.[105]

Breastfeeding and working moms

Some women find that breastfeeding is easier than expected at first, but then meet challenges after returning to work. For example, leaking breast milk on a t-shirt at home is not exactly the same as drenching a silk blouse during a meeting at work. Some new moms may also be

Going Deeper
Challenges with Breastfeeding
• • • • • • • • • • • • • • • • • • • •

I am a passionate breastfeeding advocate. However, there are legitimate challenges to overcome, especially in the beginning. Three days after the birth of my first child, my breasts became so engorged with milk I thought they were going to burst like water balloons. My doctor joked that I had turned into Dolly Parton overnight, and my husband tried to ease the situation by joking that I was our family's prize jersey cow. I was not amused. The more I pumped to relieve the pressure, the more milk I produced. Yet when I didn't pump, my ducts clogged and mastitis ensued (mastitis is inflammation of breast tissue due to infection, engorgement, or clogged ducts). Our baby couldn't begin to drink the milk I was producing, and she struggled to latch on to my fire hose. My nipples were cracked and stinging, and I had cold cabbage leaves hanging out of my bra for relief. Thankfully, family and friends helped me over the breastfeeding hump.

Truthfully, I have hardly met a nursing mom who didn't have breastfeeding challenges, and more often than not, low milk supply, not over-supply, is the major concern. Common issues, such as sore nipples, bleeding nipples, inverted nipples, and problems with baby's latch, can all lower a woman's milk supply. A good latch occurs when baby's mouth covers more of the areola above the nipple than below (like a fish kissing a wall.) A bad latch can lead to a cycle of frustration, which adversely affects the overall breastfeeding effort: a bad latch causes sore nipples, Mom is edgy with sore nipples and baby is not gaining weight, so Mom or Dad panics and supplements with formula, which contributes to further low milk supply. Repeat. Some babies need supplementation during that initial low milk supply period. However, if this happens to you, please seek help from a lactation specialist.

Did You Know?

Break Time Laws for Nursing Mothers

• •

The Patient Protection and Affordable Care Act ("Affordable Care Act") amended section 7 of the Fair Labor Standards Act ("FLSA"), requiring "employers to provide reasonable break time for an employee to express breast milk for her nursing child for one year after the child's birth each time such employee has need to express the milk. Employers are also required to provide a place, other than a bathroom, that is shielded from view and free from intrusion from coworkers and the public, which may be used by an employee to express breast milk." This breastfeeding break time requirement became effective when the Affordable Care Act was signed into law on March 23, 2010.

concerned about time allowances for pumping during the workday. Yet many do not know that federal regulations are on their side.

Getting over the hump: troubleshooting tips

Surveys often cite "lack of support" as a reason why women give up on breastfeeding. Let's flesh out a few common scenarios and provide some troubleshooting tips and solutions.

Lack of Role Models

Problem: New mothers often get information about breastfeeding from pamphlets and online resources, which can be ineffective compared to live role models, such as a sister, sister-in-law, or friend, who have breast-fed successfully.

Solution: If you want to breastfeed, seek the help of trusted friends and family members who have been successful breast feeders.

Generational Differences

Problem: At birth, a new mom's own mother may be ambivalent about breastfeeding. She didn't breastfeed, and you turned out fine (breastfeeding rates in the 1970s and 80s were between 25-35%).

Solution: Assure your mom that you respect her decisions and ask for her support. Invite her to be present when you talk with a lactation consultant.

Lack of Partner Support

Problem: In some families, fathers may feel uncertain about breastfeeding. How will he bond with baby? How will his partner work outside the home and breastfeed? How much household work will shift to him due to breastfeeding? How will breastfeeding affect the couple's sex life?

Solution: Prenatal education with fathers has shown to enhance breastfeeding support remarkably. One study from a university obstetrics practice showed a breastfeeding initiation rate of 74% among mothers whose partners attended a two-hour prenatal intervention class (led by a peer-educator), compared to a 41% rate among control groups without the class. Teach your partner about breastfeeding.[106]

Mixed Messages about Breastfeeding in the Media

Problem: If you peruse popular op-eds, you might come across cynical headlines about breastfeeding, such as "The Breastfeeding Myth," "Booby Trap: Myths about Breastfeeding," or "The Case against Breastfeeding." In the last mentioned article, the author states, "it was not the vacuum that was keeping me and my 21st-century sisters down, but another sucking sound." Personally, I don't get it. If you are going to rant and spread cynicism about something, pick a better subject.

Solution: Surround yourself with encouraging messages about breastfeeding.

What if you just can't breastfeed?

Some mothers simply cannot breastfeed or breastfeed exclusively, due to physical ailments, emotional limitations, medications, employment, and other factors. Know that good parenting is more important than breastfeeding. Your baby needs a healthy mom. So, if you are experiencing difficulties and you choose to give up breast-feeding, make lemonade and embrace the positives of formula feeding. Formula can be easier to feed on the go, without worrying about nursing in public. With formula, you know exactly how much baby is eating and your schedule is not directly tied to baby. Other caregivers can also feed baby at night or while you are at work.

Misperceptions about Low Milk Supply

Problem: New mothers are often discouraged by the common misperception they are not producing enough milk for their baby. No one has explained the physiology of lactation. One study showed that 50% of women mentioned "an insufficient milk supply" as the number one reason for stopping breastfeeding.[107]

Solution: Visual cues may help new mothers conceptualize just how much milk a baby needs in the first weeks of life, which is not that much. See the chart below.

Visual Cues: Size and Volume of a Newborn's Stomach

DAY ONE	DAY THREE	ONE WEEK	ONE MONTH
Size of a Cherry	Size of a Walnut	Size of an Apricot	Size of a Large Egg
5-7 ml or ½ tsp.	22-27 ml or .75-1 oz.	45-60 ml or 1.5-3 oz.	80-150 ml or 2.5-5 oz.

Breastfeeding Checklist

❑ **Learn as much as you can about breastfeeding before baby arrives**. Even if you are an experienced aunt, babysitter, or nanny, you may not be knowledgeable about this topic. Dad can benefit from an overview, too. Some popular breastfeeding resources are:
  ▶ Online instructional videos: These videos demonstrate breastfeeding techniques better than any words in a book.
  ▶ La Leche League International online information portal at http://www.llli.org/nb.htm
  ▶ The KellyMom website at www.KellyMom.com
  ▶ Books on breastfeeding (See: Appendix C Recommended Resources).

❑ **Overcome breastfeeding challenges with tenacity and a sense of purpose.** The initial pain and discomfort of breastfeeding should subside in two to four weeks. Nursing can be relaxing and peaceful once established.

❑ **Overcome work-schedule challenges with compromise.** No one says that baby must be 100% breastfed, especially after returning to work. Try to keep breastfeeding and supplement with formula if needed. For example, breastfeed at night and in the morning and have a care provider feed pumped milk supplemented with formula during the day. Pump what you can at work. Assess your baby's feeding situation one day at a time.

Practical Tips from Real Parents
Breastfeeding

• • • • • • • • • •

- Relax! You and baby are learning how to do this thing called breastfeeding at the same time.

- Breastfeeding is kind of like childbirth. When you talk to other women, they often remember the end result of the experience, yet they selectively forget the struggle it took to get there.

- Feed as soon as you think baby is hungry (when she first starts rooting or turning her head and opening her mouth), and she will suck with less vigor.

- Apply lanolin or nipple cream around the clock to help with cracked or bleeding nipples.

- Try a thin nipple shield if baby is having problems latching on and you are too sore to continue. It really helps!

- If you are struggling to feed, have a lactation consultant come to your house to help. Many non-profits support this type of service.

- Attend a La Leche meeting if someone cannot come to your house.

- Use a support pillow to breastfeed, or else you will be hunching over baby uncomfortably for as long as you feed.

- Breastfeeding is rough on your back and neck. Your head is always looking down and you are curled up around baby to get in the right position. Make sure that you stretch and look up while feeding to minimize the strain.

- If you are struggling with clogged ducts and mastitis, try taking lecithin, a natural food additive, to reduce the stickiness of the milk.

- If your baby continues to struggle with a good latch, have your pediatrician check to see if he is tongue-tied or has a physical reason why he can't extend his tongue. The doctor can clip the frenulum, or small webbed place under the tongue to help with feeding.

- If you have big breasts, make sure that you pinch or squeeze your nipple each time to help baby latch on. Also, don't worry if baby's nose is buried into your breast a little bit. He can still breathe since the nose tip usually extends further than the holes.

- I had problems with thrush while breastfeeding. Make sure that you contact both your pediatrician and your OB or primary care doctor to get treatment, and dump any pumped milk that may be infected. (Note: Thrush is a common yeast infection that can be shared between Mom and baby. Thrush looks like white patches of cottage cheese in baby's mouth and pink, flaky spots on Mom's nipples.)

Let's Review:
Pregnancy Dos and Don'ts

. . . .

Congratulations! We have come to the end of our checklists. I hope that you feel better equipped to tackle pregnancy and expectations for life after baby. However, before we wrap up, let's review a few pregnancy essentials. We'll cover the no-nos first to ensure that we end on a high note.

Pregnancy Don'ts

❑ **Avoid or limit exposure to potentially harmful chemicals and environmental toxins.** Focus on the worst offenders: lead, mercury, pesticides, and endocrine-disrupting chemicals, such as BPA and phthalates.[39]
  ▸ **Lead:** have your pre-1978 home tested for lead, check for chipping paint, don't renovate an old home while pregnant
  ▸ **Mercury:** eat fish and seafood low in mercury
  ▸ **Pesticides and insecticides:** eat organic foods, wash fruits and vegetables under running water, scrub with a brush, avoid household weed killers, avoid household insect sprays, be mindful if you are living near a golf course, farm, or public space that is frequently sprayed with pesticides, especially in the third trimester[108]
  ▸ **BPA:** cut down on canned goods, use BPA-free plastics, don't drink bottled water, especially those left in the car

- ▶ **Phthalates/Vinyl/PVC-plastics**: cut down on packaged and microwave-ready foods, drink from stainless steel water bottles, use glass to heat and re-heat food, lose #3, 6, and 7 plastics and choose #2, 4 and 5 plastics
- ▶ **Synthetic fragrance:** avoid the ingredient "fragrance" or "parfum" in cleaners, detergents, and personal care products
- ▶ **Brominated fire retardants/polybrominated diphenyl ethers (PBDEs):** throw away ripped items with foam padding inside, watch for PBDE dust when pulling up old carpet, don't buy baby gear, mattresses, and household products coated in fire retardants
- ▶ **Polychlorinated biphenyls (PCBs):** avoid eating fish skins and fat, eat wild salmon
- ▶ **Arsenic:** get your water tested if you drink from a well, if you live near metal smelters where metal is made, or if you live near a garbage incinerator
- ▶ **Toluene:** avoid inhaling or sniffing paint, paint thinners, gasoline, rubber cement, nail polish, and other solvents; if you smell fumes, leave the room
- ▶ **Manganese:** check your well water for manganese levels, filter your water, do not feed baby soy or rice milk beverages in place of infant formula
- ▶ **Nonstick chemicals:** keep heat at medium or below for non-stick cookware; opt for iron or stainless steel pots and pans, if possible
- ▶ **Triclosan:** limit or avoid anti-bacterial soaps and sanitizers
- ▶ **Toxic household cleaners:** mix your own cleaning ingredients or use green cleaners
- ▶ **Other chemicals brought into the home:** use a door mat, take shoes off with a shoe organizer by the door, use a HEPA-filter vacuum, dust with a wet cloth
- ❑ **Avoid problematic foods.**
  - ▶ High-mercury fish, such as swordfish, king mackerel, shark, tilefish, marlin, orange roughy, and tuna (bigeye, ahi)
  - ▶ Farmed salmon (may contain PCBs)
  - ▶ Raw sushi

- ▸ Raw seafood, such as oysters
- ▸ Refrigerated smoked seafood with labels such as "lox," "smoked," "kippered," or "nova-style"
- ▸ Undercooked meat: steaks, burgers, poultry, pork, and lamb should be fully cooked
- ▸ Cured meats with nitrates/nitrites
- ▸ Deli meat and hot dogs not heated to steaming
- ▸ Soft unpasteurized cheeses
- ▸ Unpasteurized juice: fresh-squeezed juice from farms, juice bars, or the grocery store
- ▸ Unpasteurized or raw milk
- ▸ Raw sprouts, such as alfalfa, clover, and radish
- ▸ Food that has been sitting out for more than two hours

❑ **Avoid problematic OTC drugs:** aspirin, ibuprofen, naproxen (Aleve), pseudoephedrine (decongestants), chlorpheniramine (cold and flu medicine), bismuth subsalicylate (Pepto Bismol, Kaopectate), and nicotine (Nicorette, Nicoderm patches).[27]

❑ **Avoid retinol-based skin products, skin-lightening creams, salicylic acid, and acne prescription drugs, similar to Accutane.**

❑ **Avoid alcohol, smoke, and illegal drugs.**

❑ **Avoid excessive caffeine intake** (no more than 200 mg per day—a Starbucks medium or grande 16 oz. coffee exceeds this number by 130 mg).

❑ **Always wear a seat belt.**

❑ **Do not clean the cat's litter box.** Wear gloves while gardening or handling cat feces, if you must.

❑ **Avoid hot tubs and saunas.**

❑ **Know that whatever you consume or put on your skin, your baby does, too,** including prescription medications, OTC medications, herbal supplements, and vitamin-enriched skin creams.[11]

❑ **To reference these same checklists on the go, try** *The Parent's Pocket Checklist: An Essential Guide to Pregnancy* **e-book, interactive digital book, or mobile app.**

Pregnancy Dos

Okay, now here is a joyful list of pregnancy "definitely dos."

- ❑ **Anticipate:** Look forward to meeting your child.
- ❑ **Appreciate:** Tune out the noise, and try to relish pregnancy in the moment.
- ❑ **Prioritize:** Step away from the computer. Don't over-research to the detriment of your pregnancy experience and your relationships.
- ❑ **Meditate:** Find a quiet place, breathe deeply, and think about what you want for your child. Connect with your child. Pray for your child. Meditation relaxes the body and the mind.
- ❑ **Celebrate:** Share your joy and pleasure with others to enhance the experience.
- ❑ **Reflect:** Don't forget to take lots of pictures. You will look back on these precious moments for the rest of your lives.
- ❑ **Enjoy:** This time of preparation goes by fast. Take care of yourself, spend time with loved ones, and try to laugh at the ups and downs of pregnancy.

For more lists to help you with life after baby, read *The Parent's Pocket Checklist: An Essential Guide to Baby's First Year*, which includes information and tips on baby care, colic, sleep training, starting solid foods, air travel with baby, autism and food allergy awareness, early education advice, and more.

Here's to finding immense joy in parenting!

Appendix A: Abbreviated Checklists

. . . .

Pregnancy Timeline and To Do

First Trimester

Weeks 1–8

Medical tips
- ❏ Estimate your due date
- ❏ Check health insurance coverage for pregnancy and childbirth
- ❏ Find an OB or OB/GYN or midwife
- ❏ Schedule first prenatal checkup at 6-10 weeks
- ❏ Tell your doctor about any previous miscarriages
- ❏ Bring partner to critical OB appointments, if possible
- ❏ Expect doctor visit every 4 weeks until 28 weeks pregnant
- ❏ Purchase a current week-by-week pregnancy guide

Financial tips
- ❏ Calculate how maternity leave will affect your finances
- ❏ Consider increasing life insurance coverage
- ❏ Ensure you and/or spouse have short and long-term disability
- ❏ Research maternity leave options at your firm before approaching your boss
- ❏ Consider asking for a salary raise before presenting maternity plan

Nutrition, health, and well-being tips
- ❏ If you are a single mom, seek support of family and friends
- ❏ Begin eating healthy diet
- ❏ Drink 8-10 glasses of water per day
- ❏ Take a daily prenatal vitamin

❏ Obtain prescription for prenatal vitamin with DHA supplement
❏ For nausea, eat smaller meals

Fun tips
❏ Limit sharing news early with trusted family and friends
❏ Sign up for weekly pregnancy emails, but expect your personal info to be shared
❏ Be discerning with pregnancy mobile apps
❏ Start taking pregnancy photos

Weeks 8–14

Medical tips
❏ Write down questions prior to doctor's visits
❏ Understand purpose of prenatal tests
❏ Investigate childbirth and breastfeeding classes at your hospital

Financial tips
Start buying or borrowing maternity clothes
❏ Extend your non-maternity wardrobe by looping a hair tie through the buttonhole of pants
❏ Buy or borrow new bras, or extend existing ones with bra clip extender

Nutrition, health, and well-being tips
❏ Stock up on moisturizer for your skin and growing belly
❏ Talk to doctor about exercise routine
❏ Expect bodily changes and nuisance issues:
   ▶ Congestion/sniffles
   ▶ Constipation
   ▶ Heartburn
   ▶ Headaches
   ▶ Varicose veins
   ▶ Hemorrhoids
   ▶ Vaginal discharge
   ▶ Incontinence
   ▶ Acne/pimples
   ▶ Melasma

> ► Sun sensitivity
> ► Hair growth
> ► Constant pressure in lower abdomen

Fun tips
- ❑ Record baby's heartbeat
- ❑ Give partner a few nights off
- ❑ Expect the possibility of your partner experiencing a 'sympathetic pregnancy'

Second Trimester

Weeks 14–20

Medical tips
- ❑ Triple screen testing occurs in weeks 15-20
- ❑ Option of amniocentesis occurs in weeks 16-20
- ❑ Mid-pregnancy ultrasound occurs at week 20

Financial tips
- ❑ Lay out maternity plan for boss
- ❑ Research childcare options and begin interviewing

Organizational tips
- ❑ Plan a baby shower; schedule for 6-8 weeks before due date
- ❑ Plan nursery; paint early

Fun tips
- ❑ With doctor's okay, enjoy intimacy with your partner
- ❑ Continue pregnancy photo journal
- ❑ Expect baby's first kicks
- ❑ Guess gender with fun games

Weeks 20–28

Medical tips
- ❑ Seek recommendations for pediatrician
- ❑ Research cord blood banking
- ❑ Find a doula, if desired
- ❑ Expect glucose screen test (around 28 weeks)

Nutrition, health, and well-being tips
- ❏ Make sure your diet includes enough iron
- ❏ Expect more rapid weight gain
- ❏ Make time for your marriage or relationship even if there doesn't seem to be any trouble

Organizational tips
- ❏ Update or write a will
- ❏ Send baby shower invitations
- ❏ Register for baby gifts

Fun tips
- ❏ Take a babymoon
- ❏ Search Google images for awkward pregnancy photos

Third Trimester

Weeks 29–35

Medical tips
- ❏ Doctor/midwife visits will occur every two weeks from 28-35 weeks
- ❏ Prepare your birth plan

Nutrition, health, and well-being tips
- ❏ Expect back pain
- ❏ Expect belly itching; moisturize for relief

Organizational tips
- ❏ Send thank you notes for baby shower
- ❏ Purchase items still needed; return duplicates
- ❏ Complete childbirth class
- ❏ Pre-register for your hospital or birth center; take a tour
- ❏ Pack a hospital bag
- ❏ Research baby care
- ❏ Research breastfeeding; find support from lactation consultant, if desired
- ❏ Research natural childbirth, if desired
- ❏ Install baby's car seat and have it inspected

Fun tips

- ❏ Wash baby's clothes, organize nursery
- ❏ Schedule newborn photos with photographer
- ❏ Fill out the pregnancy sections of a baby memory book
- ❏ Go out and enjoy time with family and friends

Week 35–Delivery

Medical tips

- ❏ Expect weekly doctor/midwife visits
- ❏ Avoid flying after 35 weeks
- ❏ Expect Group B strep test between 35-37 weeks
- ❏ Ask doctor about delayed cord clamping
- ❏ Call health insurance provider about adding baby to policy
- ❏ Select pediatrician

Nutrition, health, and well-being tips

- ❏ Expect interrupted sleep in final weeks
- ❏ Sleep on your left side with a pillow between your legs
- ❏ Don't push too hard in final weeks
- ❏ If due date passes, try natural labor-inducing techniques
  - ► Go for a walk
  - ► Get a massage
  - ► Stimulate nipples
  - ► Have sex if cleared
  - ► Eat spicy food
  - ► Try acupuncture or acupressure if cleared
- ❏ Stretch daily
- ❏ Expect false labor pains in the final weeks
- ❏ Use positive psychology to prepare for labor

Organizational tips

- ❏ Write an "If I go into labor tonight" plan for work and home
- ❏ Prepare electronic birth announcement
- ❏ Make a list of phone numbers to call shortly after birth
- ❏ Finalize baby names
- ❏ Divide chores and household duties with your partner
- ❏ Discuss the spiritual direction of your family with your partner

❑ Buy roomy pajamas with loose pants
❑ Buy large, cotton Granny panties and natural maxi-pads
❑ If you will breastfeed, buy nursing bras, nipple cream, nursing pads
❑ Cook and freeze meals for after delivery
❑ Have a friend set up a meal schedule for you on takethemameal .com
❑ Deep clean your home

Fun tips
❑ Read non-baby books
❑ Take older siblings on a special "date"
❑ Write a note or make a video for baby to watch later
❑ Baby is full term at 37 weeks

Is it Safe?

Food and Drink

❑ Avoid alcohol
❑ Limit coffee to one cup per day, or less than 200 mg of caffeine
❑ Avoid unpasteurized juice
❑ Avoid sushi or raw fish
❑ Fish
  ▶ *Avoid:* shark, swordfish, king mackerel, fresh tuna, tilefish, mahi-mahi, grouper, amberjack, orange roughy
  ▶ *Limit to 6 oz. per week:* canned albacore tuna, fresh caught freshwater fish
  ▶ *Limit to 12 oz. per week:* shellfish, canned light tuna, smaller ocean fish, farm-raised fish, store-bought freshwater fish
  ▶ *Safe:* wild salmon, sole, flounder, haddock, halibut, ocean perch, pollock, cod, trout
❑ Avoid imported cheeses: Brie, Camembert, Greek Feta, Montrachet, Neufchatel, goat, and queso fresco can contain listeria. Listeria may also be found in unpasteurized semi-soft cheeses: blue, Asiago, Gorgonzola, Havarti, Muenster, and Roquefort.
❑ Thoroughly cook hot dogs or deli meats
❑ Avoid nitrates and nitrites

- ❏ Avoid pâté or meat spreads
- ❏ Avoid raw eggs
- ❏ Peanuts, eggs, milk: talk to doctor (okay if no history of allergies)
- ❏ Heat leftovers until steaming
- ❏ Do not heat leftovers in plastic containers
- ❏ Avoid artificial sweeteners in food and beverages

Exercise

- ❏ Okay: swimming, walking, cycling, yoga, calisthenics, stretching routines
- ❏ Avoid: Waterskiing, diving/jumping into pools, horseback riding, downhill skiing, cross-country skiing >10,000 feet, scuba diving, cycling on wet pavement or downhill paths (where a fall is likely), sprinting, or any high impact sports that could cause injury to Mom or baby
- ❏ Seek doctor's approval for jogging
- ❏ Limit weightlifting to 5-10 pound weights

Air Travel

- ❏ "No later than" flying rules vary by airline. Talk to doctor before flying for medical clearance
- ❏ Avoid metal detectors and body scanners; ask for a "pat down" through airport security
- ❏ Choose an aisle seat on planes
- ❏ Wear loose clothing; stand and stretch often
- ❏ Program doctor or midwife's number into phone

Seat Belts

- ❏ Always wear a seat belt

X-Rays

- ❏ Tell doctor and dentist you're pregnant
- ❏ Avoid all routine x-rays

Smoking and Secondhand Smoke

- ❏ Avoid smoking
- ❏ Avoid breathing in secondhand smoke

Medications

- ❏ Pain relievers: avoid aspirin, naproxen, and ibuprofen
- ❏ Cold medicines: discuss with doctor
- ❏ Allergy medicines: continue allergy shots with approval; avoid new medication
- ❏ Herbal medicines: avoid herbal medicines unless prescribed by doctor

Cleaning Products

- ❏ Replace toxic chemicals with green products
- ❏ Make sure cleaning area is well ventilated
- ❏ Wear gloves to protect skin
- ❏ Don't mix chemicals

Household Herbicides, Insecticides, and Pesticides

- ❏ Buy organic food
- ❏ Wash food thoroughly
- ❏ Avoid chemical sprays to kill bugs and rodents in and outside
- ❏ Take shoes off when entering home
- ❏ Avoid weed killers

Cat Litter Box

- ❏ Avoid changing litter box; keep cat indoors
- ❏ Garden with gloves

Beauty and Skin Care

- ❏ Acne medications: avoid Retin-A, Retinol/retinoids, tetracycline, salicylic acid, and beta hydroxyl acid/BHA
- ❏ Avoid Botox
- ❏ Avoid spa facials that use chemicals like glycolic acid
- ❏ Coloring hair: avoid chemical-based color; use henna-based hair dye instead

Manicures and Pedicures

- ❏ Bring your own instruments from home
- ❏ Avoid manicures and pedicures if concerned with infection risk

Soap, Hand Sanitizer, and Toothpaste

❑ Avoid alcohol-based hand sanitizer
❑ Instead of sanitizer, wash hands with soap for 20 seconds
❑ Limit use of anti-bacterial soap
❑ Limit toothpaste with triclosan

Hot Tubs, Saunas, and Baths

❑ Avoid hot tubs and saunas
❑ Keep bath water to < 100°F

Massage

❑ Use only trained prenatal masseuse
❑ Make sure you are propped up on your left side, or ask for a maternity table

Scented Feminine Hygiene Products and Douches

❑ Avoid douching
❑ Avoid feminine sprays
❑ Avoid scented sanitary napkins

Thong Underwear

❑ Avoid thongs
❑ If unavoidable, wear cotton maternity variety and sleep in regular underwear

Sleep Position

❑ Sleep on left side to maximize blood flow
❑ Put pillow between your legs or beneath belly
❑ Avoid sleeping on back after 4 months

Vaccinations

For pregnant women:
❑ Ideally, be up to date on vaccinations prior to conception
❑ Discuss safety of vaccines with doctor, especially during first trimester
❑ Flu shot: request shot, not the nasal spray

Prenatal testing

Listed by timeline of availability, if required

- ❏ Week 10: Noninvasive prenatal testing (NIPT)
- ❏ Weeks 11-14: Nuchal Translucency screening (NT)
- ❏ Weeks 10-12: Chorionic villus sampling (CVS)
- ❏ Weeks 15-18: Amniocentesis (AMNIO)
- ❏ Weeks 16-22: Maternal serum alpha-fetoprotein (MSAFP) or multiple marker screening

Toxins Suspected to Contribute to Autism, ADHD, and Other Neurodevelopment Disabilities (NDDs)

- ❏ Lead
- ❏ Methylmercury
- ❏ Polychlorinated biphenyls (PCBs) or pre-1979 industrial chemicals
- ❏ Organophosphate pesticides
- ❏ Organochlorine pesticides
- ❏ Endocrine disruptors (ECDs), such as phthalates and bisphenol A (BPA)
- ❏ Automotive exhaust
- ❏ Polycyclic aromatic hydrocarbons (PAH) or fossil fuel products
- ❏ Brominated flame retardants (polybrominated diphenyl ethers, or PBDEs)
- ❏ Perfluorinated compounds (PFCs) or Teflon and Scotchgard
- ❏ Arsenic
- ❏ Toluene
- ❏ Manganese
- ❏ Fluoride
- ❏ Tetrachloroethylene or PERC

Chemicals to Avoid or Limit in Cosmetics and Personal Care

- ❏ Antibacterials (Triclosan)
- ❏ Coal tar
- ❏ DEA

- ❑ 1,4-Dioxane
- ❑ Formaldehyde
- ❑ Fragrance and phthalates
- ❑ Lead and mercury
- ❑ Nanoparticles
- ❑ Parabens
- ❑ Petroleum distillates (PDs)
- ❑ PPD (P-Phenylenediamine)
- ❑ Hydroquinone

Tips for Morning Sickness and Nausea

- ❑ Eat small meals
- ❑ Don't skip meals
- ❑ Note which foods/smells are triggers for queasiness and avoid them
- ❑ Carry citrus lotion or an herb pouch on you to mask offending smells
- ❑ Keep crackers nearby and eat a few before getting out of bed
- ❑ Try acupuncture wrist bands
- ❑ Put gentle pressure on your wrist
- ❑ Put a cool compress on your neck
- ❑ Drink cold Gatorade, freeze it into ice cubes, or suck on frozen fruit
- ❑ Avoid looking at computer monitor
- ❑ Drive instead of riding in passenger seat
- ❑ Wear loose clothing
- ❑ Take a prenatal vitamin for adequate vitamin B6
- ❑ If prenatal vitamin is too big, talk to doctor about smaller pill
- ❑ Carry a barf bag with you

Food suggestions for nausea
- ❑ Bland foods: chicken soup, broth, plain baked potato, potato chips, pasta
- ❑ Whole grains: toast, bagels, brown rice, oatmeal
- ❑ Cold foods: sandwiches, raw veggies and hummus, avocados, cheese
- ❑ Fruits and vegetables: cold applesauce, pears, citrus, potatoes
- ❑ Ginger: ginger ale, ginger tea, ginger snaps, Gin-Gins candy

❏ Crackers or pretzels, with peanut butter or almond butter for protein

❏ Lemons: sniff them, slice them, and put them in water

❏ Peppermint: decaf tea, mints

❏ Popsicles: Italian ice, real fruit bars, frozen fruit, homemade yogurt and fruit pops

❏ Lollipops or hard candy: Preggie Pops, Preggie Pop drops, B-natal candy

❏ Beverages: sparkling water, water with electrolytes: SmartWater, Vitamin Water, 365 brand

What to Eat During Pregnancy

❏ *Protein*

Cottage cheese, boneless/skinless chicken breast, fish, lentils, milk, peanut butter, quinoa, beans, and eggs

❏ *Iron*

Iron-fortified cereal, beans, spinach, lean beef, duck, poultry, quinoa, pumpkin seeds, tofu, lentils, blackstrap molasses, and edamame (cooked soybeans)

❏ *Calcium*

Milk, yogurt, cheese, ice cream, salmon, spinach, broccoli, edamame, roasted almonds, fortified cereal, and fortified orange juice

❏ *Folate*

Fortified cereal, spinach, beans, asparagus, peanut butter, oranges, and dark leafy greens

❏ *Vitamin B6*

Fortified cereal, garbanzo beans, baked potato with skin, lean beef, and chicken breast

❏ *Vitamin B12*

Wild salmon, lean beef, lamb, chicken, milk, yogurt, eggs, Kellogg's All-Bran cereal, General Mills Multi-Grain Cheerios, vitamin B12 fortified soy milk and other B12-fortified foods

❑ *Vitamin C*

Oranges, kiwi, strawberries, mango, pineapple, grapes, bell peppers, tomatoes, asparagus, broccoli, spinach, and cauliflower

❑ *Vitamin D*

Milk, low-mercury fish, asparagus, eggs (in the yolk), vitamin D fortified orange juice, and vitamin D fortified soymilk

❑ *Docosahexaenoic Acid (DHA)*

Wild salmon and fortified eggs

Tips for Pregnancy Nutrition

❑ Eat fresh whole foods
❑ Eat lots of fruits and vegetables, lean proteins, and whole grains
❑ Drink 8-10 glasses of water per day
❑ Talk with a doctor before taking supplements other than prenatal vitamin
❑ Take a prescription-level prenatal vitamin with DHA
❑ Take prenatal vitamin with orange juice
❑ Take prenatal vitamin and calcium supplement at different times
❑ Boost iron intake by pairing vitamin C-rich food with iron-rich food
❑ Talk with doctor about gluten-free diet as a non-celiac
❑ Eat breakfast cereals with 100% DV of folic acid *and* iron *and* vitamin B12: Total, Product 19, and All-Bran Complete
❑ Prioritize lean cuts of beef and pork for choline
❑ Choose light tuna over white, albacore tuna
❑ Skip canned goods in favor of glass bottles or soups in BPA-free Tetra Paks
❑ For unavoidable canned goods, stick to brands without BPA
❑ Snack on fruits, vegetables, proteins, and calcium foods
❑ Hit the salad bar for lunch
❑ Eat healthier options for dessert
❑ Cook with canola, flaxseed, and olive oils
❑ Shop for whole foods around the edges of the supermarket
❑ Don't let "nutrient eating" lead to over eating

Financial Planning for Baby

❏ Set aside three months' living expenses for emergencies
❏ Add child to your life or health insurance policies
❏ Research childcare options based on income and expenses
❏ Create a budget using software or online tool; include baby expenses
❏ Purchase life insurance or increase current coverage
❏ Make a will or update your will
❏ Consider disability insurance
❏ Investigate child tax deductions, credits, and savings programs
   ▶ Dependent Exemption
   ▶ Child Tax Credit
   ▶ The Child Care Credit
   ▶ Dependent Care Accounts
   ▶ Medical Flexible Spending Account
❏ Start college savings for child
❏ Ask for salary raise *before* baby's arrival

20 Tips for a Greener Pregnancy

❏ Go green during pregnancy, if at no other time
❏ For birth, consider a midwife at a nonhospital birth center
❏ Have a doula help at birth
❏ Focus on daily green habits over a natural birth
❏ Ask pediatrician candidates green-leaning questions
❏ Check food labels and ingredients carefully
❏ Replace family linens with organic cotton
❏ Use natural beauty and personal care products
❏ Beware of deceptive marketing and phony "green" labels
❏ Read skin and personal care ingredients online at Skin Deep or NIH Household Products
❏ Skip toxic home makeovers that could uncover lead dust
❏ Skip bottled water; install water filtration system in home
❏ Use allergen control methods to reduce indoor pollutants:
   ▶ Fix leaks and eliminate sources of moisture
   ▶ Use exhaust vent while cooking

> ▸ Hire a contractor to tune up furnaces, flues, chimneys, and gas appliances
> ▸ Install carbon monoxide detector
> ▸ Consider an air purifier for your home
> ▸ Grow air-purifying plants

❏ Use green gardening methods

❏ Use green methods of indoor pest control

❏ Be skeptical of established green brands and curious about new labels

❏ Plant a tree

❏ Vote with your dollars; choose organic and eco-friendly products over processed

❏ If access to green products is limited, go online at VineMarket.com or AbesMarket.com

❏ Recycle and re-use secondhand baby gear, maternity clothes and baby clothes

Packing for the Hospital

Packing List for Mom

❏ Practical nursing nightgowns or loose pajamas

❏ Nursing or maternity bras

❏ Large, cotton, granny panties

❏ A comfy bathrobe

❏ Socks

❏ Flip-flops

❏ Slippers with treads

❏ Sanitary pads

❏ Toiletries

❏ Makeup bag

❏ Hair dryer, flat iron, hair cream, wraps, or other hair accessories

❏ Nipple cream

❏ Nursing pads

❏ Nursing pillow with slipcover

❏ Going home outfit

Packing List for Baby

- ❏ Newborn one-piece suits or kimono-style shirts, at least two
- ❏ Baby socks, at least two pairs
- ❏ Newborn hat or skullcap, if desired
- ❏ Swaddle blankets
- ❏ Burp cloths
- ❏ Going home outfit

Packing List for Dad

- ❏ Changes of clothes
- ❏ Toiletries
- ❏ Pillow from home and a blanket, if not already provided

Packing List: General

- ❏ iPod, MP3, or CD player with headphones and speakers
- ❏ Books and magazines
- ❏ An iPad or laptop computer
- ❏ Digital camera and video camera. Don't forget chargers, batteries, and extra memory cards
- ❏ Digital watch, preferably with a second hand for timing contractions
- ❏ Hospital registration forms
- ❏ Birth plan, if you have one (See Birth Plan)
- ❏ Insurance cards
- ❏ Your drivers' licenses
- ❏ Car seat. Make sure the car seat is installed and checked.
- ❏ Cell phones and chargers
- ❏ Cash

Packing List: Optional Items

- ❏ Gift for an older sibling
- ❏ Your favorite pregnancy book or birthing technique guide
- ❏ Tennis balls, massage oil, or lotion for back massage
- ❏ Lollipops and hard candies
- ❏ Reusable shopping bags to bring home extra supplies

Baby Registry

Baby Gear

- ❏ Car seat
- ❏ Stroller
- ❏ Bouncer seat
- ❏ Activity mat or play gym
- ❏ Portable crib or play yard
- ❏ Infant swing
- ❏ Activity saucer, ExerSaucer, or Jumperoo
- ❏ Baby carrier or front carrier
- ❏ Baby wrap, sling, or soft carrier
- ❏ Doorway jumper or bouncer
- ❏ Stroller snug sack or winter bunting

Cloth Diapering Supplies

- ❏ Diapers
- ❏ Wipes
- ❏ Wipes solution
- ❏ Diaper pail with waterproof liner
- ❏ Wet bag/travel bag
- ❏ Cloth diaper sprayer
- ❏ Extra inserts
- ❏ Drying rack or clothesline

Universal Diapering Supplies

- ❏ Diapers
- ❏ Wipes
- ❏ Diaper rash cream
- ❏ Diaper pail and liners
- ❏ Wipes dispenser
- ❏ Diapering organization station
- ❏ Diaper bag

Breastfeeding: Supplies for Breastfeeding

- ❏ Nursing or feeding pillow
- ❏ Breast pump

❑ Pumping accessories
❑ Lanolin/nipple cream
❑ Soothing gel pads
❑ Nipple shields
❑ Nursing tanks
❑ Nursing bras, day and night
❑ Nursing pads
❑ Nursing cover
❑ Nursing friendly shirts

Bottle-Feeding: Supplies for Breast Milk and Formula

❑ Bottles
❑ Bottle brushes
❑ Bottle drying rack
❑ Burp cloths
❑ Formula
❑ Dishwasher basket
❑ Bottle warmer
❑ Microwave sterilization bags
❑ Bottle sterilizer (microwave or electric)
❑ Formula dispenser

Feeding Supplies

❑ Highchair
❑ Bibs
❑ Sippy cups
❑ Baby spoons
❑ Teethers
❑ Pacifiers
❑ Splat mat
❑ Roll-up travel placemat
❑ Baby food maker
❑ Baby food ice trays
❑ Electric swivel sweeper or cordless vacuum

Bathing Supplies

- ❑ Bathtub
- ❑ Bath Sponge Cushion
- ❑ Inflatable Safety Tub
- ❑ Hooded bath towels
- ❑ Washcloths
- ❑ Baby shampoo and body wash
- ❑ Bath toys

Nursery

- ❑ Crib
- ❑ Crib mattress
- ❑ Waterproof crib mattress cover or pad
- ❑ Crib sheets
- ❑ Changing table
- ❑ Changing table pad or cushion
- ❑ Changing table cover
- ❑ Baby hangers for clothes
- ❑ Rocker or glider
- ❑ Nursery paint
- ❑ Baby-safe rug or carpet
- ❑ Floor mat or covering

Sleeping Supplies

- ❑ Swaddling blankets
- ❑ Wearable blankets or sleep sacks
- ❑ Nightlight
- ❑ Sound machine or MP3 player with docking station
- ❑ Blinds, shades, or blackout curtain
- ❑ Mobile for crib
- ❑ Bassinet, cradle or co-sleeper

Health and First Aid Supplies

- ❑ Bulb syringe or nasal aspirator
- ❑ Saline drops
- ❑ Digital temporal scanner and back-up rectal thermometer
- ❑ Infant acetaminophen

- ❏ Infant ibuprofen
- ❏ Gas relief medicine
- ❏ Cough and cold relief
- ❏ Cotton balls
- ❏ Baby Q-tips
- ❏ Hair brush
- ❏ Nail clippers
- ❏ Baby nail files
- ❏ Baby lotion
- ❏ Baby sunscreen

Cleaning Supplies

- ❏ Household cleaners: Go green
  - ▶ Dishwashing soap
  - ▶ Dishwasher detergent
  - ▶ All-purpose cleaner
  - ▶ Toilet bowl cleaner
  - ▶ Scrubbing powder
  - ▶ Cleaner for food prep surfaces
  - ▶ Glass and window cleaner
- ❏ Baby friendly laundry detergent
- ❏ Baby clothes stain remover
- ❏ Steam mop

Safety Supplies

- ❏ Baby monitor, audio and video
- ❏ Breathing monitor
- ❏ Safety gates, top of stairs bolted
- ❏ Pressure-mounted gates, doorway and bottom of stairs
- ❏ Safety devices
  - ▶ Cabinet locks
  - ▶ Electrical outlet covers
  - ▶ Stove knob covers
  - ▶ Oven lock
  - ▶ Furniture edge guard
  - ▶ Toilet seat lock

    ▸ Blinds/cord wraps
    ▸ Electronics/DVD guard
❑ Water filtration system

Baby Clothing

❑ Pajamas or sleep-and-plays
❑ One-piece short sleeve bodysuits or onesies
❑ Shirts
❑ Leggings or pull-on pants
❑ Outer layers and winter gear
❑ Hats
❑ Socks and booties
❑ Shoes

Other Items

❑ Books, toys, and other fun gifts

Baby Registry: A Waste of Money

❑ Baby healthcare and grooming kit
❑ Expensive crib bedding and crib bumper pads
❑ Bassinet
❑ Moses basket
❑ Baby bath robe
❑ Ear thermometer
❑ Infant winter coats and suits
❑ Disposable breast pads
❑ Too many clothes
❑ Too many baby blankets
❑ Too many bottles and pacifiers
❑ Too many mom-to-be labeled toiletries

On a tighter budget, drop these items:
❑ Changing table
❑ Diaper Genie
❑ Bottle warmer
❑ Too many slings and baby carriers

Tips for Postpartum Recovery

For Perineum Pain Relief

- ❏ Raid your hospital room for postpartum swag
- ❏ Take a sitz bath several times per day for first week
- ❏ Line a maxi-pad with Tuck's cooling pads
- ❏ Pour witch hazel on a maxi-pad and freeze
- ❏ Use a peri-bottle to rinse perineum area
- ❏ If pain persists, try numbing spray such as Dermoplast

For Postpartum Bleeding

- ❏ Buy large supply of low-chemical, natural maxi-pads
- ❏ Use a squirt bottle or peri-bottle to rinse between baths
- ❏ If bleeding is heavy, try an adult incontinence pad or diaper

For Constipation

- ❏ Drink water
- ❏ Eat high-fiber foods
- ❏ Go for bowel-inducing walk
- ❏ Drink cup of hot water
- ❏ Ask doctor for stool softener

Other Tips

- ❏ Expect hot and cold flashes
- ❏ For incontinence, try daily kegel exercises. Use panty liners as needed
- ❏ For latch problems and breast pain, talk to a lactation specialist
- ❏ For swollen gums, gingivitis, and periodontal disease, brush and floss regularly
- ❏ For painful sex (after 4-6 weeks), use water-based lubricant. Talk to doctor about pain after deep penetration
- ❏ Wear stretchy tank top or ACE bandage for belly support during exercise
- ❏ For healthy weight loss, target a goal of one pound per week
- ❏ Stop taking narcotics as soon as possible

Typical Restrictions for C-Section Recovery

Talk to doctor about resuming activities

- ❑ Avoid lifting anything heavier than baby for six weeks
- ❑ Avoid climbing stairs, or climb slowly for two to six weeks
- ❑ Avoid driving for two to three weeks
- ❑ Avoid chores that require bending or stretching for two weeks
- ❑ No sex for six weeks or until cleared by doctor

Favorite Apps for Pregnancy

- ❑ Pregnancy (week by week): My Pregnancy Center | BabyCenter
- ❑ Pregnancy (week by week): Pregnancy & Baby | What to Expect
- ❑ Pregnancy (best 3D graphics): Pregnancy Sprout
- ❑ Pregnancy (medication safety): Pregnancy & Medication Safety
- ❑ Pregnancy (fish intake): Fish4Health
- ❑ Pregnancy (photo banners): Belly Snaps
- ❑ Pregnancy (ultrasound photos): Pimp My Ultrasound
- ❑ Pregnancy (heartbeat audio recorder): Lullabeats or My Baby's Beat
- ❑ Pregnancy (fetal monitor): BabyScope
- ❑ Pregnancy (labor contraction timer): Full Term
- ❑ Baby names: 50,000 Baby Names or Baby Names Wizard
- ❑ Shopping (nutrition): Shopwell
- ❑ Shopping (green product ratings): GoodGuide
- ❑ Shopping (personal care): Skin Deep by EWG
- ❑ Fitness (yoga): Yoga Studio or Yoga Mama
- ❑ Public restroom finder: SitOrSquat

Appendix B: Infant Formula Ingredient Labels

· · · · · · · · · · · · · · · · · ·

Conventional Formula

Milk-based Formulas:

**Similac Infant Formula
With Iron, Powder**

Ingredients:
Nonfat Milk, Lactose, High Oleic Safflower Oil, Soy Oil, Coconut Oil, Whey Protein Concentrate, and less than 2% of: C. Cohnii Oil (Source of Docosahexaenoic Acid [DHA]), M. Alpina Oil (Source of Arachidonic Acid [ARA]), Potassium Citrate, Calcium Carbonate, Ascorbic Acid, Soy Lecithin, Potassium Chloride, Magnesium Chloride, Ferrous Sulfate, Choline Chloride, Choline Bitartrate, Ascorbyl Palmitate, Sodium Chloride, Taurine, M-Inositol, Zinc Sulfate, Mixed Tocopherols, D-Alpha-Tocopheryl Acetate, Niacinamide, Calcium Pantothenate, L-Carnitine, Vitamin A Palmitate, Cupric Sulfate, Thiamine Chloride Hydrochloride, Riboflavin, Pyridoxine Hydrochloride, Folic Acid, Manganese Sulfate, Phylloquinone, Biotin, Sodium Selenate, Beta-Carotene, Vitamin D3, Cyanocobalamin, Calcium Phosphate, Potassium Phosphate, Potassium Hydroxide and Nucleotides (Adenosine 5'-Monophosphate, Cytidine 5'-Monophdsphate, Disodium Guanosine 5'-Monophosphate, Disodium Uridine 5'-Monophosphate).

Enfamil Infant Formula (Newborn)
Milk-based Infant Formula with Iron, Powder

Ingredients:

Nonfat Milk, Lactose, Vegetable Oil (Palm Olein, Coconut, Soy, and High Oleic Sunflower Oils), Whey Protein Concentrate, Galactooligosaccharides (a Type of Prebiotic), Polydextrose (a Type of Prebiotic), and less than 1% of: Mortierella Alpina Oil (a Source of Arachidonic Acid (ARA)), Crypthecodinium Cohnii Oil (a Source of Docosahexaenoic Acid (DHA)), Soy Lecithin, Vitamin A Palmitate, Vitamin D3, Vitamin E Acetate, Vitamin K1, Thiamin Hydrochloride, Riboflavin, Vitamin B6 Hydrochloride, Vitamin B12, Niacinamide, Folic Acid, Calcium Pantothenate, Biotin, Ascorbic Acid, Inositol, Calcium Carbonate, Calcium Phosphate, Magnesium Oxide, Ferrous Sulfate, Zinc Sulfate, Manganese Sulfate, Cupric Sulfate, Potassium Iodide, Sodium Selenite, Potassium Citrate, Choline Chloride, Potassium Chloride, Sodium Chloride, Nucleotides (Cytidine 5'-Monophosphate, Disodium Uridine 5'-Monophosphate, Adenosine 5'-Monophosphate, Disodium Guanosine 5'-Mono-Phosphate), Taurine, L-Carnitine.

Enfamil Infant Formula (LIPIL)
Milk-based Infant Formula with Iron, Powder

Ingredients:

Nonfat Milk, Lactose, Vegetable Oil (Palm Olein, Soy, Coconut, and High Oleic Sunflower Oils), Whey Protein Concentrate, and less than 1% of: Mortierella Alpina Oil (a Source of Arachidonic Acid [ARA]), Crypthecodinium Cohnii Oil (a Source of Docosahexaenoic Acid [DHA]), Vitamin A Palmitate, Vitamin D3, Vitamin E Acetate, Vitamin K1, Thiamin Hydrochloride, Riboflavin, Vitamin B6 Hydrochloride, Vitamin B12, Niacinamide, Folic Acid, Calcium Pantothenate, Biotin, Ascorbic Acid, Choline Chloride, Inositol, Calcium Carbonate, Magnesium Oxide, Ferrous Sulfate, Zinc Sulfate, Manganese Sulfate, Cupric Sulfate, Potassium Chloride, Potassium Citrate, Potassium Hydroxide, Sodium Selenite, Taurine, L-Carnitine, Nucleotides (Adenosine 5'-Monophosphate, Cytidine 5'-Monophosphate, Disodium Guanosine 5'-Monophosphate, Disodium Uridine 5'-Monoposphate).

Gerber Infant Formula (gentle)
Milk-based Powder With Iron

Ingredients:

Whey Protein Concentrate (from Cow's Milk, Enzymatically Hydrolyzed, Reduced in Minerals), Vegetable Oils (Palm Olein, Soy, Coconut, and High-Oleic Safflower or High-Oleic Sunflower), Corn Maltodextrin, Lactose, Galacto-Oligosaccharides (a Prebiotic Fiber Sourced from Milk), and less than 2% of: Potassium Citrate, Potassium Phosphate, Calcium Chloride, Calcium Phosphate, Sodium Citrate, Magnesium Chloride, Ferrous Sulfate, Zinc Sulfate, Sodium Chloride, Copper Sulfate, Potassium Iodide, Manganese Sulfate, Sodium Selenate, M. Alpina Oil (a Source of Arachidonic Acid [ARA]), C. Cohnii Oil (a Source of Docosahexaenoic Acid [DHA]), Sodium Ascorbate, Inositol, Choline Bitartrate, Alpha-Tocopheryl Acetate, Niacinamide, Calcium Pantothenate, Riboflavin, Vitamin A Acetate, Pyridoxine Hydrochloride, Thiamine Mononitrate, Folic Acid, Phylloquinone, Biotin, Vitamin D3, Vitamin B12, Taurine, Nucleotides (Cytidine 5'-Monophosphate, Disodium Uridine 5'-Monophosphate, Adenosine 5'-Monophosphate, Disodium Guanosine 5'-Monophosphate), Ascorbyl Palmitate, Mixed Tocopherols, L-Carnitine, Soy Lecithin.

Parent's Choice Infant Formula
Newborn

Ingredients:

Nonfat Milk, Lactose, Vegetable Oils (Palm Olein, Soy, Coconut, High Oleic (Safflower Or Sunflower) Oil), Whey Protein Concentrate, Galacto-Oligosaccharid (Gos), and less Than 1% of: Mortierella Aplina Oil*, Crypthecodinium Cohnii Oil**, Soy Lecithin, Vitamin A Palmitate, Vitamin D3, Vitamin E Acetate, Vitamin K, Thiamine Hydrochloride, Riboflavin, Vitamin B6 Hydrochloride, Vitamin B12, Niacinamide, Folic Acid, Calcium Pantothenate, Biotin, Ascorbic Acid, Choline Bitartrate, Inositol, Calcium Carbonate, Calcium Chloride, Calcium Hydroxide, Magnesium Chloride, Ferrous Sulfate, Zinc Sulfate, Manganese Sulfate, Cupric Sulfate, Potassium Bicarbonate, Potassium Iodide, Potassium Hydroxide, Potassium Phosphate, Sodium Selenite, Sodium Citrate, Taurine, L-Carnitine, Beta-Carotene, Mixed Tocopherol Concentrate, Ascorbyl Palmitate, Monoglycerides, Nucleotides (Adenosine-5'-Monophosphate,

Cytidine-5'-Monophosphate, Disodium Guanosine-5'-Monophosphate, Disodium Uridine-5'-Monophosphate). Contains Milk and Soy Ingredients. *A Source of Anachidonic Acid (Ara). **A Source of Docosahexaenoic Acid (DHA).

Sensitive milk-based formulas (for fussiness and gas):

Similac Sensitive Infant Formula:
With Iron for Fussiness & Gas, Powder

Ingredients:
Corn Syrup, Sugar, Milk Protein Isolate, High Oleic, Safflower Oil, Soy Oil, Galacto-Oligosaccaride, and less Than 2% of: C. Cohnii Oil, M. Alpina Oil, Beta-Carotene, Lutein, Lycopene, Calcium Phosphate, Potassium Citrate, Potassium Chloride, Sodium Citrate, Magnesium Phosphate, Ascorbic Acid, Calcium Carbonate, Choline Chloride, Ferrous Sulfate, Magnesium Chloride, Ascorbyl Palmitate, Choline Bitartrate, Taurine, M-Inositol, D-Alpha-Tocopheryl Acetate, Zinc Sulfate, Mixed Tocopherols, L-Carnitine, Niacinamide, Calcium Pantothenate, Vitamin A Palmitate, Cupric Sulfate, Thiamine Chloride Hydrochloride, Riboflavin, Pydroxide Hydrochloride, Folic Acid, Manganese Sulfate, Potassium Iodide, Phylloquinone, Biotin, Sodium Selenate, Vitamin D3, Cyanocobalamin, Potassium Hydroxide And Nucleotide (Adenosine 5'monophosphate, Cytide 5'-Monophosphate, Disodium Guanosine 5'-Monophosphate, Disodium Uridine 5'-Monophosphate). Galacto-Oligosaccharides Are Sourced from Milk (Gos). C. Cohnii Oil Is A Source of DHA. M. Alpina Oil Is A Source of Ara.

Enfamil Infant Formula (Gentlease)
For Fussiness & Gas

Ingredients:
Corn Syrup Solids, Partially Hydrolyzed Nonfat Milk and Whey Protein Concentrate Solids (Soy), Vegetable Oil (Palm Olein, Soy, Coconut, and High Oleic Sunflower Oils), and less than 2% of: Mortierella Alpina Oil (a Source of Arachidonic Acid (ARA)), Crypthecodinium Cohnii Oil (a Source of Docosahexaenoic Acid (DHA)), Vitamin A Palmitate, Vitamin D3, Vitamin E Acetate, Vitamin K1, Thiamin Hydrochloride, Riboflavin, Vitamin B6 Hydrochloride, Vitamin B12, Niacinamide, Folic Acid, Calcium Pantothenate, Biotin, Ascorbic Acid, Choline Chloride, Inositol,

Calcium Carbonate, Calcium Phosphate, Magnesium Phosphate, Ferrous Sulfate, Zinc Sulfate, Manganese Sulfate, Cupric Sulfate, Sodium Selenite, Sodium Citrate, Potassium Chloride, Taurine, and L-Carnitine.

Soy-based formulas:

Similac Infant Formula
Isomil Soy for Fussiness & Gas with Iron, Powder

Ingredients:
Corn Syrup Solids (39%), Soy Protein Isolate (15%), High Oleic Safflower Oil (11%), Sugar (10%), Soy Oil (8%), Coconut Oil (8%), and less than 2% of: C. Cohnii Oil, M, Alpina Oil, Beta-Carotene, Lutein, Lycopene, Fructooligosaccharides, Calcium Phosphate, Potassium Citrate, Potassium Chloride, Magnesium Chloride, Salt, Ascorbic Acid, Choline Chloride, L-Methionine, Taurine, Ascorbyl Palmitate, Ferrous Sulfate, M-Inositol, Mixed Tocopherols, Zinc Sulfate, D-Alpha Tocopheryl Acetate, L-Carnitine, Niacinamide, Calcium Pantothenate, Cupric Sulfate, Thiamine Chloride Hydrochloride, Vitamin A Palmitate, Riboflavin, Pyridoxine Hydrochloride, Folic Acid, Potassium Iodide, Potassium Hydroxide, Phylloquinone, Biotin, Sodium Selenate, Vitamin D3 and Cyanocobalamin. C. Cohnii is a Source of DHA. M. Alpina Oil is a Source of ARA.

Enfamil Infant Formula (ProSoBee)
Soy, Iron Fortified, Powder

Ingredients:
Corn Syrup Solids (55 %), Vegetable Oil (Palm Olein, Soy, Coconut, and High Oleic Sunflower Oils) (27 %), Soy Protein Isolate (15 %), and less Than 1% of: Vitamin A Palmitate, Vitamin D3, Vitamin E Acetate, Vitamin K1, Thiamin Hydrochloride, Riboflavin, Vitamin B6 Hydrochloride, Vitamin B12, Niacinamide, Folic Acid, Calcium Pantothenate, Magnesium Phosphate, Ferrous Sulfate, Zinc Sulfate, Cupric Sulfate, Potassium Hydroxide, Potassium Chloride, Sodium Citrate, Sodium Selenite, L-Methionine, Taurine, L-Carnitine.

Gerber Infant Formula
With Iron Soy, Powder

Ingredients:

Corn Maltodextrin, Vegetable Oils (Palm Olein, Soy, Coconut, and High-Oleic Safflower or High-Oleic Sunflower), Enzymatically Hydrolyzed Soy Protein Isolate, Sucrose, and less than 2% of: Calcium Phosphate, Potassium Citrate, Sodium Citrate, Calcium Citrate, M. Alpina Oil (A Source of Arachidonic Acid [ARA]), C. Cohnii Oil (A Source of Docosahexaenoic Acid [DHA]), Magnesium Chloride, Calcium Chloride, Potassium Chloride, Ferrous Sulfate, Zinc Sulfate, Copper Sulfate, Potassium Iodide, Sodium Selenate, Soy Lecithin, Sodium Ascorbate, Choline Chloride, Inositol, Alpha-Tocopheryl Acetate, Niacinamide, Calcium Pantothenate, Vitamin A Acetate, Riboflavin, Thiamine Mononitrate, Pyridoxine Hydrochloride, Folic Acid, Biotin, Phylloquinone, Vitamin 03, Vitamin B12, Ascorbyl Palmitate, Mixed Tocopherols, L-Methionine, Taurine, L-Carnitine.

Organic Formula

Earth's Best Infant Formula
Milk Based With Iron, Powder

Ingredients:

Organic Lactose, Organic Nonfat Milk, Organic High Oleic Sunflower Oil, Organic Coconut Oil, Organic Soy Oil, Organic Whey Protein Concentrate, and less Than 1% of each of the following: Soy Lecithin, Vitamins: (Vitamin A Palmitate, Vitamin D3, dI-Alpha-Tocophero, Phytonadione, Thiamin Hydrochloride, Riboflavin, Pyridoxine Hydrochloride, Vitamin B12, Niacinamide, Folic Acid, Calcium Pantothenate, Biotin, Sodium Ascorbate, Ascorbic Acid, Ascorbyl Palmitate, Choline Chloride, Inositol), Minerals: (Calcium Phosphate, Calcium Citrate, Magnesium Chloride, Ferrous Sulfate, Zinc Sulfate, Manganese Sulfate, Cupric Sulfate, Potassium Iodide, Potassium Citrate, Potassium Chloride, Potassium Hydroxide, Sodium Hydroxide, Sodium Selenite), L-Carnitine, Taurine, Nucleotides: (Adenosine 5' Monophosphate, Cytidine 5 Monophosphate, Disodium Guanosine 5' Monophosphate, Disodium Uridine 5' Monophosphate).

Earth's Best Infant Formula
Soy Infant Formula with Iron, Powder

Ingredients:

Organic Corn Syrup, Organic Soy Protein, Organic High Oleic Sunflower Oil, Organic Coconut Oil, Organic Soy Oil, and less than 1% of: Soy Lecithin, Vitamins: (Vitamin A Palmitate, Vitamin D3, Dl-Alpha-Tocopherol, Phytonadione, Thiamin Hydrochloride, Riboflavin, Pyridoxine Hydrochloride, Vitamin B12, Niacinamide, Folic Acid, Calcium Pantothenate, Biotin, Sodium Ascorbate, Ascorbic Acid, Ascorbyl Palmitate, Choline Chloride, Inositol), Minerals: (Calcium Phosphate, Calcium Citrate, Magnesium Chloride, Ferrous Sulfate, Zinc Sulfate, Cupric Sulfate, Potassium Iodine, Potassium Citrate, Potassium Chloride, Potassium Phosphate, Sodium Chloride, Sodium Hydroxide, Sodium Selenite), L-Carnitine, Taurine, Methionine, Lipids: DHA (Docosahexaenoic Acid), ARA (Arachidonic Acid).

Baby's Only Organic Toddler Formula
Dairy Iron Fortified

Ingredients:

Organic Brown Rice Syrup, Organic Nonfat Milk, Organic High Oleic Sunflower and/or Organic High Oleic Safflower Oil, Organic Soybean Oil, Organic Coconut Oil, Calcium Phosphate, Calcium Ascorbate (Vit. C), Organic Soy Lecithin, Calcium Citrate, Choline Bitartrate, Organic Vanilla, Taurine, Ferrous Sulfate, Inositol, Natural Vitamin E Acetate, Zinc Sulfate, Niacinamide, Vitamin A Palmitate, Calcium Pantothenate, Thiamin Hydrochloride (Vit. B1), Copper Sulfate, Riboflavin (Vit. B2), Pyridoxine Hydrochloride (Vit. B6), Folic Acid, Phylloquinone (Vit. K1), Potassium Iodide, Sodium Selenate, Biotin, Vitamin D3, Cyanocobalamin (Vit. B12). Gluten free.

Baby's Only Organic Toddler Formula
Soy Iron Fortified

Ingredients:

Organic Brown Rice Syrup, Organic Soy Protein Concentrate, Organic High Oleic Sunflower and/or Organic High Oleic Safflower Oil, Organic Coconut Oil, Organic Soybean Oil, Calcium Phosphate, Organic Vanilla, Organic Soy Lecithin, Potassium Phosphate, Magnesium Sulfate,

Calcium Carbonate, Calcium Ascorbate (Vit. C), Sodium Chloride, Potassium Chloride, Calcium Citrate, Choline Bitartrate, L-Methionine, Taurine, Ferrous Sulfate, Inositol, Zinc Sulfate, D-Alpha Tocopheryl Acetate (Vit. E), L-Carnitine, Niacinamide, Calcium Pantothenate, Vitamin A Palmitate, Thiamin Hydrochloride (Vit. B1), Riboflavin (Vit. B2), Pyridoxine Hydrochloride (Vit. B6), Copper Sulfate, Folic Acid, Phylloquinone (Vit. K1), Potassium Iodide, Sodium Selenate, Biotin, Vitamin D3, Cyanocobalamin (Vit. B12). Gluten free.

Similac Organic Infant Formula

Ingredients:
Organic Nonfat Milk, Organic Maltodextrin, Organic Sugar from Evaporated Cane Juice, Organic High Oleic Sunflower Oil, Organic Soy Oil, Organic Coconut Oil, and less than 2% of: C. Cohini Oil (Source of Docosahexaenoic Acid [DHA]), M. Alpina Oil (Source of Arachidonic Acid [ARA]), Potassium Citrate, Soy Lecithin, Calcium Carbonate, Ascorbic Acid, Magnesium Chloride, Sodium Chloride, Ferrous Sulfate, Choline Chloride, Choline Bitartrate, Ascorbyl Palmitate, Taurine, M-Inositol, Zinc Sulfate, Mixed Tocopherol, D-Alpha-Tocopheryl Acetate, Niacinamide, Calcium Pantothenate, L-Carnitine, Vitamin A Palmitate, Cupric Sulfate, Thiamine Chloride Hydrochloride, Riboflavin, Pyridoxine Hydrochloride, Folic Acid, Manganese Sulfate, Phylloquinone, Biotin, Beta-carotene, Sodium Selenate, Vitamin D3, Cyanocobalamin, Potassium Hydroxide and Nucleotides (Cytodyne 5'-Monophosphate, Disodium Guanosine 5'-Monophsopahte, Disodium Uridine 5'-Monophosphate, Adenosine 5'-Monophosphate).

Appendix C: Recommended Books and Resources

• •

Pregnancy

❑ *Mayo Clinic Guide to A Healthy Pregnancy* by Mayo Clinic

❑ *What To Expect When You're Expecting* by Heidi Murkoff, Arlene Eisenberg, and Sandee Hathaway

❑ *Pregnancy, Childbirth and the Newborn: The Complete Guide* by Penny Simkin, Janet Walley, April Bolding, and Ann Kepler

❑ *Your Pregnancy Week by Week* by Glade B. Curtis and Judith Schuler

❑ *The Pregnancy Book: Month-by-Month, Everything You Need to Know from America's Baby Experts* by William Sears, Martha Sears, and Linda Hughey Holt

❑ *Raising Baby Green: The Earth-Friendly Guide to Pregnancy, Childbirth, and Baby Care* by Alan Greene (author), Jeanette Pavini (contributor), and Theresa Foy DiGeronimo (contributor)

Natural Childbirth

❑ *Ina May's Guide to Childbirth* by Ina May Gaskin

❑ *Birthing From Within: An Extra-Ordinary Guide to Childbirth Preparation* by Pam England and Rob Horowitz

❑ *The Thinking Woman's Guide to a Better Birth* by Henci Goer

❑ *Spiritual Midwifery* by Ina May Gaskin

❑ *Natural Childbirth the Bradley Way: Revised Edition* by Susan McCutcheon, Erick Ingraham, Robin Yoko Burningham, and Robert A. Bradley

Breastfeeding

- ❑ *The Womanly Art of Breastfeeding* by La Leche League International
- ❑ *Breastfeeding Made Simple: Seven Natural Laws for Nursing Mothers* by Kathleen Kendall-Tackett, Nancy Mohrbacher, and Jack Newman
- ❑ *The Nursing Mother's Companion* by Kathleen Huggins
- ❑ *The Breastfeeding Mother's Guide to Making More Milk* by Diana West and Lisa Marasco

Pregnancy Nutrition

- ❑ *Eating for Pregnancy: The Essential Nutrition Guide and Cookbook for Today's Mothers-to-Be* by Catherine Jones and Rose Ann Hudson
- ❑ *Expect the Best: Your Guide to Healthy Eating Before, During, and After Pregnancy* by Elizabeth Ward
- ❑ *What to Expect: Eating Well When You're Expecting* by Heidi Murkoff and Sharon Mazel

Baby Registry

- ❑ *Baby Bargains* by Denise Fields and Alan Fields

Baby Care

- ❑ *Caring for Your Baby and Young Child: Birth to Age 5* by the American Academy of Pediatrics
- ❑ *The Baby Book: Everything You Need to Know About Your Baby from Birth to Age Two* by William, Martha, Robert, and James Sears
- ❑ *Mayo Clinic Guide to Your Baby's First Year* by Mayo Clinic
- ❑ *Baby 411: Clear Answers and Smart Advice for Your Baby's First Year* by Denise Fields and Ari Brown

For Dads-to-be

❑ *The Baby Owner's Manual: Operating Instructions, Trouble-Shooting Tips, and Advice on First-Year Maintenance* by Louis Borgenicht, Joe Borgenicht, and Paul Kepple (illustrator)

❑ *The Expectant Father: Facts, Tips, and Advice for Dads-to-Be* by Armin Brott and Jennifer Ash

❑ *The Birth Partner: A Complete Guide to Childbirth for Dads, Doulas, and All Other Labor Companions* by Penny Simkin, April Bolding, Ann Keppler, and Janelle Durham

Humorous, Light, and Funny

❑ *The Girlfriends' Guide to Pregnancy* by Vicki Iovine

❑ *Belly Laughs: The Naked Truth about Pregnancy and Childbirth* by Jenny McCarthy

❑ *What to Expect When Your Wife Is Expanding: A Reassuring Month-by-Month Guide for the Father-to-Be, Whether He Wants Advice or Not* by Thomas Hill

Notes

· · · · · · ·

Pregnancy

1. Murkoff, H.E., S. Mazel, and C.J. Lockwood, *What to expect when you're expecting*. 4th ed. 2008, New York: Workman Publishing, 153-165.
2. Centers for Disease Control and Prevention. *Unmarried Childbearing*. CDC Fast Stats 2012, updated April 26, 2014; Available from: http://www.cdc.gov/nchs/data/nvsr/nvsr62/nvsr62_09.pdf.
3. American Pregnancy Association. *Miscarriage*. 2011, updated April 26, 2014; Available from: http://americanpregnancy.org/pregnancycomplications/miscarriage.html.
4. American College of Obstetricians and Gynecologists (ACOG). *Frequently Asked Questions: Pregnancy*. 2014; Available from: https://www.acog.org/~/media/For%20Patients/faq001pdf?dmc=1&ts=20140721T1211223119.
5. United States Department of Agriculture (USDA). *High fructose corn syrup: estimated number of per capita calories consumed daily, by calendar year*. 2014; Available from: http://www.ers.usda.gov/data-products/sugar-and-sweeteners-yearbook-tables.aspx.
6. Curtis, G.B. and J. Schuler, *Your pregnancy week by week*. 6th ed. Lifelong books. 2008, Cambridge, MA: Da Capo/Lifelong Books, 24-197.
7. Harms, R.W., M. Wick, and Mayo Clinic., *Mayo Clinic guide to a healthy pregnancy*. 1st ed. 2011, Intercourse, PA: Good Books, part 5 Symptoms Guide.
8. Masoni, S., and others, *The couvade syndrome*. J Psychosom Obstet Gynaecol, 1994. 15(3): 125-31.
9. American Diabetes Association. *How to Treat Gestational Diabetes*. 2014, updated Apr 22, 2014; Available from: http://www.diabetes.org/diabetes-basics/gestational/how-to-treat-gestational.html.
10. McDonald, S.J., and others, *Effect of timing of umbilical cord clamping of term infants on maternal and neonatal outcomes*. Cochrane Database Syst Rev, 2013. DOI: 10.1002/14651858.CD004074.pub3.

11. Greene, A.R., *Raising baby green : the earth-friendly guide to pregnancy, childbirth, and baby care.* 1st ed. 2007, San Francisco: Jossey-Bass: 9-11.

12. Saunders, N.R., S.A. Liddelow, and K.M. Dziegielewska, *Barrier mechanisms in the developing brain.* Front Pharmacol, 2012. 3, DOI: 10.3389/fphar.2012.00046.

13. Environmental Protection Agency (EPA). *DDT - A Brief History and Status: Current Status.* 2014, updated July 7, 2014; Available from: http://www.epa.gov/pesticides/factsheets/chemicals/ddt-brief-history-status.htm.

14. Stotland, N.E., and others, *Counseling patients on preventing prenatal environmental exposures - a mixed-methods study of obstetricians.* PLoS One, 2014. 9, DOI: 10.1371/journal.pone.0098771.

15. Staud, F., L. Cerveny, and M. Ceckova, *Pharmacotherapy in pregnancy; effect of ABC and SLC transporters on drug transport across the placenta and fetal drug exposure.* J Drug Target, 2012. 20, DOI: 10.3109/1061186X.2012.716847.

16. Morgan, S., G. Koren, and P. Bozzo, *Is caffeine consumption safe during pregnancy?* Can Fam Physician, 2013. 59(4): 361-2.

17. Sengpiel, V., and others, *Maternal caffeine intake during pregnancy is associated with birth weight but not with gestational length: results from a large prospective observational cohort study.* BMC Med, 2013. 11: 42.

18. Murkoff, H.E. and S. Mazel, *What to expect : eating well when you're expecting.* 2005, New York: Workman Publishing: 74-107.

19. Oceana, *Ocean Study Reveals Seafood Fraud Nationwide.* 2014; Available from: http://oceana.org/sites/default/files/National_Seafood_Fraud_Testing_Results_Highlights_FINAL.pdf.

20. American Pregnancy Association. *Is It Safe.* 2014; Available from: http://americanpregnancy.org/isitsafe.

21. Pogoda, J.M. and S. Preston-Martin, *Maternal cured meat consumption during pregnancy and risk of paediatric brain tumour in offspring: potentially harmful levels of intake.* Public Health Nutr, 2001. 4(2): 183-9.

22. Sarasua, S. and D.A. Savitz, *Cured and broiled meat consumption in relation to childhood cancer: Denver, Colorado (United States).* Cancer Causes Control, 1994. 5(2): 141-8.

23. Griesenbeck, J.S., and others, *Development of estimates of dietary nitrates, nitrites, and nitrosamines for use with the Short Willet Food Frequency Questionnaire.* Nutr J, 2009. 8, DOI: 10.1186/1475-2891-8-16.

24. Frazier, A.L., and others, *Prospective study of peripregnancy consumption of peanuts or tree nuts by mothers and the risk of peanut or tree nut allergy in their offspring.* JAMA Pediatr, 2014. 168, DOI: 10.1001/jamapediatrics.2013.4139.

25. U.S. Department of Health and Human Services, National Center for Chronic Disease Prevention and Health Promotion, Office on Smoking and Health, *Let's Make the Next Generation Tobacco-Free: Your Guide to the*

50th Anniversary Surgeon General's Report on Smoking and Health. 2014; Available from: http://www.surgeongeneral.gov/library/reports/50-years-of-progress/consumer-guide.pdf.

26. Hyland, A., and others, *Associations of lifetime active and passive smoking with spontaneous abortion, stillbirth and tubal ectopic pregnancy: a cross-sectional analysis of historical data from the Women's Health Initiative.* Tob Control, 2014. DOI: 10.1136/tobaccocontrol-2013-051458.

27. U.S. Department of Health and Human Services Office on Women's Health. *Pregnancy and Medicine.* 2014; Available from: https://www.womenshealth.gov/publications/our-publications/fact-sheet/pregnancy-medicines.pdf.

28. Liew, Z., and others, *Acetaminophen use during pregnancy, behavioral problems, and hyperkinetic disorders.* JAMA Pediatr, 2014. 168, DOI: 10.1001/jamapediatrics.2013.4914.

29. Cooper, M., K. Langley, and A. Thapar, *Antenatal acetaminophen use and attention-deficit/hyperactivity disorder: an interesting observed association but too early to infer causality.* JAMA Pediatr, 2014. 168, DOI: 10.1001/jamapediatrics.2013.5292.

30. Llop, S., and others, *Prenatal and postnatal residential usage of insecticides in a multicenter birth cohort in Spain.* Sci Total Environ, 2013. 445-446, DOI: 10.1016/j.scitotenv.2012.12.031.

31. Cuhra, M., T. Traavik, and T. Bohn, *Clone- and age-dependent toxicity of a glyphosate commercial formulation and its active ingredient in Daphnia magna.* Ecotoxicology, 2013. 22(2): 251-62.

32. Antoniou, M., and others, *Roundup and birth defects: Is the public being kept in the dark?* Earth Open Source 2011; Available from: http://www.earthopensource.org/files/pdfs/Roundup-and-birth-defects/RoundupandBirthDefectsv5.pdf

33. Li, D.K., and others, *Hot tub use during pregnancy and the risk of miscarriage.* Am J Epidemiol, 2003. 158(10): 931-7.

34. Huang, H., and others, *The in Vitro estrogenic activities of triclosan and triclocarban.* J Appl Toxicol, 2014. DOI: 10.1002/jat.3012.

35. Dimmitt, B.S. *Safest Sleep Positions During Pregnancy* Parenting 2013, updated April 25, 2014; Available from: http://www.parenting.com/article/safest-sleep-positions-during-pregnancy.

36. Harms, R. *Is it safe to get a flu shot during pregnancy?* 2014; Available from: http://www.mayoclinic.org/healthy-living/pregnancy-week-by-week/expert-answers/influenza/faq-20058522.

37. Poehling, K.A., and others, *Impact of maternal immunization on influenza hospitalizations in infants.* Am J Obstet Gynecol, 2011. 204, DOI: 10.1016/j.ajog.2011.02.042.

38. Akolekar, R., and others, *Procedure-related risk of miscarriage following amniocentesis and chorionic villus sampling: a systematic review*

and meta-analysis. Ultrasound Obstet Gynecol, 2014. DOI: 10.1002/uog.14636.

39. Grandjean, P. and P.J. Landrigan, *Neurobehavioural effects of developmental toxicity.* Lancet Neurol, 2014. 13, DOI: 10.1016/S1474-4422(13)70278-3.

40. Woodruff, T.J., A.R. Zota, and J.M. Schwartz, *Environmental chemicals in pregnant women in the United States: NHANES 2003-2004.* Environ Health Perspect, 2011. 119, DOI: 10.1289/ehp.1002727.

41. Landrigan, P.J., L. Lambertini, and L.S. Birnbaum, *A research strategy to discover the environmental causes of autism and neurodevelopmental disabilities.* Environ Health Perspect, 2012. 120, DOI: 10.1289/ehp.1104285.

42. Grandjean, P. and P.J. Landrigan, *Developmental neurotoxicity of industrial chemicals.* Lancet, 2006. 368, DOI: 10.1016/S0140-6736(06)69665-7.

43. Jusko, T.A., and others, *Blood lead concentrations < 10 microg/dL and child intelligence at 6 years of age.* Environ Health Perspect, 2008. 116(2): 243-8.

44. Hillyer, M.M., and others, *Multi-technique quantitative analysis and socioeconomic considerations of lead, cadmium, and arsenic in children's toys and toy jewelry.* Chemosphere, 2014. 108, DOI: 10.1016/j.chemosphere.2014.01.041.

45. Oken, E., and others, *Maternal fish intake during pregnancy, blood mercury levels, and child cognition at age 3 years in a US cohort.* Am J Epidemiol, 2008. 167, DOI: 10.1093/aje/kwn034.

46. Winneke, G., *Developmental aspects of environmental neurotoxicology: lessons from lead and polychlorinated biphenyls.* J Neurol Sci, 2011. 308, DOI: 10.1016/j.jns.2011.05.020.

47. Weaver, D.E., *Contaminant levels in farmed salmon.* Science, 2004. 305, DOI: 10.1126/science.305.5683.478a.

48. Fleming, L., and others, *Parkinson's disease and brain levels of organochlorine pesticides.* Ann Neurol, 1994. 36(1): 100-3.

49. Eskenazi, B., and others, *Pesticide toxicity and the developing brain.* Basic Clin Pharmacol Toxicol, 2008. 102, DOI: 10.1111/j.1742-7843.2007.00171.x.

50. Braun, J.M., and others, *Impact of early-life bisphenol A exposure on behavior and executive function in children.* Pediatrics, 2011. 128, DOI: 10.1542/peds.2011-1335.

51. Volk, H.E., and others, *Residential proximity to freeways and autism in the CHARGE study.* Environ Health Perspect, 2011. 119, DOI: 10.1289/ehp.1002835.

52. Perera, F.P., and others, *Prenatal airborne polycyclic aromatic hydrocarbon exposure and child IQ at age 5 years.* Pediatrics, 2009. 124, DOI: 10.1542/peds.2008-3506.

53. Herbstman, J.B., and others, *Prenatal exposure to PBDEs and neurodevelopment.* Environ Health Perspect, 2010. 118, DOI: 10.1289/ehp.0901340.

54. Stapleton, H.M., and others, *Identification of flame retardants in polyurethane foam collected from baby products.* Environ Sci Technol, 2011. 45, DOI: 10.1021/es2007462.

55. Stein, C.R. and D.A. Savitz, *Serum perfluorinated compound concentration and attention deficit/hyperactivity disorder in children 5-18 years of age.* Environ Health Perspect, 2011. 119, DOI: 10.1289/ehp.1003538.

56. Woolf, A., and others, *A child with chronic manganese exposure from drinking water.* Environ Health Perspect, 2002. 110(6): 613-6.

57. Wright, R.O., and others, *Neuropsychological correlates of hair arsenic, manganese, and cadmium levels in school-age children residing near a hazardous waste site.* Neurotoxicology, 2006. 27(2): 210-6.

58. Crinella, F.M., *Does soy-based infant formula cause ADHD? Update and public policy considerations.* Expert Rev Neurother, 2012. 12, DOI: 10.1586/ern.12.2.

59. Cockell, K.A., G. Bonacci, and B. Belonje, *Manganese content of soy or rice beverages is high in comparison to infant formulas.* J Am Coll Nutr, 2004. 23(2): 124-30.

60. Choi, A.L., and others, *Developmental fluoride neurotoxicity: a systematic review and meta-analysis.* Environ Health Perspect, 2012. 120, DOI: 10.1289/ehp.1104912.

61. Environmental Protection Agency (EPA). *Fact Sheet on Perchloroethylene, also known as Tetrachloroethylene.* 2012; Available from: http://www.epa .gov/oppt/existingchemicals/pubs/perchloroethylene_fact_sheet.html.

62. Cosmetic Ingredient Review (CIR). *Ingredients found unsafe for use in cosmetics (11 total, through June 2013).* 2013; Available from: http://www .cir-safety.org/sites/default/files/U-unsafe062013.pdf.

63. National Geographic Society and C. Zandonella, *Green Guide Families.* 2010. National Geographic Society: Washington, D.C.

64. Sahakian, V., and others, *Vitamin B6 is effective therapy for nausea and vomiting of pregnancy: a randomized, double-blind placebo-controlled study.* Obstet Gynecol, 1991. 78(1): 33-6.

65. DeNavas-Walt, C., B. Proctor, and J. Smith. *Income, Poverty, and Health Insurance Coverage in the United States.* U.S. Census Bureau, 2013; Available from: http://www.census.gov/prod/2013pubs/p60-245.pdf.

66. Scott, K.D., G. Berkowitz, and M. Klaus, *A comparison of intermittent and continuous support during labor: a meta-analysis.* Am J Obstet Gynecol, 1999. 180(5): 1054-9.

67. Leighton, B.L. and S.H. Halpern, *The effects of epidural analgesia on labor, maternal, and neonatal outcomes: a systematic review.* Am J Obstet Gynecol, 2002. 186(5 Suppl Nature): S69-77.

68. Pesticide Action Network North America. *Cotton.* 2014; updated March 31, 2014; Available from: http://www.panna.org/resources/cotton.

69. Saleh, M.A., and others, *Chemical, microbial and physical evaluation of commercial bottled waters in greater Houston area of Texas.* J Environ Sci Health A Tox Hazard Subst Environ Eng, 2008. 43(4): 345-7.

70. Environmental Working Group. *Bottled Water Quality Investigation: 10 Major Brands, 38 Pollutants.* 2011; Available from: http://www.ewg.org/research/ewg-bottled-water-scorecard-2011.

71. Wolverton, B.C., *How to grow fresh air : 50 houseplants that purify your home or office.* 1997, New York, N.Y.: Penguin Books, 38-138.

72. Child Care Aware. *Choosing Child Care.* 2013; updated April 11, 2014; Available from: http://childcareaware.org/parents-and-guardians/child-care-101/choosing-child-care.

73. Zero to Three: National Center for Infants Toddlers and Families. *Choosing Quality Child Care.* 2014; Available from: http://www.zerotothree.org/early-care-education/child-care/choosing-quality-child-care.html.

74. Chu, S., F.A. Chervenak, and A. Grunebaum, *Are planned home births really low risk?* Obstet Gynecol, 2014. 123 Suppl 1, DOI: 10.1097/01.AOG.0000447326.13142.ac.

75. Watterberg, K. and Committee on Fetus and Newborn, *Policy statement on planned home birth: upholding the best interests of children and families.* Pediatrics, 2013. 132, DOI: 10.1542/peds.2013-2596.

76. ACOG Committee on Obstetric Practice, *ACOG Committee Opinion No. 476: Planned home birth.* Obstet Gynecol, 2011. 117, DOI: 10.1097/AOG.0b013e31820eee20.

77. American College of Nurse-Midwives, *Writing a birth plan.* J Midwifery Womens Health, 2014. 59(2): 227-8.

78. Hadar, E., and others, *Obstetrical outcome in women with self-prepared birth plan.* J Matern Fetal Neonatal Med, 2012. 25, DOI: 10.3109/14767058.2012.678438.

79. Rosenberg, J. and W.B. Wilcox. *Fathers and Their Impact on Children's Well-Being* The Importance of Fath ers in the Healthy Development of Children 2006, updated July 29, 2014; Available from: https://www.childwelfare.gov/pubs/usermanuals/fatherhood/chaptertwo.cfm#fn7.

Baby Registry

80. Decina, L. and K. Lococo, *Child Restraint Use Survey (LATCH Use and Misuse): Coding Manual.* 2013, National Highway Traffic Safety Administration: Report No. DOT HS 811 852.

81. Henary, B., and others, *Car safety seats for children: rear facing for best protection.* Inj Prev, 2007. 13(6): 398-402.

82. Kallan, M.J., D.R. Durbin, and K.B. Arbogast, *Seating patterns and corresponding risk of injury among 0- to 3-year-old children in child safety seats.* Pediatrics, 2008. 121, DOI: 10.1542/peds.2007-1512.

83. Kornhauser Cerar, L., and others, *A comparison of respiratory patterns in healthy term infants placed in car safety seats and beds.* Pediatrics, 2009. 124, DOI: 10.1542/peds.2009-0160.

84. Armstrong, L. and A. Scott, *Whitewash: Exposing the Health and Environmental Dangers of Women's Sanitary Products and Disposable Diapers, What You Can Do About It.* 1993, New York: Harper Collins, 194 pages.

85. Thomas, D.W., and others, *Probiotics and prebiotics in pediatrics.* Pediatrics, 2010. 126(6): 1217-31.

86. Simmer, K., S.K. Patole, and S.C. Rao, *Long-chain polyunsaturated fatty acid supplementation in infants born at term.* Cochrane Database Syst Rev, 2008. DOI: 10.1002/14651858.CD000376.pub2.

87. Bronnenberg, B.J., and others, *Do Pharmacists Buy Bayer? Sophisticated Shoppers and the Brand Premium.* Chicago Booth Research Paper No. 14-17 2013; Available from: http://papers.ssrn.com/sol3/papers.cfm?abstract_id=2460893.

88. Swan, S.H., *Prenatal phthalate exposure and anogenital distance in male infants.* Environ Health Perspect, 2006. 114(2): A88-9.

89. Sathyanarayana, S., and others, *Baby care products: possible sources of infant phthalate exposure.* Pediatrics, 2008. 121, DOI: 10.1542/peds.2006-3766.

90. Environmental Working Group. *Top Tips for Safer Products.* EWG's Skin Deep Database 2014; Available from: http://www.ewg.org/skindeep/top-tips-for-safer-products/.

Preparing for Baby

91. Alehagen S, W.K., Lundberg U, Melin B, and Wijma B., *Catecholamine and cortisol reaction to childbirth.* International journal of behavioral medicine, 2001, 8(1): 50-65.

92. Livingston, G. and D.V. Cohn. *Record Share of New Mothers are College Educated.* Pew Research Social & Demographic Trends, 2013; Available from: http://www.pewsocialtrends.org/2013/05/10/record-share-of-new-mothers-are-college-educated/.

93. Noble, R.E., *Depression in women.* Metabolism, 2005. 54(5 Suppl 1): 49-52.

94. Dietz, P.M., and others, *Clinically identified maternal depression before, during, and after pregnancies ending in live births.* Am J Psychiatry, 2007. 164(10): 1515-20.

95. Heinrichs, M., and others, *Selective amnesic effects of oxytocin on human memory.* Physiol Behav, 2004. 83(1): 31-8.

96. Ko, J.Y., and others, *Depression and treatment among U.S. pregnant and non-pregnant women of reproductive age, 2005-2009.* J Womens Health, 2012. 21, DOI: 10.1089/jwh.2011.3466.

97. Beck, C.T., *A meta-analysis of predictors of postpartum depression.* Nurs Res, 1996. 45(5): 297-303.

98. Muscat, T., and others, *Beliefs About Infant Regulation, Early Infant Behaviors and Maternal Postnatal Depressive Symptoms.* Birth, 2014. 41, DOI: 10.1111/birt.12107.

99. Oppo, A., and others, *Risk factors for postpartum depression: the role of the Postpartum Depression Predictors Inventory-Revised (PDPI-R). Results from the Perinatal Depression-Research & Screening Unit (PNDReScU) study.* Arch Womens Ment Health, 2009. 12, DOI: 10.1007/s00737-009-0071-8.

100. Center for Disease Control and Prevention, *Breastfeeding Report Card: United States 2014.* 2014, National Center for Chronic Disease Prevention and Health Promotion.

101. DiSanto, J. *Breast or Bottle?* KidsHealth.org, 2012; Available from: http://kidshealth.org/parent/pregnancy_newborn/formulafeed/breast_bottle_feeding.html#cat20583.

102. Christakis, D.A., *Breastfeeding and cognition: Can IQ tip the scale?* JAMA Pediatr, 2013. 167, DOI: 10.1001/jamapediatrics.2013.470.

103. Brion, M.J., and others, *What are the causal effects of breastfeeding on IQ, obesity and blood pressure? Evidence from comparing high-income with middle-income cohorts.* Int J Epidemiol, 2011. 40, DOI: 10.1093/ije/dyr020.

104. Varendi, H., and others, *Soothing effect of amniotic fluid smell in newborn infants.* Early Hum Dev, 1998. 51(1): 47-55.

105. DeCasper, A.J. and W.P. Fifer, *Of Human Bonding: Newborns Prefer their Mothers' Voices.* Science, 1980. 208, DOI: 10.2307/1683733.

106. Wolfberg, A.J., and others, *Dads as breastfeeding advocates: results from a randomized controlled trial of an educational intervention.* Am J Obstet Gynecol, 2004. 191(3): 708-12.

107. Li, R., and others, *Why mothers stop breastfeeding: mothers' self-reported reasons for stopping during the first year.* Pediatrics, 2008. 122 Suppl 2, DOI: 10.1542/peds.2008-1315i.

108. Shelton, J.F., and others, *Neurodevelopmental Disorders and Prenatal Residential Proximity to Agricultural Pesticides: The CHARGE Study.* Environ Health Perspect, 2014. 122, DOI: 10.1289/ehp.1307044.

Photo Credits

· · · · · · · · · · · · · ·

Cover Photo: © Thinkstock/Sergey Borisov

Author Photo: © Dawnielle Westerman, All These Years Photography

All product photos in this book were used with permission. Specific requested notations are written below.

Page 161, © 2011 Jolly Jumper

Page 177, © 2011, The Boppy Company, LLC. All rights reserved. Used with permission.

Page 177, Boppy Two-Side Nursing Pillow. © 2012, The Boppy Company, LLC. All rights reserved. Used with permission.

Page 178, Medela Pump In Style. Copyright © Medela, Inc.

Page 180, Medela Contact Nipple Shields. Copyright © Medela, Inc.

Page 181, Medela Sleep Bra. Copyright © Medela, Inc.

Page 198, Green Toys Green Eats, © Green Toys, Inc.

Page 200, Martin Juul for Natursutten by EcoBaby/DK.

Page 205, Green Toys Ferry Boat with Mini Cars Bathtub Toy, © Green Toys, Inc.

Page 212, NaturePedic Organic Cotton Contoured Changing Pad. Copyright © NaturePedic.

Page 239, Green Toys Twist Teether Toy, © Green Toys, Inc.

Fisher-Price and related trademarks, copyrights, and character designs are used with permission of Fisher-Price, Inc., East Aurora, New York 14052.

Index

· · · · · · ·

Made in the USA
Middletown, DE
19 February 2016